Letts study aids

Revise Mathematics

A complete revision course for O level and CSE

Duncan Graham   BSc, BSc(Hons), MSc

Lecturer in Mathematics, Rolle College,
Exmouth

Charles Letts & Co Ltd
London, Edinburgh & New York

First published 1979
by Charles Letts & Co Ltd
Diary House, Borough Road, London SE1 1DW

Revised 1981, 1984
Reprinted 1986

Design: Ben Sands
Illustrations: Tim Marshall DipAD and Chartwell Illustrators

© J. Duncan Graham 1979, 1981, 1984
© Illustrations: 1979, 1981, 1984 Charles Letts & Co Ltd

ISBN 0 85097 637 5

Printed and bound by
Charles Letts (Scotland) Ltd

Preface

Revise Mathematics aims to be a clear, concise and comprehensive guide for a student revising for a GCE O level, SCE or CSE examination in Mathematics. Although it was designed to be used as a final year revision text offering self-help to students, teachers have used it in planning and implementing their examination courses in schools. The format of the book also looks forward to the day when the two existing examinations of GCE and CSE are replaced by a common system of examination at 16 +.

   Revise Mathematics has been produced after analysing the forty-two most popular Mathematics syllabuses of all the Examination Boards in the United Kingdom. Most of the Mathematics required by these syllabuses has been divided into 55 topics and a table of analysis clearly shows which of these topics are included in each syllabus. A blank column is left for completion by the student whose examination is not listed. Section II of the book contains the revision notes on all these topics but the student is advised to revise only those which are necessary for his, or her, syllabus. A second table details the format and requirements of the examination.

   This book offers the student a wide range of help and advice. The introduction gives a description of how to use the tables of analysis, guidance on the use of the book and hints on revision technique. As well as advice on actual examination technique, various types of Mathematics examination question are described and advice is offered on how to answer each type. The self-test section contains numerous questions from previous examination papers, each question being keyed back to the relevant topic in Section II, and answers for checking solutions are provided. An index and a formula check list have been included for quick and easy reference.

   This third edition of *Revise Mathematics* incorporates a number of changes in current GCE, CSE and SCE syllabuses and the Northern Ireland syllabuses have been added. Extensive revision has been made to the main text and several extra topics included. Some changes are based on comments kindly sent by users of the previous editions of this book: I should like to thank them for their letters. Since this book is revised and up-dated regularly, comments on the content and presentation of this edition would be most welcome (write care of the publishers), so that they can be taken into account in the next edition.

   I wish to thank my wife, Christine Graham BEd(Hons), who acted as consultant on the original book, giving constant help, advice, criticism and encouragement, and who has made major contributions to the subsequent revised editions.

   My grateful thanks also go to the following people for their help in producing this book: Tim Marshall DipAD and Chartwell Illustrators, for the clarity of their illustrations; the late Gay Redfern for the professionalism of her typing; and the staff of Charles Letts & Co Limited.

   I should also like to express my gratitude to Cambridge University Press for their permission to reproduce the extracts from *Four-figure tables* by C. Godfrey and A. W. Siddons, and to the examination boards from whom I received permission to reproduce questions from past examination papers.

Duncan Graham 1984

Contents

Section I Introduction and guide to using this book

The main aim of this book is to help you revise for a GCE O level, SCE or CSE examination in Mathematics.

This book can help you to revise because it:
- gives you detailed information about the examination you are taking,
- tells you which topics you need to revise for your syllabus,
- refreshes your memory with important facts,
- reminds you of important words and their meanings,
- reminds you of methods for solving problems,
- gives you advice and hints for answering examination questions,
- gives you a selection of past examination questions to work through, so that you can practise your skills.

YOUR SYLLABUS

To use this book most effectively you need to know exactly which syllabus you are studying. The answers to the following questions will help you to find out.
- Which examination are you preparing for: GCE O level, Scottish O grade or CSE?
- What is the name of your Examination Board?
- What is the reference number of your syllabus?
- Which options (if any) are you taking?

YOUR TOPICS

Most of the mathematics required by the forty-two syllabuses analysed in this book have been divided into 55 topics with easily recognizable titles, *e.g.* Percentages, Linear equations, Trigonometry, *etc.* Section II of this book contains revision notes on all these topics.

To find out which of these topics are on your syllabus:
- turn to Table 1* on pages 4–5,
- look along the top of the table and find your Examination Board,
- look down the column for your syllabus. (You may find this easier if you place a ruler alongside your column.)

Each of the boxes in the column relates to a topic in this book. If a box:

(*i*) is blank ☐—ignore that topic because you do not need it,

(*ii*) has a dot ☑—study that topic because it is on your syllabus,

(*iii*) has an o ☒—study that topic if it is one of your options (your teacher will advise you which options you should study),

(*iv*) has another letter—study only part of that topic (look for the letter(s) in the table footnotes to find out what to do).

If the syllabus you are studying does not appear in Table 1 you should either ask your teacher or write to your Examination Board (address on page 7) for the details. You can then enter your syllabus in the blank end column of the table.

YOUR EXAMINATION

Table 2* on page 6 lists some of the main details of the examinations for each syllabus included in this book. If your examination is given, it will tell you:
- the number of papers you will take,
- the form of each paper, *i.e.* its length and the percentage of the total marks it carries,
- whether your teacher will assess a project or your course work and award a percentage of the total marks,
- whether you are allowed to use an electronic calculator in the examination,
- the type of mathematical tables (3- or 4-figure) you may use.

*Although Tables 1 and 2 have been prepared very carefully from the most recent syllabuses and this book is revised regularly, syllabuses sometimes change slightly from year to year. If in doubt, ask your teacher to check the information for your syllabus. Alternatively, you can check the syllabus yourself.

YOUR REVISION

Plan ahead   Research has shown that revising topics regularly throughout your course will help you to remember them more easily. Spread your final intensive revision sensibly over several months. In this way you will be able to refresh your memory frequently with the things you need to know and to practise the things you need to be able to do.

When to study   When you study often depends on the time you have, or make, available. Be realistic about how much work you need to do and how much time you should spend on it.

Organise your time into fixed study sessions, say one to two hours long, and break these up into three or four short periods with planned breaks of about five minutes. In this way you will help yourself to keep concentrating. Follow each study session by a slightly longer break for recreation and relaxation.

If you are working in the evening, begin work as early as possible, leaving yourself time to relax and do something different before going to bed.

Where to study   If possible, work in a quiet room which is not too warm but well ventilated and away from distractions. A desk or table, on which you can spread your books, is ideal for working on. The light should be good: the best form of lighting being a reading lamp.

Try to make somewhere 'your study place'. This can have a good psychological effect on you, helping you to settle down to work more easily, and on your friends and family, who will know that you are studying there and, hopefully, not disturb you unnecessarily. It also saves time during study periods if you can keep all your books, paper, calculator and other essential equipment at hand in one place.

How to study   Once you know which topics you must revise for your syllabus it will be easier to revise them first in the order in which they appear in this book. When revising you need to have with you a pen or pencil and an exercise book in which to make notes and 'do some Mathematics'.

Throughout the book key words and phrases are given in **bold type**. You should know the meaning of these words as they are likely to occur in examination questions. One way to learn these words is to make your own glossary. To do this label each page in a small notebook with a letter of the alphabet. When you meet a key word write it on the appropriate page of your glossary and beside it write down its meaning. In this way you will build up your own mathematical dictionary.

While you are working on a topic in the book, jot down notes and try to work through the mathematics for yourself. **Simply reading through the topic will not do**. When you come to an example, cover the given solution and try to answer the question yourself in your exercise book. Then compare your working with that given in the book. When you feel that you understand a topic, try to answer some questions from Section III, the Self-test units (pages 149–199), on that topic. Section III also shows you the different types of examination question you might meet and gives you some hints on answering questions. If you have difficulty in answering these questions, you should work through the topic again before trying them a second time. You can also practise answering other questions from past examination papers which you can buy directly from your Board (address on page 7). If you are a pupil at school your teacher should have a stock of these papers.

Test yourself regularly. Write out important definitions, formulae, *etc.*, checking them against the units and Formula check list (pages 203–211) in this book. Rework problems you have solved before, without looking at your previous solutions, as well as attempting questions that you have not looked at before.

Make special revision notes for quick reference on cards which you can keep in your pocket and look at in spare moments. Hang charts giving definitions, formulae, *etc.*, on the wall of your study room.

Try questions in mock examination conditions. Allow yourself only the 'examination time' for each question and the equipment you can take into the examination room. Save a few complete examination papers so that you can use them to practise your examination technique: do them as mock examinations 'against the clock' and in 'examination conditions'. Section IV gives you some hints for the examination itself.

SOME USEFUL SYMBOLS

Throughout this book you will find mathematical symbols which you must remember. Below is a short list of some of the most common ones. At the side of each there is an explanation of its meaning and an example of its use.

Symbol	Meaning	Example
$=$	is equal to	$6 \div 2 = 3$
$\neq$	is not equal to	$8 \times 5 \neq 21$
$\approx$	is approximately equal to	$3.142 \approx 3.14$
$<$	is less than	$4 < 5$
$\leqslant$	is less than or equal to	if x is a positive integer and $x \leqslant 2$ then $x = 1$ or 2
$>$	is greater than	$8 > 5$
$\geqslant$	is greater than or equal to	if x is a negative integer and $x \geqslant -2$ then $x = -2$ or -1
$^\circ$	degrees	45° means '45 degrees'
$\angle$	angle	$\angle A = 45^\circ$ means 'angle A equals 45°'
$\sqrt{\ }$	the positive square root of	$\sqrt{4}$ means 'the positive square root of 4', *i.e.* 2
$\pm$	positive or negative	± 2 means '2 or -2'
$\Rightarrow$	implies	$x = 2 \Rightarrow x^2 = 4$

Table 1: Analysis of examination syllabuses

	AEB				Cambridge	JMB	London		NI	Oxford		O and C	SUJB		WJEC		
Level	GCE	GCE	GCE	GCE	GCE	G	G	G	G	GCE	GCE	GCE	GCE	GCE	G/C	G/C	G/C
Syllabus	100	101	102	103	D	B	A	B		4851	4852		A	B	P1 P2	P1 P4	P2 P3
1 Sets & algebra of sets	●	●	●	●	●		●	●	●	O	●	●		●	●	●	●
2 Numbers	●	●	●	●	●	●	●	●	●	●	●	●	●	●	●	●	●
3 Number bases	●	●	●	●						●	●			●			
4 Fractions	●	●	●	●	●	●	●	●	●	●	●	●	●	●	●	●	●
5 Decimals	●	●	●	●	●	●	●	●	●	●	●	●	●	●	●	●	●
6 Standard form & significant figures	●	●	●	●	●	●	●	●	●	●	●	●	●	●	●	●	●
7 Units of measure	●	●	●	●	●	●	●	●	●	●	●	●	●	●	●	●	●
8 Time & timetables	●	●	●	●	●	●	●	●	●	●	●	●	●	●	●	●	●
9 Conversion	●	●	●	●	●	●	●	●	●	●	●	●	●	●	●	●	●
10 Squares & square roots	●	●	●	●	●	●	●	●	●	●	●	●	●	●	●	●	●
11 Perimeters & areas of plane shapes	●	●	●	●	●	●	●	●	●	●	●	●	●	●	●	●	●
12 Vol. & surface area of solid shapes	●	●	●	●	●	●	●	●	●	●	●	●	●	●	●	●	●
13 Ratio, proportion & scale	●	●	●	●	●	●	●	●	●	●	●	●	●	●	●	●	●
14 Percentages	●	●	●	●	●	●	●	●	●	●	●	●		●	●	●	●
15 Money	●	●	●	●	●	●	●	●	●	●	●	●	●	●	●	●	●
16 Averages	●	●	●	●	●	●	●	●	●	●	●	●	●	●	●	●	●
17 Symmetry	●	●	●	●	●	●	●	●	●	●	●	●	●	●			
18 Composition tables					●				●								
19 Simple algebra	●	●	●	●	●		●	●	●	●	●	●		●	●	●	●
20 Linear equations	●	●	●	●	●	●	●	●	●	●	●	●	●	●	●	●	●
21 Relations & functions	●	●		●			●	●	●				●				●
22 Co-ordinates	●	●	●	●	●		●	●	●	●	●	●	●		●	●	●
23 The straight line	●	●	●	●	●		●	●	●	●	●	●	●	●	●	●	●
24 Simultaneous equations	●	●	●	●	●	●	●	●	●	●	●	●	●	●	●	●	●
25 Inequalities & linear programming	a	a	●	●	●		a	a	●	O	●	●		●	a		a
26 Matrices	●	●	●	●	●		●	●	●	O	●			O	●		●
27 Factorisation	●	●	●	●	●	●	●	●	●	●	●	●	●	●	●	●	●
28 Algebraic fractions	●	●	●	●	●		●	●	●	●	●	●	●				●
29 Quadratics	●	●	●	●	●		●	●	●	●	●	●	●	●	●		●
30 Algebraic graphs	●	●	●	●	●		●	●	●	●	●	●	●	●			●
31 Indices & logarithms	●	●	●	●	c	●	c	c	c	c	●		c	c			c
32 Transformation of formulae	●	●	●	●	●	●	●	●	●	●	●	●	●	●			●
33 Variation	●	●	●				●	●	●	●	●	●	●	●			●
34 Angles & parallels	●	●	●	●	●		●	●	●	●	●	●	●	●	●	●	●
35 Quadrilaterals	●	●	●	●	●		●	●	●	●	●	●	●	●	●	●	●
36 Similarity & congruence	●	●	●	●	●		●	●	●	●	●	●	●	●	●	●	●
37 Bearings & scale drawing	●	●	●	●			●	●	●	●	●	●	●	●			●
38 Isometries & enlargement	●	●	●	●	●		●	●	●	O	●	●	●	●			●
39 Shear & stretch				●	●					O	●						
40 Pythagoras' theorem	●	●	●	●	●		●	●	●	●	●	●	●	●			●
41 Trigonometry	●	●	●	●	●		●	●	●	●	●	●	●	●			●
42 The sine & cosine rules	●	●	●	●	●		●	●			O	●	●	O			●
43 Further trigonometry		●	●	●	●		●	●	●	●	●	●	●	O			●
44 Three-dimensional trigonometry	●		●	●	●		●	●	●	●	●	●	●	●			●
45 The circle	●	●	●	●	●		●	●	●	●	●	●	●	●	●		●
46 Arc length, sectors, & segments	●	●	●	●	●		●	●	●	●	●	●	●	●	●		●
47 Latitude & longitude		●	●	●	●		●	●		●	●	●	●	O			
48 Constructions & loci	●	●	●	c	●		●	●	●	●	●	●	●	●	●	●	●
49 Vectors	●	●	●	●			●	●	●	●	●	O	●	O	●		●
50 Graphical representation of data	●	●				●	●	●	●	O	●	●	●	O	●	●	●
51 Probability			●		●		●	●		O	●						
52 Calculus	●		●			●		●	●	O	O						
53 Graphs in kinematics	●	●	●	●	●	●	●	●	●	O	●	●	●	●	●	●	●
54 Use of tables or calculator	●	●	●	●	●	●	●	●	●	●	●	●	●	●	●	●	●
55 Approximations & errors	●	●	●	●	●	●	●	●	●	●	●	●	●	●	●	●	●

Key (see also page 1):

ALSEB		EAEB				EMREB	LREB		NI	NREB	NWREB		SREB			SEREB	SWEB	WMEB	YHREB			SCEEB
CSE	CSE	C	C	C	C	C	C	C	C	C	CSE	CSE	CSE	CSE	CSE	CSE	CSE	C	CSE	CSE	CSE	O
A	B	†	‡	‖	$	1	A	B	A	F	A	B	RA	RB	RC				A	B	C	
	•	O	•	O	•	•	•	•	•	•		•		•	•	•	•	•		•	•	•
•	•	•	•	•	•	•	•	•	•	•	•	•	•	•	•	•	•	•	•	•	•	•
•	•	•	•	•	•	•	•	•	•		•	•		•	•	•	•	•	•	•	•	•
•	•	•	•	•	•	•	•	•		•	•	•	•	•	•	•	•	•	•	•	•	•
•	•	•	•	•	•	•	•	•	•	•	•	•	•	•	•	•	•	•	•	•	•	•
•	•	•	•	•	•	•	•	•	•	•	•	•	•	•	•	•	•	•	•	•	•	•
•	•	•	•	•	•	•	•	•	•	•	•	•	•	•	•	•	•	•	•	•	•	•
•	•	•	•	•	•	•	•	•	•	•	•	•	•	•	•	•	•	•	•	•	•	•
•	•	•	•	•	•	•	•	•	•	•	•	•	•	•	•	•	•	•	•	•	•	•
•	•	•	•	•	•	•	•	•	•	•	•	•	•	•	•	•	•	•	•	•	•	•
•	•	•	•	•	•	•	•	•	•	•	•	•	•	•	•	•	•	•	•	•	•	•
•	•	•	•	•	•	•	•	•	•	•	•	•	•	•	•	•	•	•	•	•	•	•
•	•	•	•	•	•	•	•	•	•	•	•	•	•	•	•	•	•	•	•	•	•	•
•	•	•	•	•	•	•	•	•	•	•	•	•	•	•	•	•	•	•	•	•	•	•
•	•	•	•	•	•	•	•	•	•	•	•	•	•	•	•	•	•	•	•	•	•	•
	•		•		•	O	•	•			•		•	•	•	•	•	O		•	•	•
•	•	•	•	•	•	•	•	•	•	•	•	•	•	•	•	•	•	•	•	•	•	•
•	•	•	•	•	•	•	•	•	•	•	•	•	•	•	•	•	•	•	•	•	•	•
	•	•	•	•	•	•	•	•			•		•	•	•	•	•			•	•	•
•	•	•	•	•	•	•	•	•	•	•	•	•	•	•	•	•	•	•	•	•	•	•
•	•	•	•	•	•	O	•	•	•	•	•	•	•	•	•	•	•	•	•	•	•	•
•	•	•	•	•	•	•	•	•	•	•	•	•	•	•	•	•	•	•	•	•	•	•
a	a	O	•	O	•	a	•	•	a	a	•	•	a	•	a	a	a	•	a	•	•	•
	•	O	•	O	•	O			•	•		•		•	•	•	•	O		•	•	•
•	•	•	•	•	•	•	•	•	•	•	•	•	•	•	•	•	•	•	•	•	•	•
•		•	O		•		•	•		•	O		•	•	•	•	•	•	•	•	•	•
b	•	•	•	•	•	O	•	b	b	•	b	b	b	b	b	•	b	•	b	b	•	•
O	•	•	•	•	•	O	•	•	O	•	O	•	•	•	•	•	•	•	•	•	•	•
•	•	•	•	•	•	c	c	c	•	c	c	•	c	c	c	•	•	•	•	•	•	•
•	•	•	•	•	•	O	•	•	•	•	O	•	•	•	•	•	•	•	•	•	•	•
•	•	O	•	O	•	•	•	•	•	•	O	•	•	•	•	•	•	•	•	•	•	•
•	•	•	•	•	•	•	•	•	•	•	•	•	•	•	•	•	•	•	•	•	•	•
•	•	•	•	•	•	•	•	•	•	•	•	•	•	•	•	•	•	•	•	•	•	•
•	•	•	•	•	•	•	•	•	O	•	•	•	•	•	•	•	•	•	•	•	•	•
•	•	•	•	•	•	•	•	•	•	•	•	•	•	•	•	•	•	•	•	•	•	•
	•	O	•	O	•	•	•	•	•	•	•		•	•	•	•	•	•		•	•	•
	•	O	•	•	•	•	•	•			•		•	•	•	•	•			•	•	•
•	•	•	•	•	•	•	•	•	•	•	•	•	•	•	•	•	•	•	•	•	•	•
O		O	•	O	•	O		•		•	O		•	•	•	•	•			•		•
	•	O	•	•	•	O	•	•	•	•	O	•	•	•		•				•		•
O	•	•	•	O	•	O	•	•	O	•	O	•	•	•	•	•	•	•		•	•	•
•	•	•	•	•	•	O	•	•	•	•	•	•	•	•	•	O	•	O	•	•	•	•
•	•	•	•	O	•	•	•	•	•	•	•	•	•	•	•	•	•	O	•	•	•	•
O				O									•	•	•	•		O			•	•
•	•	•	e	•	•	•	e	•	•	•	•	•	•	•	e	•	•	•	•	•	e	•
	•	O	•	O	•	O	•	•	•	•	•	•	•	•	•	O	•	O		•	•	•
•	•	•	•	•	•	•	•	•	•	•	•	•	•	•	•	•	•	O	•	•	•	•
	•	O	•	O	•	•	•	•	•	O	•	•	•	•	•	•	•	O		•	•	•
O								O														
O		•	•	•	•	•	•	•	•	•	•	•	•	•	•	•	•	•	•	•	•	•
•	•	•	•	•	•	•	•	•	•	•	•	•	•	•	•	•	•	•	•	•	•	•
•	•	•	•	•	•	•	•	•	•	•	•	•	•	•	•	•	•	•	•	•	•	•

Table 2: Analysis of examination format

Board	Level	Syllabus	Number of papers	Form of examination	Project/ Course work assessment	Electronic calculator permitted	Maths. Tables (type)
AEB	GCE	100	3	P1–1h(20%), P2–$1\frac{1}{2}$h(30%), P3–$2\frac{1}{2}$h(50%)	None	Yes for P3	4 fig.
	GCE	101	3	P1–1h(20%), P2–$1\frac{1}{2}$h(30%), P3–$2\frac{1}{2}$h(50%)	None	Yes for P3	4 fig.
	GCE	102	3	P1–1h(20%), P2–$1\frac{1}{2}$h(30%), P3–$2\frac{1}{2}$h(50%)	None	Yes for P3	4 fig.
	GCE	103	3	P1–1h(20%), P2–$1\frac{1}{2}$h(30%), P3–$2\frac{1}{2}$h(50%)	None	Yes for P3	4 fig.
Cambridge	GCE	D	2	P1–$2\frac{1}{2}$h(50%), P2–$2\frac{1}{2}$h(50%)	None	Yes for P2	4 fig.
JMB	GCE	A	2	P1–$2\frac{1}{2}$h(50%), P2–$2\frac{1}{2}$h(50%)	None	Yes	4 fig.
	GCE	B	2	P1–$2\frac{1}{2}$h(50%), P2–$2\frac{1}{2}$h(50%)	None	Yes	4 fig.
London	GCE	B	2	P1–$1\frac{1}{4}$h($33\frac{1}{3}$%), P2–$2\frac{1}{2}$h($66\frac{2}{3}$%)	None	Yes for P2	3 or 4 fig. (P2)
NI	GCE		2	P1–$2\frac{1}{2}$h, P2–$2\frac{1}{2}$h	None	Yes for P2	4 fig.
Oxford	GCE	4851	2	P1–$2\frac{1}{2}$h(50%) + P2–$2\frac{1}{2}$h(50%) or P3–$2\frac{1}{2}$h(50%)	None	Yes for P3	4 fig.
	GCE	4852	2	P1–$2\frac{1}{2}$h(50%) + P2–$2\frac{1}{2}$h(50%) or P3–$2\frac{1}{2}$h(50%)	None	Yes for P3	3 or 4 fig.
O + C	GCE		2	P1–2h, P2–2h	None	Yes for P2	4 fig.
SUJB	GCE	A	2	P1–$2\frac{1}{2}$h, P2–$2\frac{1}{2}$h	None	Yes	4 fig.
		B	2	P1–$2\frac{1}{2}$h, P2–$2\frac{1}{2}$h	None	Yes	3 fig.
WJEC	GCE(C)/CSE(1)		2	P1–2h, P2–2h Optional P3–$2\frac{1}{2}$h		Yes except for P1	4 fig.
	GCE(D)/CSE(2)		2	P1–2h, P4–2h Od–Trigonometry			
	GCE(A)/CSE(1)		2	P2–2h, P3–$2\frac{1}{2}$h Oe–Coordinate Geometry and Calculus			
ALSEB	CSE	A	2	P1–$1\frac{1}{2}$h(40%), P2–2h(30%)	TA(30%)	Yes for P2	4 fig.
	CSE	B	2	P1–$1\frac{1}{2}$h(35%), P2–$1\frac{1}{2}$h(35%)	TA(30%)	Yes for P2	4 fig.
EAEB	CSE	N/8/-/A	2	P1–$2\frac{1}{2}$h(50%), P2–$2\frac{1}{2}$h(50%)	None	Yes for P2	3 or 4 fig.
	CSE	N/8/-/B	2	P1–$2\frac{1}{2}$h(50%), P2–$2\frac{1}{2}$h(50%)	None	Yes for P2	3 or 4 fig.
	CSE	S/8/-/A	2	P1–2h(50%), P2–2h(50%)	None	Yes for P2	3 or 4 fig.
	CSE	S/8/-/B	2	P1–2h(50%), P2–2h(50%)	None	Yes	3 or 4 fig.
EMREB	CSE	1	2 or 3	P1–1h(30%), P2–$1\frac{1}{2}$h(30%), P3–$2\frac{1}{4}$h(40%)	TA(40%) (instead of P3)	No except in P3	3 or 4 fig.
LREB	CSE	A	2	P1–2h(50%), P2–2h(50%)	None	Yes	3 fig.
	CSE	B	2	P1–2h(50%), P2–2h(50%)	None	Yes	3 fig.
NI	CSE	A	3	P1–$1\frac{1}{4}$h($33\frac{1}{3}$%), P2–$1\frac{1}{2}$h($33\frac{1}{3}$%), P3–$1\frac{3}{4}$h($33\frac{1}{3}$%)	None	No	3 fig.
NREB	CSE	F	3	P1–$1\frac{1}{4}$h(20%), P2–$1\frac{1}{2}$h(30%), P3–2h(30%)	TA(20%)	Yes for P2 + P3	3 or 4 fig.
NWREB	CSE	A	2 or 3	P1–1h(30%), P2–$1\frac{1}{2}$h(40%), P3–$1\frac{1}{2}$h(30%)	TA(30%) (instead of P3)	Yes for P3	3 fig.
	CSE	B	2 or 3	P1–1h(30%), P2–1h(20%), P3–2h(50%)	TA(20%) (instead of P2)	Yes for P3	3 fig.
SREB	CSE	RA	2	P1–2h(40%), P2–$2\frac{1}{2}$h(60%)	None	Yes for P2	3 fig.
	CSE	RB	2	P1–2h(40%), P2–$2\frac{1}{2}$h(60%)	None	Yes for P2	3 fig.
	CSE	RC	2	P1–2h(40%), P2–$2\frac{1}{2}$h(60%)	None	Yes for P2	3 fig.
SEREB	CSE		2	P1–1h(20%), P2–$1\frac{1}{2}$h(30%)	TA(50%)	Yes for P2	3 or 4 fig.
SWEB	CSE		2	P1–2h(50%), P2–2h(50%)	None	Yes for P2	3 or 4 fig.
WMEB	CSE		2	P1–$2\frac{1}{2}$h(50%), P2–$2\frac{1}{2}$h(50%)	None	Yes for P2	4 fig.
YHREB	CSE	A	2	P1–2h, P2–2h	TA	Yes for P2	4 fig.
	CSE	B	2	P1–2h, P2–2h	TA	Yes for P2	4 fig.
	CSE	C	2	P1–2h, P2–2h	TA	Yes for P2	3 fig.
	CSE	D	2	P1–$2\frac{1}{2}$h(50%), P2–$2\frac{1}{2}$h(50%)	None	No	4 fig.
	CSE	E	2	P1–$2\frac{1}{2}$h(50%), P2–$2\frac{1}{2}$h(50%)	None	No	4 fig.
SCEEB	O		2	P1–$1\frac{3}{4}$h(80 marks), P2–2h(100 marks)	None	Yes	3 fig.

Key: P1–$2\frac{1}{2}$h(50%): Paper 1 is a $2\frac{1}{2}$ hour paper and carries 50% of total marks.
TA(20%): Teacher Assessment contributes 20% of total marks.
3 or 4 fig. (P2): 3 or 4 figure tables can be used for paper 2.

EXAMINATION BOARDS

GCE Boards

AEB	Associated Examining Board Wellington House, Aldershot, Hampshire GU11 1BQ
Cambridge	University of Cambridge Local Examinations Syndicate Syndicate Buildings, 17 Harvey Road, Cambridge CB1 2EU
JMB	Joint Matriculation Board, Manchester M15 6EU
London	University Entrance and School Examinations Council University of London, 66–72 Gower Street, London WC1 6EE
Oxford	Oxford Local Examinations Delegacy of Local Examinations, Ewert Place, Summertown, Oxford OX2 7BX
O and C	Oxford and Cambridge Schools Examination Board 10 Trumpington Street, Cambridge; Elsfield Way, Oxford
SUJB	Southern Universities' Joint Board for School Examinations Cotham Road, Bristol BS6 6DD
WJEC	Welsh Joint Education Committee, 245 Western Avenue, Cardiff CF5 2YX

SCE Board

SEB	Scottish Examination Board Ironmills Road, Dalkeith, Midlothian EH22 1BR

CSE Boards

ALSEB	Associated Lancashire Schools Examining Board 77 Whitworth Street, Manchester M1 6HA
EAEB	East Anglian Examinations Board The Lindens, Lexden Road, Colchester, Essex CO3 3RL
EMREB	East Midland Regional Examinations Board Robins Wood House, Robins Wood Road, Apsley, Nottingham NG8 3NH
LREB	London Regional Examinations Board Lyon House, 104 Wandsworth High Street, London SW18 4LF
NREB	North Regional Examinations Board Wheatfield Road, Westerhope, Newcastle upon Tyne NE5 5JZ
NWREB	North West Regional Examinations Board Orbit House, Albert Street, Eccles, Manchester M30 0WL
SREB	Southern Regional Examinations Board, 53 London Road, Southampton SO9 4YL
SEREB	South East Regional Examinations Board Beloe House, 2/4 Mount Ephraim Road, Royal Tunbridge Wells, Kent TN1 1EU
SWEB	South Western Examinations Board 23–29 Marsh Street, Bristol BS1 4BP
WJEC	Welsh Joint Education Committee 245 Western Avenue, Cardiff CF5 2YX
WMEB	West Midlands Examinations Board Norfolk House, Smallbrook Queensway, Birmingham B5 4NJ
*WY&LREB**	West Yorkshire & Lindsey Regional Examining Board Scarsdale House, 136 Derbyshire Lane, Sheffield S8 8SE
*YREB**	Yorkshire Regional Examinations Board 31–33 Springfield Avenue, Harrogate, North Yorkshire HG1 2HW

*Yorkshire and Humberside Regional Examinations Board, at the *YREB* address, now embraces *WY & LREB* and *YREB*

Section II Core Units 1–55

1 Sets and algebra of sets

1.1 SETS

A **set** is a collection of **elements**. The elements are the **members** of the set. Braces { } are usually used to denote a set. For example, $S = \{2, 4, 6\}$ is a set with three members 2, 4 and 6.

A set can be described in one of the following ways:

(i) by listing all the members. The order of the members does not matter and each member is listed only once. For example, $A = \{1, 2, 3, 4, 5\}$.

(ii) by listing the first few members and then indicating that the pattern shown continues by the use of dots. For example, $Y = \{1, 3, 5, \ldots\}$.

(iii) by a verbal description or rule which would give the members. For example, $Y = \{\text{odd numbers}\}$.

(iv) by using an algebraic expression. For example, $A = \{x : 0 < x < 6,\ x \text{ an integer}\}$. (This is read: 'The set of members x is such that x is an integer greater than 0 and less than 6'.)

If an element e belongs to a set S, we write $e \in S$. If e does not belong to S, we write $e \notin S$. For example, if $S = \{\text{even numbers}\}$, then $2 \in S$ and $3 \notin S$.

The **order** of a set is the number of elements in the set. If a set S has m members, we write $n(S) = m$. For example, if S has 4 members, $n(S) = 4$ and the order of S is 4.

Two sets are **equal** if they have exactly the same members. For example, if $S = \{2, 4, 6\}$ and $T = \{6, 2, 4\}$, then $S = T$.

Two sets are said to be **equivalent** if they have the same number of members. For example, if $X = \{1, 2, 3\}$ and $Y = \{a, b, c\}$ then $n(X) = n(Y) = 3$ and the two sets X and Y are equivalent.

Two sets are said to be **disjoint** if they have no elements in common. For example, if $A = \{\text{even numbers}\}$ and $B = \{\text{odd numbers}\}$, then A and B are disjoint sets.

The **empty** or **null set** is the set with no members. It is usually denoted by { } or ϕ. For example, {quadrilaterals with three sides} $= \phi$. *Note*: $\{0\}$ is a set with one member, *viz.* zero (0), not a null set.

An **infinite set** is a set with an infinite number of members. The elements of such a set cannot be listed. For example, $E = \{\text{even numbers}\}$ is an infinite set.

A **finite set** is a set with a finite number of members. For example, $F = \{1, 7\}$ is a finite set with two members.

The **universal set** is the set which contains all possible members. It is usually denoted by $\mathscr{E}$. The context of a problem will usually make $\mathscr{E}$ clear. For example, if a problem is concerned with sets of whole numbers, then $\mathscr{E} = \{\text{integers}\}$.

The **complement** of a set S is the set of members of $\mathscr{E}$ which do not belong to S. The complement of S is written S'. For example, if $\mathscr{E} = \{2, 4, 6, 8\}$ and $S = \{2, 6\}$ then $S' = \{4, 8\}$.

1.2 SUBSETS

Let S and T be two sets. If all the members of S are also members of T, then S is called a **subset** of T, written $S \subset T$. For example, if $S = \{a, b\}$ and $T = \{a, b, c\}$ then $S \subset T$.

Every set has at least two subsets, the set itself and the empty set ϕ.

Every possible subset of a given set, except the set itself, is called a **proper subset**.

Example
List all the subsets of $S = \{1, 2, 3\}$.

The subsets of S are:

$$\phi, \{1\}, \{2\}, \{3\}, \{1, 2\}, \{2, 3\}, \{1, 3\}, \{1, 2, 3\}.$$

1.3 OPERATIONS ON SETS

The **union** of two sets A and B, written $A \cup B$, is another set whose members belong to either A or B or both. For example, if $A = \{1, 2\}$ and $B = \{2, 3, 4\}$ then $A \cup B = \{1, 2, 3, 4\}$.

The **intersection** of two sets A and B, written $A \cap B$, is another set whose members belong to both A and B. For example, if $A = \{1, 2\}$ and $B = \{2, 3, 4\}$ then $A \cap B = \{2\}$. If $A \cap B = \phi$, then A and B are **disjoint** sets, *i.e.* they have no members in common.

The **symmetric difference** of two sets A and B, written $A \triangle B$, is another set whose members belong to the union of the two sets but do not belong to the intersection set. For example, if $A = \{1, 2\}$ and $B = \{2, 3, 4\}$ then $A \triangle B = \{1, 3, 4\}$.

The **Cartesian Product** of two sets A and B, written $A \times B$, is the set of all possible ordered pairs consisting of a first element from A and a second element from B, *i.e.*: $A \times B = \{(a, b): a \in A, \; b \in B\}$. For example, if $A = \{1, 2\}$ and $B = \{3, 5, 7\}$ then $A \times B = \{(1, 3), (1, 5), (1, 7), (2, 3), (2, 5), (2, 7)\}$.

Laws of union, intersection and symmetric difference

If A, B and C are any three sets, then the following laws hold:

The **commutative** laws: (*i*) for union: $\qquad\qquad\qquad A \cup B = B \cup A$

(*ii*) for intersection: $\qquad\qquad\quad A \cap B = B \cap A$

(*iii*) for symmetric difference: $\qquad A \triangle B = B \triangle A$

The **associative** laws: (*i*) for union: $\qquad\qquad\qquad A \cup (B \cup C) = (A \cup B) \cup C$

(*ii*) for intersection: $\qquad\qquad\quad A \cap (B \cap C) = (A \cap B) \cap C$

(*iii*) for symmetric difference: $\quad A \triangle (B \triangle C) = (A \triangle B) \triangle C$

The **distributive** laws (*i*) for intersection over union: $A \cap (B \cup C) = (A \cap B) \cup (A \cap C)$

(*ii*) for union over intersection: $A \cup (B \cap C) = (A \cup B) \cap (A \cup C)$

The **absorption** laws: (*i*) $A \cup (A \cap B) = A$

(*ii*) $A \cap (A \cup B) = A$

De Morgan's Laws: $(A \cup B)' = A' \cap B'$

$(A \cap B)' = A' \cup B'$.

If A is any set, $\mathscr{E}$ the universal set and ϕ the empty set, then:

$$A \cup A = A \qquad \mathscr{E} \cup A = \mathscr{E} \qquad A \cup \phi = A \qquad \mathscr{E} \cup \phi = \mathscr{E}$$
$$A \cap A = A \qquad \mathscr{E} \cap A = A \qquad A \cap \phi = \phi \qquad \mathscr{E} \cap \phi = \phi.$$

1.4 VENN DIAGRAMS

Venn diagrams are pictures which help to illustrate relationships between sets.

The universal set is usually shown by a rectangle and subsets of this set are shown by closed curves.

Figure 1.1 shows the relationships between sets using six Venn diagrams:

 (*i*) The shaded area represents A, the unshaded area represents A'.

(*ii*) The shaded area represents $A \cup B$.

(*iii*) The shaded area represents $A \cap B$.

(*iv*) The shaded area represents $A \triangle B$.

 (*v*) Shows two disjoint sets A and B.

(*vi*) Shows three sets in which $A \subset B$ and $B \subset C$.

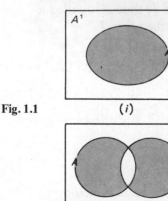

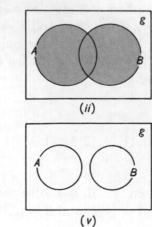

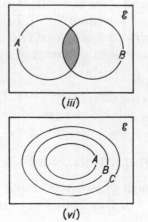

Fig. 1.1   (*i*)   (*ii*)   (*iii*)

(*iv*)   (*v*)   (*vi*)

Venn diagrams are useful for solving problems of the following type:

Example

In a sports club of 30 members, 17 play soccer, 19 play rugby and 2 do not play either. How many play (a) both soccer and rugby, (b) soccer only, and (c) rugby only?

First draw two intersecting circles to represent the members who play soccer (S) and rugby (R), (Fig. 1.2).

Next, list the given information at the side of the diagram:

$n(S) = 17$ $n(\mathscr{E}) = 30$
$n(R) = 19$ 2 play neither game.

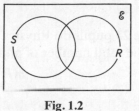

Fig. 1.2

Next begin to fill in the number of members who play the different games, *starting at the centre of the diagram.*

Since we do not know how many members play both games, we must let $n(S \cap R) = x$, (Fig. 1.3).

$n(S) = 17 = x + (17 - x)$

$n(R) = 19 = x + (19 - x)$

$n(S \cap R) = x.$

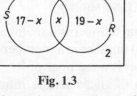

Fig. 1.3

Since we know there are 30 members of the club altogether, we have from the diagram,

$$(17 - x) + x + (19 - x) + 2 = 30$$
$$38 - x = 30$$
$$x = 8.$$

(*a*) So 8 members play both soccer and rugby.

(*b*) $(17 - x)$ members play soccer only, *i.e.* $17 - 8 = 9$ members play soccer only.

(*c*) $(19 - x)$ members play rugby only, *i.e.* $19 - 8 = 11$ members play rugby only.

Harder examples usually require three sets to be included as well as the universal set.

Example

In the sixth form of a school a pupil who studies science does one or more of the subjects Physics, Chemistry, Biology. In a group of science pupils 33 do Biology, 15 do Biology only, 2 do Chemistry only, 7 do Physics only, 15 do Biology and Chemistry, 11 do Biology and Physics and 13 do Physics and Chemistry. How many people do (a) all three subjects, (b) Chemistry, (c) Physics? How many science pupils are there altogether in the group?

Draw three intersecting circles to represent the pupils who do Physics (P), Chemistry (C) and Biology (B), (Fig. 1.4).

List the given information at the side of the diagram.

Begin to fill in the numbers of pupils doing the different combinations of subjects, starting at the centre of the diagram.

Let $n(P \cap C \cap B) = x$

$n(B) = 33,$ 15 do B only, 2 do C only, 7 do P only.

$n(B \cap C) = 15$ also $n(B \cap C) = x + (15 - x)$

$n(B \cap P) = 11$ also $n(B \cap P) = x + (11 - x)$

$n(P \cap C) = 13$ also $n(P \cap C) = x + (13 - x).$

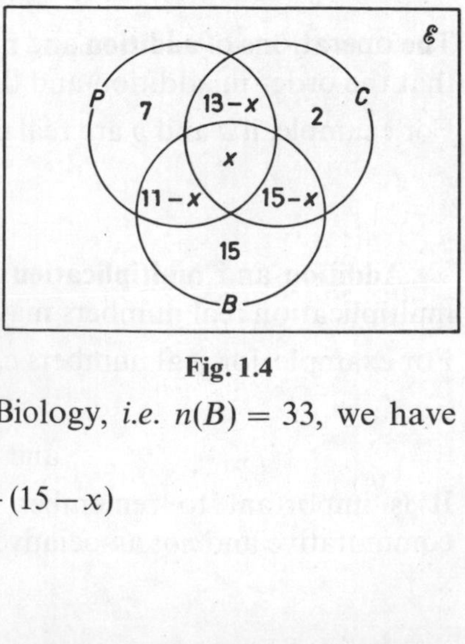

Fig. 1.4

Since we know the total number of pupils who do Biology, *i.e.* $n(B) = 33$, we have from the diagram:

(*a*)
$$33 = 15 + (11 - x) + x + (15 - x)$$
$$i.e.\ 33 = 41 - x, \text{ so } x = 8$$

Hence 8 pupils do all three subjects.

(b)
$$n(C) = 2 + (15 - x) + x + (13 - x)$$
$$= 30 - x = 22, \text{ since } x = 8$$

Hence 22 pupils do Chemistry.

(c)
$$n(P) = 7 + (13 - x) + x + (11 - x)$$
$$= 31 - x = 23, \text{ since } x = 8$$

Hence 23 pupils do Physics.

The total number of pupils altogether, *i.e.* $n(P \cup C \cup B)$, is given by:
$$n(P \cup C \cup B) = 33 + 7 + (13 - x) + 2$$
$$= 42 + 13 - 8 = 47.$$

---

2 Numbers

2.1 REAL NUMBERS

A **counting number** is a member of $\{1, 2, 3, \ldots\}$.

A **natural number** is a member of $\{0, 1, 2, \ldots\}$.

An **integer** is a member of $\{\ldots {}^-3, {}^-2, {}^-1, 0, 1, 2, 3, \ldots\}$.

Each of these sets is infinite, *i.e.* each set contains an infinite number of members. However, the first two sets each contain a smallest member (1 and 0 respectively), but the set of integers has neither a smallest member nor a largest member.

A **rational number** is a number of the form $\dfrac{p}{q}$ $(q \neq 0)$ where p and q are both integers.

For example, $\dfrac{1}{2}, \dfrac{7}{43}$ and $\dfrac{1979}{2001}$ are all rational numbers.

An **irrational number** is one which is not rational, *i.e.* a number which cannot be written in the form $\dfrac{p}{q}$ $(q \neq 0)$ where p and q are both integers.

For example, $\sqrt{2}$ is an irrational number, *i.e.* it is not possible to find the ratio of two integers which when squared equal 2. π is another irrational number.

All these numbers—counting, natural, integer, rational and irrational—together form the set of **real numbers**. Indeed, if they are all put on a line in order of size, there are no holes or gaps and the line is called a **real number line**.

Figure 2.1 shows part of the real number line. The positions of some of the different types of numbers are also shown.

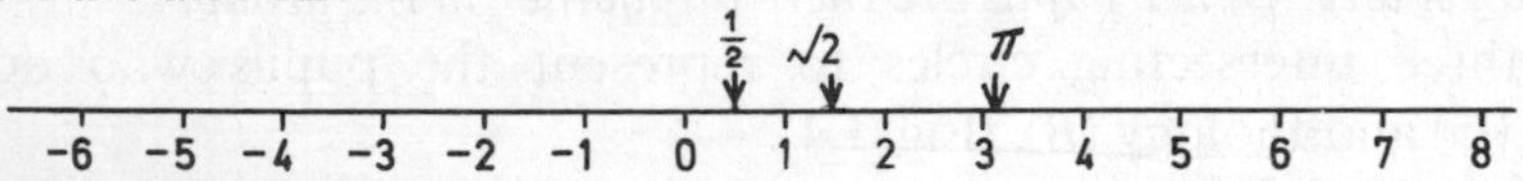

Fig. 2.1

2.2 OPERATIONS ON REAL NUMBERS

The operations of **addition** and **multiplication** on real numbers are **commutative**. This means that the order in addition and the order in multiplication of real numbers does not matter.

For example, if a and b are real numbers, then
$$a + b = b + a$$
and $ab = ba$.

Addition and **multiplication** are also **associative** for real numbers, *i.e.* in addition and multiplication real numbers may be bracketed in any way without their value changing.

For example, for real numbers a, b and c
$$(a + b) + c = a + (b + c)$$
and $(a \times b) \times c = a \times (b \times c)$.

It is important to remember that subtraction and division of real numbers are *not* commutative and *not* associative.

Multiplication is also **distributive over addition** (and subtraction). For example, if a, b and c are real numbers, then

$$a(b+c) = ab+ac \quad \text{(left distributive law)}$$
$$(a+b)c = ac+bc \quad \text{(right distributive law)}.$$

The **identity element** for **addition** is zero (0), since, if p is any real number, then

$$p+0 = 0+p = p.$$

The **additive inverse** of p is (^-p) and read as '**negative** p', since, if p is any real number, then

$$p+(^-p) = (^-p)+p = 0.$$

For example, $3+{}^-3 = {}^-3+3 = 0$ and $^-3$ is the additive inverse of 3. Likewise, 3 is the additive inverse of $^-3$.

Two similar results are true for the operation multiplication.

The **identity element** for **multiplication** is 1, since if q is any real number, then

$$q \times 1 = 1 \times q = q.$$

The **multiplicative inverse** of $q(q \neq 0)$ is $\dfrac{1}{q}$, the **reciprocal** of q, since

$$q \times \frac{1}{q} = \frac{1}{q} \times q = 1.$$

For example, $3 \times \dfrac{1}{3} = \dfrac{1}{3} \times 3 = 1$ and $\dfrac{1}{3}$ is the multiplicative inverse of 3. Likewise, 3 i

the multiplicative inverse of $\dfrac{1}{3}$.

2.3 DIRECTED NUMBERS

Positive numbers (*e.g.* $^+1, ^+2, ^+3, \ldots$) and negative numbers (*e.g.* $^-1, ^-2, ^-3, \ldots$) are often called **directed numbers**. Directed numbers can be combined using the operations addition, subtraction, multiplication and division. For example,

for addition:

$$^+2+{}^+5 = {}^+7, \qquad ^+7+{}^-4 = {}^+3, \qquad ^+3+{}^-8 = {}^-5, \qquad ^-3+{}^-5 = {}^-8;$$

for subtraction:

$$^+7-{}^+2 = {}^+5, \qquad ^+2-{}^+7 = {}^-5, \qquad ^-3-{}^-2 = {}^-1, \qquad ^-2-{}^-3 = {}^+1;$$

for multiplication:

$$^+2 \times {}^+3 = {}^+6, \qquad ^-2 \times {}^+3 = {}^-6, \qquad ^+2 \times {}^-3 = {}^-6, \qquad ^-2 \times {}^-3 = {}^+6;$$

for division:

$$^+6 \div {}^+3 = {}^+2, \qquad ^-6 \div {}^+3 = {}^-2, \qquad ^+6 \div {}^-3 = {}^-2, \qquad ^-6 \div {}^-3 = {}^+2.$$

The examples for addition and subtraction should be studied carefully. You may find that using a number line helps you to understand them (see Fig. 2.1).

For multiplication, the following rules should be remembered:

positive $\times$ positive $=$ positive   *i.e.* $(+) \times (+) = (+)$;

positive $\times$ negative $=$ negative   *i.e.* $(+) \times (-) = (-)$;

negative $\times$ positive $=$ negative   *i.e.* $(-) \times (+) = (-)$;

negative $\times$ negative $=$ positive   *i.e.* $(-) \times (-) = (+)$.

Similar rules apply if the multiplication sign ($\times$) is replaced by the division sign ($\div$).

2.4 NUMBER PATTERNS

Some subsets of the set of counting numbers make interesting patterns. Three well known ones are: **odd numbers** $1, 3, 5, 7, 9, \ldots$;

        even numbers $2, 4, 6, 8, 10, \ldots$;

        square numbers $1, 4, 9, 16, 25, \ldots$.

A **square number** can be represented by a square of dots:

$$1 \times 1 = 1 \qquad 2 \times 2 = 4 \qquad 3 \times 3 = 9 \qquad 4 \times 4 = 16 \qquad 5 \times 5 = 25$$
$$1^2 \qquad\qquad 2^2 \qquad\qquad 3^2 \qquad\qquad 4^2 \qquad\qquad 5^2$$

We include 1 in the set of square numbers for completeness.

A **rectangular number** can be represented by a rectangle of dots. (A line of dots is not considered to be a rectangle.)

For example, 12 is a rectangular number. It can be represented by two different patterns of dots:

$$2 \times 6 = 12 \qquad\qquad 3 \times 4 = 12$$

Notice that five dots do not make a rectangular pattern and so five is not a rectangular number.

The sequence of rectangular numbers is: 4, 6, 8, 9, 10, 12, 14, ...

A **triangular number** can be represented by a triangle of dots, for example:

represents 3. The sequence of triangular numbers is: 1, 3, 6, 10, 15, ...

A **prime number** is a counting number which is neither a square number nor a rectangular number.

If we take out of the set of counting numbers all the square and rectangular numbers, we are left with the set of prime numbers.

For example, 1, 2, 3, 4, 5, 6, 7, 8, 9, 10, 11, 12, 13, 14, ...

The sequence of prime numbers is: 2, 3, 5, 7, 11, 13, ...

Another description of a prime number is a number with two, and only two, factors, *viz.* 1 and itself (see unit 2.5).

2.5 FACTORS AND MULTIPLES

If an integer divides exactly into another integer (*i.e.* without leaving a remainder) the first number is called a **factor** of the second.

For example, 2 is a factor of 6 (since $6 \div 2 = 3$, a whole number).

If an integer divides exactly into another integer, the second number is called a **multiple** of the first. For example, 6 is a multiple of 2 and 15 is a multiple of 3.

A **prime factor** is a factor which is a prime number.

A very important result in arithmetic says that every integer greater than 1 can be written as a product of its prime factors in one, and only one way. (A product is the result of multiplication.)

For example:
$$294 = 2 \times 3 \times 7 \times 7$$
$$= 2 \times 3 \times 7^2$$

working
```
2 | 294
3 | 147
7 | 49
7 |  7
       1
```

The **highest common factor (HCF)** of two or more numbers is the largest number which will divide into them exactly (*i.e.* without leaving a remainder).

Example
Find the HCF of 84 *and* 108.

$$84 = 2 \times 2 \times 3 \times 7 \qquad \text{and} \qquad 108 = 2 \times 2 \times 3 \times 3 \times 3$$
$$= 2^2 \times 3 \times 7 \qquad\qquad\qquad = 2^2 \times 3^3$$

Since 2^2 is a factor of both 84 and 108
and 3 is a factor of both 84 and 108
$2^2 \times 3$ must be the largest factor of 84 and 108.

Therefore, $2^2 \times 3 = 12$ is the HCF of 84 and 108.

The **lowest common multiple (LCM)** of two or more numbers is the smallest number which is exactly divisible by them.

Example
Find the LCM of 28, 90 *and* 525.

$$28 = 2 \times 2 \times 7 \qquad 90 = 2 \times 3 \times 3 \times 5 \qquad 525 = 3 \times 5 \times 5 \times 7$$
$$ = 2^2 \times 7 \qquad\qquad = 2 \times 3^2 \times 5 \qquad\qquad = 3 \times 5^2 \times 7.$$

The LCM must contain 2^2, 3^2, 5^2 and 7 as factors, since these are the highest powers of the prime factors of 28 or 90 or 525.

Therefore, $2^2 \times 3^2 \times 5^2 \times 7 = 6300$ is the LCM of 28, 90 and 525.

2.6 SURDS

Since an irrational number cannot be expressed as a ratio of two integers its exact value cannot be stated as a decimal. We can say $\sqrt{2} \approx 1.414$ and $\sqrt{3} \approx 1.732$. However, if a calculation requires an exact result, irrational numbers such as these must be left in what is called **surd form**. That is, they must be left with the square root sign, for example $\sqrt{2}$ and $\sqrt{3}$.

Example
Simplify $\sqrt{300}$ *leaving your answer in surd form.*

$$\sqrt{300} = \sqrt{(3 \times 100)}$$
$$= \sqrt{3} \times \sqrt{100} \qquad \text{since} \qquad \sqrt{ab} = \sqrt{a} \times \sqrt{b}$$
$$= \sqrt{3} \times 10$$
$$= 10\sqrt{3}.$$

Two irrational numbers can be added if they each simplify to the same surd form.

Example
Simplify $\sqrt{8} + \sqrt{50}$.

$$\sqrt{8} + \sqrt{50} = \sqrt{(4 \times 2)} + \sqrt{(25 \times 2)}$$
$$= \sqrt{4} \times \sqrt{2} + \sqrt{25} \times \sqrt{2} \qquad \text{since} \qquad \sqrt{ab} = \sqrt{a} \times \sqrt{b}$$
$$= 2\sqrt{2} + 5\sqrt{2}$$
$$= (2 + 5)\sqrt{2}$$
$$= 7\sqrt{2}.$$

Two irrational numbers cannot be added if their surd forms are different.

Example
Simplify as far as possible $\sqrt{45} + \sqrt{48}$.

$$\sqrt{45} + \sqrt{48} = \sqrt{(9 \times 5)} + \sqrt{(3 \times 16)}$$
$$= \sqrt{9} \times \sqrt{5} + \sqrt{3} \times \sqrt{16}$$
$$= 3\sqrt{5} + 4\sqrt{3}$$

(which cannot be simplified further).

Irrational numbers, written in surd form, can be multiplied and divided as follows:

$$\sqrt{3} \times \sqrt{7} = \sqrt{(3 \times 7)} = \sqrt{21}$$
$$\sqrt{15} \div \sqrt{5} = \sqrt{(15 \div 5)} = \sqrt{3}.$$

If the division of surds is written in fractional form, the denominator is usually changed to a whole number.

For example:
$$\sqrt{3} \div \sqrt{7} = \frac{\sqrt{3}}{\sqrt{7}} = \frac{\sqrt{3} \times \sqrt{7}}{\sqrt{7} \times \sqrt{7}} = \frac{\sqrt{21}}{7}.$$

3 Number bases

3.1 DECIMAL NOTATION (Base 10)

The value of each digit in a numeral is dependent upon its position in the numeral. For example, in the numeral 3607 the left-hand digit has a value '3 thousands' and the right-hand digit has a value '7 units'. The numeral 3607 can be written using powers of 10 (see unit 27.1) as: $3607 = 3 \times 10^3 + 6 \times 10^2 + 0 \times 10^1 + 7 \times 10^0$.

We can show this also by writing the digits in columns:

Base 10 column headings:	thousands	hundreds	tens	units
or	1000	100	10	1
or	10^3	10^2	10^1	10^0
	3	6	0	7

This way of writing the number 3607 shows that we are using a base of 10 called **decimal notation**. Sometimes numbers written in decimal notation are called **denary numbers**.

3.2 CHANGING BASES

Numbers can be written using bases other than 10. The column headings used will be powers of the base. The largest digit which can appear in a numeral is always one less than the order of the base. For example, 7 is the largest digit which can appear in an octal (or base 8) numeral. Naturally, 9 is the largest digit used in base 10.

To change a base ten (decimal) number to another base, write down the column headings for the new base and then work out how many of each power of the base will be needed, starting at the largest possible power.

Example

Write 65 in base 3.

In base 3 the column headings are powers of 3. 3^4 or higher powers are not needed because $3^4 = 81$ and $81 > 65$.

Base 3 column headings:	3^3	3^2	3^1	3^0
or	27	9	3	1

Find the number of 27's in 65 first:

$$2 \times 27 = 54, \text{ so } 65 - 54 = 11 \text{ left.}$$

Then the number of 9's in 11:

$$1 \times 9 = 9, \text{ so } 11 - 9 = 2 \text{ left.}$$

There are no 3's left, only 2 units.

So $65_{10} = (2 \times 27) + (1 \times 9) + (0 \times 3) + (2 \times 1)$

$$= 2102_3.$$

To change any number to decimal notation, first set down the column headings for the base of the given number, write the number under the correct column headings and then multiply each digit by the appropriate column heading.

Example

Write 504_7 in decimal notation.

Here we have a 3 digit numeral and so need three column headings.

Base 7 column headings:	7^2	7^1	7^0
or	49	7	1
	5	0	4

So $504_7 = (5 \times 49) + (0 \times 7) + (4 \times 1)$

$$= 245 \quad + 0 \quad + 4$$

$$= 249 \text{ in decimal notation.}$$

To change a number in one base to another, first change the number into decimal notation and then from decimal notation into the new base.

3.3 BINARY NOTATION

Binary, or base 2, notation uses only two digits 0 and 1. The column headings in binary notation are all powers of 2.

Example

Write $110\,101\,111_2$ *in decimal notation.*

Base 2 column headings:

2^8	2^7	2^6	2^5	2^4	2^3	2^2	2^1	2^0
256	128	64	32	16	8	4	2	1
1	1	0	1	0	1	1	1	1

So $110\,101\,111_2$

$$= (1 \times 256) + (1 \times 128) + (0 \times 64) + (1 \times 32) + (0 \times 16) + (1 \times 8) + (1 \times 4) + (1 \times 2) + (1 \times 1)$$
$$= 256 + 128 + 32 + 8 + 4 + 2 + 1$$
$$= 431_{10}.$$

3.4 FRACTIONS

Just as in base 10, the point (.) is used in a numeral to indicate the position of the units digit, *i.e.* immediately to the left of the point.

Example

Change 101.101_2 *to decimal notation.*

Base 2 column headings:

2^2	2^1	2^0	.	2^{-1}	2^{-2}	2^{-3}
4	2	1	.	$\frac{1}{2}$	$\frac{1}{4}$	$\frac{1}{8}$
1	0	1	.	1	0	1

So $101.101_2 = (1 \times 4) + (0 \times 2) + (1 \times 1) + (1 \times \frac{1}{2}) + (0 \times \frac{1}{4}) + (1 \times \frac{1}{8})$

$$= 4 + 1 + \tfrac{1}{2} + \tfrac{1}{8}$$
$$= 5\tfrac{5}{8}$$
$$= 5.625 \text{ in decimal notation.}$$

3.5 OPERATIONS IN VARIOUS BASES

The operations of addition, subtraction, multiplication and division can be performed using numbers written in any base. The methods used are similar to those used for numbers written in decimal notation.

(The four bases used in this unit seem to be the most popular with examiners but these operations can be performed in any base.)

(a) Addition and multiplication

Remember that the 'carried' amount will vary in each base.

For example, in base 3 we 'carry lots of 3', *e.g.* $2 + 2 = 11_3$,

in base 8 we 'carry lots of 8', *e.g.* $6 + 7 = 15_8$, and so on.

The following additions (with the working shown) illustrate this and should be studied carefully.

Base 2	Base 3	Base 5	Base 8
1011	102	4213	674
+111	+22	+340	+376
10	201	22	1272
10100	1 1	10130	1 1
1 1		1 1 1	

The following examples illustrate multiplication in these four bases. Again, the amount carried differs in each base.

Base 2	Base 3	Base 5	Base 8
1011	102	431	7264
× 111	× 12	× 42	× 35
1011	211	1412	44604
10110	1	11	4142
101100	1020	33240	260340
1001101	2001	32	2121
1111	11	40202	325144
		111	1 1

(b) Subtraction

In subtraction, the amount 'borrowed' will vary with each base.

The following subtractions should be studied carefully; make sure you understand them. (No working is shown because there are two basic methods of subtraction. Follow your own method and fill in the missing working in pencil.)

Base 2	Base 3	Base 5	Base 8
1101	201	4301	7021
− 111	− 22	− 342	− 4564
110	102	3404	2235

(c) Division

The following two examples illustrate the process of division in base 2 and base 8.

They involve both multiplication and subtraction in these bases. Again, follow your own method of subtraction and fill in the missing working in pencil.

Division in base 2 is very easy since there are only two digits, 0 and 1. So, at each stage, the divisor will divide only once (1) or not at all (0).

Base 2	Base 8	
$\phantom{11\overline{)}}1011$	$\phantom{23\overline{)}}2714$ remainder 6	
$11\overline{)100001}$	$23\overline{)67052}$	
$\phantom{11\overline{)}}11$	$\phantom{23\overline{)}}46$	$(2 \times 23 = 46)$
$\phantom{11\overline{)}}100$	$\phantom{23\overline{)}}210$	
$\phantom{11\overline{)}}11$	$\phantom{23\overline{)}}205$	$(7 \times 23 = 205)$
$\phantom{11\overline{)}}11$	$\phantom{23\overline{)}}35$	
$\phantom{11\overline{)}}11$	$\phantom{23\overline{)}}23$	$(1 \times 23 = 23)$
$\phantom{11\overline{)}}00$	$\phantom{23\overline{)}}122$	
	$\phantom{23\overline{)}}114$	$(4 \times 23 = 114)$
	$\phantom{23\overline{)}}6$	

4 Fractions

A **common** or **vulgar fraction** is simply called a **fraction**.

In a fraction, *e.g.* $\dfrac{2}{3}$ ← the top number is called the **numerator**,
← the bottom number is called the **denominator**.

A **proper fraction** is one in which the numerator is less than the denominator, for example, $\frac{1}{2}$.

An **improper fraction** is one in which the numerator is bigger than the denominator, for example, $\frac{11}{5}$.

A **mixed number** is the sum of an integer and a fraction, for example, $3 + \frac{1}{4}$. This is usually written as $3\frac{1}{4}$.

Since an improper fraction is bigger than 1, it can be changed to a mixed number, for example, $\frac{7}{3} = 2\frac{1}{3}$.

4.1 EQUIVALENT FRACTIONS

Two fractions are said to be **equivalent** if they have the same value. The value of a fraction remains the same if both the numerator and denominator are multiplied by the same number ($\neq 0$).

For example, $\frac{2}{3}$ is equivalent to $\frac{4 \times 2}{4 \times 3} = \frac{8}{12}$.

To compare the size of two fractions, we must find two fractions equivalent to the given ones having the same denominator.

For example, to compare the size of $\frac{2}{3}$ and $\frac{3}{5}$ we first find two fractions equivalent to $\frac{2}{3}$ and $\frac{3}{5}$ having the same denominator.

Since the LCM of 3 and 5 (the two denominators) is 15,

$\frac{2}{3}$ is equivalent to $\frac{5 \times 2}{5 \times 3} = \frac{10}{15}$, and $\frac{3}{5}$ is equivalent to $\frac{3 \times 3}{3 \times 5} = \frac{9}{15}$.

Since $\frac{10}{15}$ is bigger than $\frac{9}{15}$ $\left(i.e. \frac{10}{15} > \frac{9}{15} \right)$, we can say that $\frac{2}{3} > \frac{3}{5}$.

If both the numerator and the denominator of a fraction contain a common factor, this factor may be cancelled and the value of the fraction remains the same. This is often called 'expressing the fraction in its **simplest form** or **lowest terms**'.

For example, $\frac{14}{16} = \frac{2^1 \times 7}{2_1 \times 8}$ which is equivalent to $\frac{7}{8}$.

4.2 OPERATIONS ON FRACTIONS

(a) Addition
Two fractions having the same denominator can be added together.

For example, $\frac{2}{7} + \frac{3}{7} = \frac{5}{7}$, *i.e.* two sevenths + three sevenths = five sevenths.

Two fractions having different denominators cannot be added directly. However, if two fractions equivalent to the given ones and having the same denominator are found, they can be added.

Example

Add $\frac{1}{7}$ and $\frac{5}{21}$.

$\frac{1}{7}$ and $\frac{5}{21}$ cannot be added directly.

But $\frac{1}{7}$ is equivalent to $\frac{3 \times 1}{3 \times 7} = \frac{3}{21}$.

So $\frac{1}{7} + \frac{5}{21} = \frac{3}{21} + \frac{5}{21} = \frac{8}{21}$.

If mixed numbers are to be added, the integers and fractions must be added separately.

Example

Evaluate $2\frac{1}{5} + 5\frac{9}{10}$.

$$2\frac{1}{5} + 5\frac{9}{10} = 7 + \frac{1}{5} + \frac{9}{10}$$

$$= 7 + \frac{2}{10} + \frac{9}{10}$$

$$= 7 + \frac{11}{10} = 7 + 1\frac{1}{10} = 8\frac{1}{10}.$$

(b) Subtraction
Two fractions having the same denominator can be subtracted.

For example, $\frac{5}{9} - \frac{4}{9} = \frac{1}{9}$, *i.e.* five ninths − four ninths = one ninth.

To subtract two fractions with different denominators, first find two fractions equivalent to them, having the same denominator.

Example

Subtract $\dfrac{4}{7}$ *from* $\dfrac{8}{9}$.

The LCM of 7 and 9 is 63.

$\dfrac{4}{7}$ is equivalent to $\dfrac{9 \times 4}{9 \times 7} = \dfrac{36}{63}$ and $\dfrac{8}{9}$ is equivalent to $\dfrac{7 \times 8}{7 \times 9} = \dfrac{56}{63}$

Hence, $\dfrac{8}{9} - \dfrac{4}{7} = \dfrac{56}{63} - \dfrac{36}{63} = \dfrac{20}{63}$.

If two mixed numbers are to be subtracted, first subtract the integers.

Example

Calculate $7\dfrac{5}{8} - 3\dfrac{1}{6}$.

$$7\dfrac{5}{8} - 3\dfrac{1}{6} = 4 + \dfrac{5}{8} - \dfrac{1}{6}$$

$$= 4 + \dfrac{15}{24} - \dfrac{4}{24} = 4\dfrac{11}{24}.$$

The problem sometimes arises where, having subtracted the integers, the second fraction is larger than the first.

Example

Work out $6\dfrac{1}{5} - 2\dfrac{2}{3}$.

$$6\dfrac{1}{5} - 2\dfrac{2}{3} = 4 + \dfrac{1}{5} - \dfrac{2}{3}$$

$$= 3 + 1 + \dfrac{1}{5} - \dfrac{2}{3} \quad \text{since } \dfrac{2}{3} > \dfrac{1}{5}$$

$$= 3 + \dfrac{6}{5} - \dfrac{2}{3} \quad \text{we can now subtract since } \dfrac{6}{5} > \dfrac{2}{3}$$

$$= 3 + \dfrac{18}{15} - \dfrac{10}{15}$$

$$= 3 + \dfrac{8}{15} = 3\dfrac{8}{15}.$$

(c) Multiplication

To multiply two fractions, multiply their numerators and multiply their denominators.

For example, $\dfrac{1}{2} \times \dfrac{3}{5} = \dfrac{1 \times 3}{2 \times 5} = \dfrac{3}{10}$.

If any factors are common to both the numerator and the denominator, they should be cancelled first.

For example, $\dfrac{3}{{}_2 8} \times \dfrac{4^1}{5} = \dfrac{3 \times 1}{2 \times 5} = \dfrac{3}{10}$.

If one or more of the numbers to be multiplied is a mixed number, first convert the mixed numbers to improper fractions.

Example

Evaluate $2\dfrac{5}{8} \times \dfrac{5}{7}$.

$2\dfrac{5}{8}$ is equivalent to $\dfrac{21}{8}$,

hence, $2\dfrac{5}{8} \times \dfrac{5}{7} = \dfrac{21}{8} \times \dfrac{5}{7} = \dfrac{15}{8} = 1\dfrac{7}{8}$.

(d) Division

The inverse of a fraction $\frac{a}{b}$ $(a, b \neq 0)$ is $\frac{b}{a}$ since $\frac{a}{b} \times \frac{b}{a} = 1$.

For example, the inverse of $\frac{2}{3}$ is $\frac{3}{2}$ since $\frac{2}{3} \times \frac{3}{2} = 1$.

To divide by a fraction, multiply by its inverse.

Example

Divide $\frac{2}{5}$ *by* $\frac{3}{4}$.

$$\frac{2}{5} \div \frac{3}{4} = \frac{2}{5} \times \frac{4}{3} \quad \text{multiplying by } \frac{4}{3}, \text{ the inverse of } \frac{3}{4},$$

$$= \frac{8}{15}.$$

If a mixed number is involved, first change it to an improper fraction.

Example

Divide $3\frac{1}{7}$ *by* $\frac{2}{5}$.

$$3\frac{1}{7} \div \frac{2}{5} = \frac{22}{7} \div \frac{2}{5} \quad \text{since } 3\frac{1}{7} = \frac{22}{7}$$

$$= \frac{22}{7} \times \frac{5}{2} \quad \text{multiplying by } \frac{5}{2}, \text{ the inverse of } \frac{2}{5},$$

$$= \frac{{}^{11}\cancel{22}}{7} \times \frac{5}{\cancel{2}_1}$$

$$= \frac{55}{7} = 7\frac{6}{7}.$$

5 Decimals

5.1 Introduction

Our ordinary number system is a **decimal** system, *i.e.* it is based on 10 (see unit 3.1). When writing a decimal number in columns the column headings are powers of ten. The **decimal point (.)** shows the position of the units digit: it is placed immediately after the units digit and before the decimal fraction.

... ← whole numbers →	.	← decimal fractions → ...		

...	thousands	hundreds	tens	units	.	tenths	hundredths	thousandths	...
	1000	100	10	1	.	$\frac{1}{10}$	$\frac{1}{100}$	$\frac{1}{1000}$	
	10^3	10^2	10^1	10^0	.	10^{-1}	10^{-2}	10^{-3}	
		2	5	6	.	7	4		

So the numeral 256.74 means:

 2 hundreds   5 tens   6 units   7 tenths   4 hundredths

When there are no whole numbers it is usual to write a zero in front of the decimal point. For example, .275 is usually written 0.275.

Decimal fractions, often just called decimals, are fractions whose denominators are powers of ten, *i.e.* 10, 100, 1000,.... The position of each digit in a numeral indicates its value.

For example, $0.4 = \dfrac{4}{10}$, $0.03 = \dfrac{3}{100}$, $0.007 = \dfrac{7}{1000}$,

$$0.295 = \dfrac{2}{10} + \dfrac{9}{100} + \dfrac{5}{1000} = \dfrac{295}{1000}.$$

5.2 DECIMAL PLACES

Decimal places (dp) come after the decimal point. For example, 72.591 has three decimal places (3 dp).

The digit in the *first* decimal place is *tenths*,
in the *second* decimal place is *hundredths*,
in the *third* decimal place is *thousandths*,
and so on.

Numbers can be **corrected** or **approximated** to a given number of decimal places.

To correct a number:
to 1 *dp*, look at the 2*nd dp*,
to 2 *dp*, look at the 3*rd dp*,
to 3 *dp*, look at the 4*th dp*,
and so on.

If the digit you look at is:

(*i*) less than 5, leave the digit in front of it alone;
(*ii*) 5 or more, add one to the digit in front of it.

Example
Correct the number 27.0375 to (*a*) 1 *dp*, (*b*) 2 *dp*, (*c*) 3 *dp*.

(*a*) 27.0375 = 27.0   (1 dp).

(*b*) 27.0375 = 27.04   (2 dp).

(*c*) 27.0375 = 27.038 (3 dp).

If an answer is to be given correct to a stated number of decimal places, then it must be calculated to at least one more decimal place than needed before it can be corrected.

Note: A calculator will often give answers with many more decimal places than required. These must be corrected to the stated number of decimal places as shown above.

5.3 OPERATIONS ON DECIMALS

(a) Addition and subtraction
When adding and subtracting numbers, care must be taken to set down digits with the same place value under each one. For numbers written with decimal points this is most easily done if they are set down with the decimal points in line.

Example
Evaluate (*i*) 274.28 + 36.075 + 0.92, (*ii*) 362.05 − 78.57.

```
(i)    274.28          (ii)    362.05
      + 36.075                 − 78.57
         0.92                  283.48
      _____
       311.275
```

(b) Multiplication and division by powers of 10
When **multiplying** a number:

by   10, *i.e.* 10^1, we move each *digit* 1 place to the *left*,
by   100, *i.e.* 10^2, we move each *digit* 2 places to the *left*,
by 1000, *i.e.* 10^3, we move each *digit* 3 places to the *left*,
and so on.

For example, the table below shows the result of multiplying the number $N = 24.17$ by 10, 100 and 1000.

	10 000	1000	100	10	units	.	$\frac{1}{10}$	$\frac{1}{100}$	
N				2	4	.	1	·7	
$10 \times N$			2	4	1	.	7		
$100 \times N$		2	4	1	7	.			
$1000 \times N$	2	4	1	7	0	.			

Note: A zero has been inserted in the units column to keep the place value correct.

When **dividing** a number:

    by   10, *i.e.* 10^1, we move each *digit* 1 place to the *right*,

    by 100, *i.e.* 10^2, we move each *digit* 2 places to the *right*,

    by 1000, *i.e.* 10^3, we move each *digit* 3 places to the *right*,

and so on.

For example, the table below shows the result of dividing the number $N = 5.79$ by 10, 100 and 1000.

	units	.	$\frac{1}{10}$	$\frac{1}{100}$	$\frac{1}{1000}$	$\frac{1}{10\,000}$	$\frac{1}{100\,000}$	
N	5	.	7	9				
$N \div 10$	0	.	5	7	9			
$N \div 100$	0	.	0	5	7	9		
$N \div 1000$	0	.	0	0	5	7	9	

Note: Zeros have been inserted into empty columns to keep the place value correct.

(c) Multiplication

To multiply decimals the 'quick way':

  (*i*) count the number of decimal places in the two numbers;

 (*ii*) forget the decimal points and multiply the numbers like whole numbers;

(*iii*) use the total number of decimal places to fix the position of the point in the answer.

It is a good idea to check your answer by finding an approximate answer (see unit 55).

Example

Evaluate 49.7×0.15.

$$
\begin{array}{r}
49.7 \longleftarrow 1\ dp \\
\times\, 0.15 \longleftarrow 2\ dp
\end{array} \Big\} total\ 3\ dp
$$

$$
\begin{array}{r}
\underline{} \\
2485 \\
4970 \\
\hline
7.455 \longleftarrow 3\ dp\ in\ answer
\end{array}
$$

Check: $49.7 \times 0.15 \approx 50 \times 0.2 = 10$—*right size of answer*.

(d) Division of a decimal by a whole number

To divide a decimal by a whole number, do the division as if both numbers were whole numbers, keeping the correct position of the decimal point.

Example
Divide 758.4 by 12.

$$
\begin{array}{r}
63.2 \\
12\overline{\smash{)}758.4} \\
72 \\
\hline
38 \\
36 \\
\hline
24 \\
24 \\
\hline
00 \\
\hline
\end{array}
$$

(e) Division of a decimal by a decimal

To divide a decimal by a decimal:

  (*i*) write the division as a fraction,

 (*ii*) change the denominator to a whole number by multiplying it by 10, 100, 1000,... as necessary and multiply the numerator by the same number,

(*iii*) work it out as in section (**d**).

Example
Evaluate $5.642 \div 0.13$.

$$
\begin{aligned}
5.642 \div 0.13 &= \frac{5.642}{0.13} \\
&= \frac{5.642 \times 100}{0.13 \times 100} \\
&= \frac{564.2}{13} \\
&= 43.4
\end{aligned}
$$

working
$$
\begin{array}{r}
43.4 \\
13\overline{\smash{)}564.2} \\
52 \\
\hline
44 \\
39 \\
\hline
52 \\
52 \\
\hline
00 \\
\hline
\end{array}
$$

5.4 CHANGING DECIMALS TO FRACTIONS AND FRACTIONS TO DECIMALS

Changing decimals less than 1 to fractions is easy because decimal fractions have denominators which are powers of 10, *i.e.* 10, 100, 1000,.... The 'column heading' of the last digit tells you the type of fraction.

For example, $0.2 = \frac{2}{10}$, $0.36 = \frac{36}{100}$, $0.054 = \frac{54}{1000}$ and so on.
↑ tenths   ↑ hundredths   ↑ thousandths

However, it is usual to express the fraction in its **lowest terms** after conversion.

For example, $0.2 = \frac{2}{10} = \frac{1}{5}$, $0.36 = \frac{36}{100} = \frac{9}{25}$, $0.054 = \frac{54}{1000} = \frac{27}{500}$.

Changing decimals bigger than 1 to fractions is done in a similar way. The whole numbers stay the same, the decimal fractions are changed as before.

For example, $5.8 = 5\frac{8}{10} = 5\frac{4}{5}$, $17.65 = 17\frac{65}{100} = 17\frac{13}{20}$.

To change a fraction to a decimal, divide the denominator into the numerator. This is done in the same way as dividing a decimal by a whole number (see unit 5.1(**d**)).

For example, $\frac{1}{4} = \frac{1.00}{4} = 0.25$, $\frac{5}{8} = \frac{5.000}{8} = 0.625$.

Not all fractions can be expressed as **terminating** decimals. Some fractions give **recurring** decimals.

For example, $\frac{1}{3} = 0.333\ldots$ which never terminates (stops). To show that the same pattern

of 3's continues we write $\frac{1}{3} = 0.\dot{3}$, which is read as 'nought point three recurring.'

Similarly, $\dfrac{1}{7} = 0.142857142857\ldots$

$$= 0.\dot{1}4285\dot{7}$$

Note: The dots are placed over the first and last digits of the group of recurring digits.

---

6 Standard form and significant figures

6.1 STANDARD FORM

When a positive number is written in **standard form**, it is written as $A \times 10^n$ where n is a positive or negative integer and $1 \leqslant A < 10$. For numbers less than 1, n is always negative.

This way of expressing positive numbers is very useful if the numbers are very large or very small.

Example

Express (a) 6 740 000, and (b) 0.00048 in standard form.

(a) $6\,740\,000 = 6.74 \times 1\,000\,000 = 6.74 \times 10^6$

(b) $0.00048 \quad = 4.8 \div 10\,000 = 4.8 \div 10^4 = 4.8 \times 10^{-4}$ (see unit 27.1(**4**)).

Remember: multiplying a number by 10^6 moves each digit 6 places to the left whereas multiplying a number by 10^{-4} (*i.e.* dividing it by 10^4) moves each digit 4 places to the right.

Arithmetical calculations are often simplified when standard form is used.

Example

Find the positive value of v in standard form, given that $\frac{1}{2}mv^2 = 6 \times 10^5$ and $m = 3 \times 10^{-3}$.

$$\tfrac{1}{2}mv^2 = 6 \times 10^5$$

$$v^2 = \frac{2 \times 6 \times 10^5}{3 \times 10^{-3}} \qquad \text{(since } m = 3 \times 10^{-3})$$

$$= 4 \times 10^8 \qquad \text{(since } 10^5 \div 10^{-3} = 10^5 \times 10^3 = 10^8)$$

Hence $v = 2 \times 10^4 \qquad$ (since $\sqrt{10^8} = 10^4$).

6.2 SIGNIFICANT FIGURES

The value of any digit in a number is dependent upon its position. We call the first non-zero digit the first **significant figure**.

These three numbers all have four significant figures (sf):

$$
\begin{array}{ccc}
3607, & 360.7, & 0.0003607 \\
\uparrow\ \uparrow & \uparrow\ \uparrow & \uparrow\ \uparrow \\
\text{1st 4th} & \text{1st 4th} & \text{1st 4th}
\end{array}
$$

In scientific experiments quantities are often measured. If we then use these measurements in a calculation, the answer we give cannot be more accurate than the measurements used. In many cases the answer must be rewritten to a smaller number of significant figures. We call this 'correcting to a stated number of significant figures'. It is essential to retain correct place values when doing this.

Example

Correct the number 187 340 to (a) 4 sf, (b) 3 sf, (c) 2 sf and (d) 1 sf.

(a) 187 340 correct to 4 sf is 187 300,

(b) 187 340 correct to 3 sf is 187 000,

(c) 187 340 correct to 2 sf is 190 000,

(d) 187 340 correct to 1 sf is 200 000.

Note: This is similar to correcting to a given number of decimal places. (See unit 5.3.) For example, in (c) to correct to 2 sf we look at the 3rd sf and as this is 5 or more we increase the 2nd sf by 1.

7 Units of measure

7.1 Metric units

The **metric units** of **length** are:

$$1 \text{ metre (m)} \quad = \quad 10 \text{ decimetres (dm)} \quad \left(\text{so } 1 \text{ dm} = \frac{1}{10} \text{ m or } 0.1 \text{ m}\right).$$

$$= \quad 100 \text{ centimetres (cm)} \quad \left(\text{so } 1 \text{ cm} = \frac{1}{100} \text{ m or } 0.01 \text{ m}\right).$$

$$= \quad 1000 \text{ millimetres (mm)} \left(\text{so } 1 \text{ mm} = \frac{1}{1000} \text{ m or } 0.001 \text{ m}\right).$$

1 **kilometre (km)** = 1000 m.

The prefixes deci-, centi-, milli, come from the Latin words for 10, 100, 1000.

The prefix kilo- comes from the Greek word for 1000.

The metric units of **mass** are:

$$1 \text{ kilogram (kg)} \quad = 1000 \text{ grams (g)} \quad \left(\text{so } 1 \text{ g} = \frac{1}{1000} \text{ kg or } 0.001 \text{ kg}\right).$$

$$1 \text{ milligram (mg)} = \frac{1}{1000} \text{ g or } 0.001 \text{ g}.$$

1 metric **tonne** = 1000 kg.

The metric units of **volume** are:

$$1 \text{ cubic metre (m}^3) = 1000 \text{ litres (l)} \quad \left(\text{so } 1 \text{ l} = \frac{1}{1000} \text{ m}^3 \text{ or } 0.001 \text{ m}^3\right).$$

$1 \text{ l} = 1000 \text{ cm}^3.$

The metric units of **area** are:

$$1 \text{ square metre (m}^2) = 10\,000 \text{ square centimetres (cm}^2) \quad \left(\text{so } 1 \text{ cm}^2 = \frac{1}{10\,000} \text{ m}^2\right).$$

$$1 \text{ cm}^2 = 100 \text{ square millimetres (mm}^2) \quad \left(\text{so } 1 \text{ mm}^2 = \frac{1}{100} \text{ cm}^2 \text{ or } 0.01 \text{ cm}^2 \text{ or } 0.001 \text{ m}^2\right).$$

$1 \text{ square kilometre (km}^2) = 1\,000\,000 \text{ m}^2.$

7.2 Imperial units and approximate metric equivalents

Questions are sometimes set which give you approximate equivalents and ask you to convert quantities using the values given. **Do not**, therefore, attempt to learn the equivalents, but the following two worked examples illustrate how to use them.

Example

A sack of potatoes weighs 56 lb. If 1 lb ≈ 0.45 kg, approximately how many kg is this?

$1 \text{ lb} \approx 0.45 \text{ kg}$

$56 \text{ lb} \approx 56 \times 0.45 \text{ kg} = 25.2 \text{ kg}.$

Example

On a run a car can travel 36 miles on one gallon of petrol. How many km per litre is this? (Use 1 gallon ≈ 4.6 l and 1 mile ≈ 1.6 km.)

On 1 gallon the car travels 36 miles.

On 4.6 litres the car travels 36 miles (since 1 gallon ≈ 4.6 l).

On 1 litre the car travels $\dfrac{36}{4.6}$ miles.

On 1 litre the car travels $\dfrac{36}{4.6} \times 1.6$ km (since 1 mile ≈ 1.6 km)

$$= 12.5 \text{ km (to 1 dp)}.$$

8 Time and timetables

8.1 UNITS

You may need to use these in questions:

60 seconds (s) = 1 minute (min)	365 days = 1 year
60 minutes (min) = 1 hour (h)	366 days = 1 leap year
24 hours (h) = 1 day (d)	52 weeks = 1 year
	12 months = 1 year

8.2 12- AND 24-HOUR TIMES

The time of day can be given as either a '12-hour' or a '24-hour' time.

In a '12-hour' time we use a.m. and p.m. to indicate whether a time is before noon (a.m.) or after noon (p.m.). For example, 3.30 a.m. is 'half past three in the morning', 9.40 p.m. is 'twenty to ten at night'.

In a '24-hour' time we use four figures to give the time. The first two figures give the 'number of hours after midnight'; the last two figures give the 'number of minutes past the hour'. For example, 20 53 means '20 hours after midnight' and '53 minutes past the hour'. Sometimes a point or a gap is used to separate the hours from the minutes and the word 'hours' or 'h' may be written after the figures. For example, 12 noon may be written as 1200, 12 00, 12.00, 1200 hours, ...

'12-hour' times may be converted to '24-hour' times and vice versa. When doing this, always check whether the time is 'before noon' or 'after noon' remembering that 12 noon is 12 00.

Example

Express (a) 08 00 *and* 13 30 *as '12-hour' times,*
    (b) 5 a.m. *and* 9.35 p.m. *as '24-hour' times.*

(a)   08 00 is 'before noon' (a.m.).
    It is   8.00 a.m.

            13 30 is 'after noon' (p.m.).
    Noon is 12 00
    So it is   1.30 p.m.

(b)   5 a.m. is 'before noon'.
    It is 05 00.

            9.35 p.m. is 'after noon'.
    Noon is 12 00
    So it is   21 35.

Timetables are usually written using '24-hour' times. Calculations using '24-hour times' are easy if we remember that 60 minutes = 1 hour.

Example

A train left Birmingham at 15 35 h, *taking* 2 *hours* 40 *minutes for its journey to Exeter. At what time did the train arrive at Exeter?*

    15 35   *Note*: 75 min = 1 h 15 min
  + 2 40
   ―――――
    18 15
     1 75

The train arrives at Exeter at 18 15 h.

For calculations that span midnight, remember that midnight is either 24 00 or 00 00.

Example

A train left Exeter at 23 43 h *and arrived in London at* 02 01 h. *How long did the journey take?*

    From 23 43 h to midnight (24 00) →   17 min
    From midnight (00 00) to 02 01 h → 2 h 01 min
            Total time for journey   2 h 18 min

9 Conversion

9.1 CURRENCY CONVERSION

Each country in the world has its own system of currency and each day an exchange rate for the pound is quoted. For example, the exchange rate between France and Britain may be 8.4 francs to the pound. This means that for each pound which you exchange for French money you will receive 8.4 French francs. This is called **currency conversion**.

Example

The exchange rate between Britain and the USA is $2.36 to the pound. How many dollars would you receive for £55?

$$£1 = \$2.36$$
$$£55 = \$55 \times 2.36$$
$$= \$129.80$$

Sometimes you may wish to convert one foreign currency to another, but you only know the exchange rate of each with respect to the pound.

Example

If £1 = 8.4 francs and £1 = 4.6 marks how many marks would you expect to receive for 60 francs?

$$1 \text{ franc} = £\frac{1}{8.4} \text{ and } £1 = 4.6 \text{ marks}$$

$$1 \text{ franc} = £\frac{1}{8.4} = 4.6 \times \frac{1}{8.4} \text{ marks}$$

$$60 \text{ francs} = 60 \times 4.6 \times \frac{1}{8.4} \text{ marks}$$

$$= 32.86 \text{ marks}.$$

9.2 CONVERSION GRAPHS

A straight line graph is often useful as a means of converting units.

Example

Given that £1 = 8.4 francs, draw a graph to convert amounts up to £12. Use a scale of 1 cm to 10 francs on the vertical axis and 1 cm to £1 on the horizontal axis. Use your graph to find the approximate values of (a) £11 in francs, (b) 65 francs in pounds sterling.

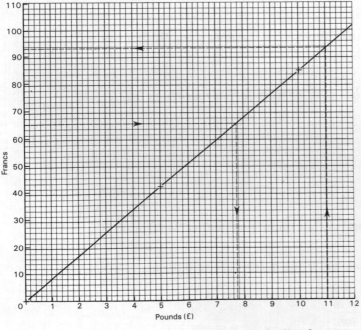

Since £0 = 0 francs, £5 = 42 francs and £10 = 84 francs, we can plot the points (0, 0), (5, 42) and (10, 84) on a grid and join them by a straight line. Not every point on the line will have a meaning; we do not have, for example, coins smaller than 1p. However, in this kind of conversion graph we draw a straight line to make it easier to read.

From Fig. 9.1, the conversion graph for converting pounds (£) to francs,

(a) £11 ≈ 92 francs (to the nearest franc),

(b) 65 francs ≈ £7.70 (to the nearest 10p).

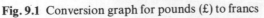

Fig. 9.1 Conversion graph for pounds (£) to francs

10 Squares and square roots

10.1 SQUARES

To **square** a number we multiply it by itself. For example, $5^2 = 5 \times 5 = 25$.

Note: The square of a negative number is positive. For example, $(^-5)^2 = {}^-5 \times {}^-5 = +25$.

A calculator or tables of squares (see unit 54) can be used to square numbers, but remember that these may give answers which may not be exact.

Some tables of squares list numbers with decimal points, whilst others do not. When **using tables to square** a number, write the number in standard form $A \times 10^n$ (see unit 6.1) before using the tables. An approximate answer is a useful check.

Example
Find 547.9^2 by using tables.

$$547.9 = 5.479 \times 10^2 \qquad \text{standard form } A \times 10^n$$
$$547.9^2 = 5.479^2 \times (10^2)^2 \qquad (a \times b)^2 = a^2 \times b^2$$
$$= 30.02 \times 10^4 \qquad \text{tables and } (10^2)^2 = 10^4$$
$$= 300\,200$$

Check: $547.9^2 \approx 500^2 = 250\,000$—the right size of answer!

Squaring a number less than 1 is done in a similar way.

Example
Calculate $(0.285)^2$ to 2 sf.

$$0.285 = 2.85 \times 10^{-1} \qquad \text{standard form}$$
$$(0.285)^2 = 2.85^2 \times (10^{-1})^2$$
$$= 8.123 \times 10^{-2} \qquad \text{tables and } (10^{-1})^2 = 10^{-2}$$
$$= 0.081 \quad (2\text{ sf})$$

Check: $(0.285)^2 \approx (0.3)^2 = 0.09$—the right size of answer!

Note: Sometimes the number to be squared has more significant figures than the table to be used. Before using four-figure tables, the number must be corrected to 4 sf; before using three-figure tables, the number must be corrected to 3 sf. For example, before squaring 73 856.14 using four-figure tables, it must be corrected to 73 860 (4 sf).

10.2 SQUARE ROOTS

The inverse of the operation 'square' is '**square root**'.

Remember: (*i*) since the square of a real number is positive, we can only find the square root of positive numbers;

(*ii*) every positive real number has two square roots.

The square root of a perfect square may be found by factorisation.

Example
Find the two square roots of 36.

Since $6 \times 6 = 36$, one square root of 36 is 6,

but $^-6 \times {}^-6 = 36$ so the other square root of 36 is $^-6$.

It is worth remembering the sequence of square numbers and their square roots:

Square numbers 1 4 9 16 25 36 ...

Square roots -1 1 -2 2 -3 3 -4 4 -5 5 -6 6 ...

Note: $\sqrt{n}$ means the positive square root of n.

A calculator or tables of square roots can be used to find the square roots. There are two sets of square root tables: one gives the square roots of numbers 1 to 10, the other gives the square roots of numbers from 10 to 100. Sometimes both sets of tables are presented on the same page.

To find the **square root** of a number **from tables**:

(*i*) correct the number to 4 sf for four-figure tables, to 3 sf for three-figure tables;

(*ii*) write the number in the form;

$$B \times 10^m$$

number between 1 and 100 $\uparrow$ $\uparrow$ even power of ten

(*iii*) use the correct table to find the square root of *B* and work out the square root of 10^m;

(*iv*) place the decimal point correctly.

Calculating the square of an approximation of your answer is a useful check.

Example

Evaluate, to 3 sf, using tables: (*a*) $\sqrt{(375.9)}$, (*b*) $\sqrt{(8276)}$, (*c*) $\sqrt{(0.005\,86)}$.

$$
\begin{aligned}
(a) \quad 375.9 &= 3.759 \times 10^2 \qquad &&\text{in the form } B \times 10^m \\
\sqrt{(375.9)} &= \sqrt{(3.759)} \times \sqrt{(10^2)} \qquad &&\sqrt{(a \times b)} = \sqrt{a} \times \sqrt{b} \\
&= 1.938 \quad \times \quad 10^1 \qquad &&\text{1–10 tables and } \sqrt{(10^2)} = 10^1 \\
&= 19.38 \\
&= 19.4 \quad \text{(to 3 sf)}.
\end{aligned}
$$

Check: $19.4 \approx 20$; $20^2 = 400$; $400 \approx 375.9$.

$$
\begin{aligned}
(b) \quad 8276 &= 82.76 \times 10^2 \qquad &&\text{in the form } B \times 10^m \\
\sqrt{(8276)} &= \sqrt{(82.76)} \times \sqrt{(10^2)} \\
&= \quad 9.097 \times \quad 10^1 \qquad &&\text{10–100 tables and } \sqrt{(10^2)} = 10^1 \\
&= 90.97 \\
&= 91.0 \quad \text{(to 3 sf)}.
\end{aligned}
$$

Check: $91.0 \approx 90$; $90^2 = 8100$; $8100 \approx 8276$.

$$
\begin{aligned}
(c) \quad 0.005\,86 &= 58.6 \times 10^{-4} \qquad &&\text{in the form } B \times 10^m \\
\sqrt{(0.005\,86)} &= \sqrt{(58.6)} \times \sqrt{(10^{-4})} \\
&= \quad 7.655 \times \quad 10^{-2} \qquad &&\text{10–100 tables and } \sqrt{(10^{-4})} = 10^{-2} \\
&= 0.076\,55 \\
&= 0.0766 \quad \text{(3 sf)}.
\end{aligned}
$$

Check: $0.0766 \approx 0.08$; $0.08^2 = 0.0064$; $0.0064 \approx 0.005\,86$.

---

11 Perimeters and areas of plane shapes

The **perimeter** of a plane shape is the length of its boundary, *i.e.* the distance around its edge. For example, if the shape is a polygon its perimeter is the sum of the lengths of its sides. It is measured in **length units** such as metres (m), centimetres (cm), etc.

The **area** of a plane shape is the amount of surface it encloses. It is measured in **square units** such as square metres (m^2), square centimetres (cm^2), etc.

When calculating perimeters or areas, make sure that all the linear dimensions are measured in the same unit.

For example, in m to give the area in m^2,
in cm to give the area in cm^2, etc.

If the measurements are given in different units, then they must be converted to the same unit before the calculation can be done.

11.1 A SQUARE

Perimeter of a square $= 4 \times$ (length of a side)
$$= 4a$$

Area of a square $=$ (length of a side)^2
$$= a^2.$$

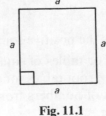

Fig. 11.1

For example, for a square of side 6 cm,

the perimeter of the square $= 4 \times 6$ cm $= 24$ cm,

the area of the square $= 6$ cm $\times 6$ cm $= 36$ cm².

11.2 A RECTANGLE

Perimeter of a rectangle $= 2 \times$ (length + breadth)

$$= 2(l \times b)$$

Area of a rectangle $=$ length $\times$ breadth

$$= lb.$$

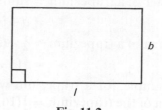

Fig. 11.2

For example, for a rectangle of length 3 m and breadth 2 m,

the perimeter of the rectangle $= 2(3+2)$ m $= 10$ m,

the area of the rectangle $= 3$ m $\times 2$ m $= 6$ m².

Note: A square is a special case of a rectangle with $l = b$.

11.3 A TRIANGLE

Perimeter of a triangle $=$ sum of lengths of sides

$$= a+b+c$$

Area of a triangle $= \frac{1}{2} \times$ base $\times$ perpendicular height

$$= \frac{1}{2}bh.$$

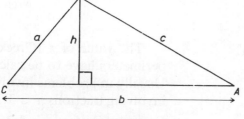

Fig. 11.3

If the perpendicular height is not known but two sides and the angle included between these sides are,

then the area of a triangle $= \frac{1}{2}$ (product of two sides) $\times$ (sine of the included angle)

$$= \frac{1}{2}ab \sin c \text{ or } \frac{1}{2}bc \sin A \text{ or } \frac{1}{2}ac \sin B.$$

If the lengths of all three sides are known, then

the area of a triangle $= \sqrt{S(S-a)(S-b)(S-c)}$ where $S = \frac{1}{2}(a+b+c)$.

For example, for a triangle with sides measuring 7 cm, 5 cm and 4 cm,

the perimeter of the triangle $= (7+5+4)$ cm $= 16$ cm.

The semi-perimeter $S = \frac{1}{2}(7+5+4)$ *cm* $= 8$ *cm*,

hence, the area of the triangle $= \sqrt{8(8-7)(8-5)(8-4)}$ cm²,

$$= \sqrt{8 \times 1 \times 3 \times 4} \text{ cm}^2,$$

$$= 4\sqrt{6} \text{ cm}^2 = 9.8 \text{ cm}^2 \quad \text{(1 dp)}.$$

11.4 A PARALLELOGRAM

(*A quadrilateral with opposite sides parallel*)

Perimeter of a parallelogram $= 2 \times$ (sum of lengths of two adjacent sides)

$$= 2(b+m)$$

Area of a parallelogram $=$ base $\times$ perpendicular height

$$= bh.$$

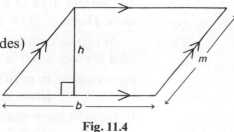

Fig. 11.4

For example, for a parallelogram with base 37 mm and height 19 mm,

the area of the parallelogram $= 37$ mm $\times 19$ mm $= 703$ mm².

(To find the perimeter, the lengths of the two sides not parallel to the base would have to be known.)

Note: A rhombus is a special case of a parallelogram in which all the sides are equal, *i.e.* $b = m$.

11.5 A TRAPEZIUM

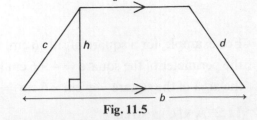

Fig. 11.5

(A quadrilateral with one pair of parallel sides)

Perimeter of a trapezium = sum of lengths of sides

$$= a + b + c + d$$

Area of a trapezium = $\frac{1}{2} \times$ (sum of the parallel sides) × (perpendicular height)

$$= \frac{1}{2}(a + b)h.$$

For example, for a trapezium with parallel sides 16 cm and 1.4 m long and 0.2 m apart, the area of the trapezium = $\frac{1}{2}(16 + 140)$ cm × 20 cm   since 1.4 m = 140 cm and 0.2 m = 20 cm

$$= 78 \text{ cm} \times 20 \text{ cm}$$

$$= 1560 \text{ cm}^2.$$

11.6 A CIRCLE

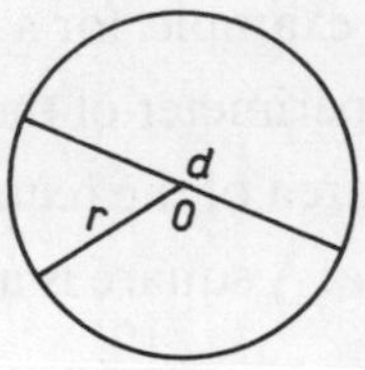

Perimeter (circumference) of a circle = $2 \times \pi \times$ radius = $\pi \times$ diameter

$$= 2\pi r = \pi d \qquad \text{(since } d = 2r\text{).}$$

Area of a circle = $\pi \times$ (radius)^2

$$= \pi r^2.$$

Fig. 11.6

The value of π (Greek letter pi) cannot be stated exactly. However, when areas and perimeters have to be calculated you will be given an approximate value for this number. Usually in problems involving decimals π is given as 3.142 correct to 3 dp and in problems involving fractions $\pi \approx 3\frac{1}{7}$.

For example, for a circle with radius 14 cm,

the circumference of the circle = $2\pi r = 2 \times 3\frac{1}{7} \times 14$ cm   (taking π as $3\frac{1}{7}$)

$$= 2 \times \frac{22}{7} \times 14 \text{ cm}$$

$$= 88 \text{ cm},$$

the area of the circle = $\pi r^2 = 3\frac{1}{7} \times 14^2 \; cm^2$

$$= \frac{22}{7} \times 14 \times 14 \; cm^2$$

$$= 616 \; cm^2.$$

---

12 Volume and surface area of solid shapes

The **volume** of a solid shape is the amount of space it occupies. It is measured in **cubic units** such as cubic metres (m^3), cubic centimetres (cm^3), etc.

The **surface area** of a solid shape is the total area of its surface and is measured in **square units**. This is easily worked out if a **net** of the solid is drawn.

When calculating volumes and surface areas, make sure that all the linear dimensions used are measured in the same unit.

For example, in m to give the volume in m^3 and the surface area in m^3;

in cm to give the volume in cm^3 and the surface area in cm^2, etc.

If the measurements are given in different units, then they must be converted to the same unit before the calculation can be done.

12.1 A CUBE

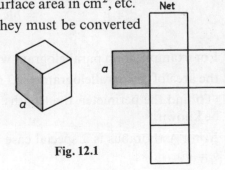

Volume of a cube = (length of an edge)^3

$$= a^3.$$

Surface area of a cube = $6 \times$ (area of one face)

$$= 6a^2.$$

Fig. 12.1

For example, for a cube of edge 4 cm,

the volume of the cube $= 4^3 \text{ cm}^3 = 64 \text{ cm}^3$,

the surface area of the cube $= 6 \times 4^2 \text{ cm}^2 = 6 \times 16 \text{ cm}^2 = 96 \text{ cm}^2$.

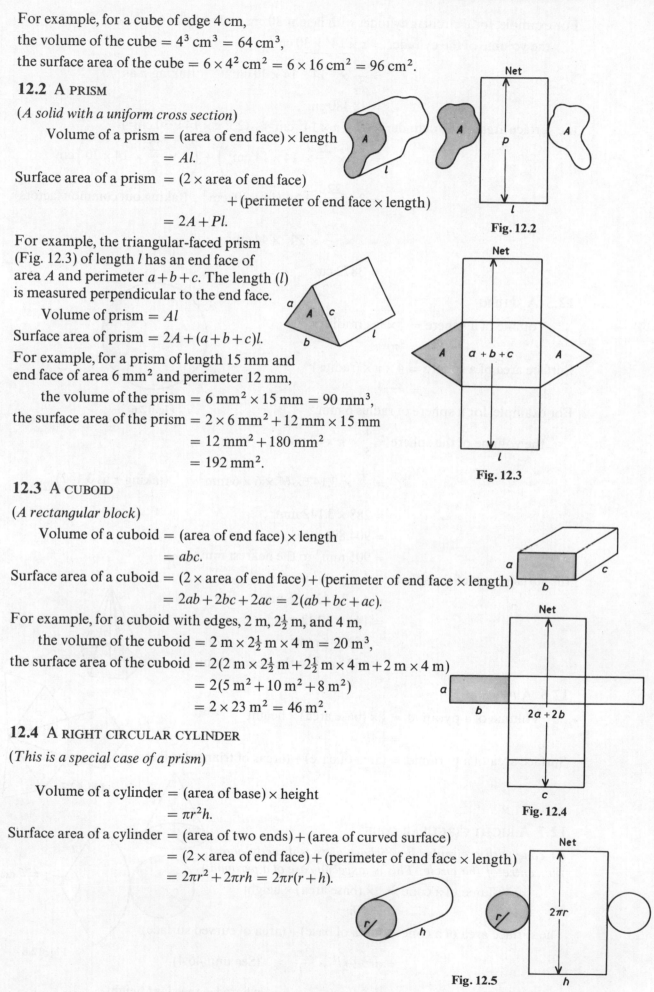

12.2 A PRISM

(A solid with a uniform cross section)

$$\text{Volume of a prism} = (\text{area of end face}) \times \text{length}$$
$$= Al.$$

$$\text{Surface area of a prism} = (2 \times \text{area of end face})$$
$$+ (\text{perimeter of end face} \times \text{length})$$
$$= 2A + Pl.$$

Fig. 12.2

For example, the triangular-faced prism
(Fig. 12.3) of length l has an end face of
area A and perimeter $a + b + c$. The length (l)
is measured perpendicular to the end face.

$$\text{Volume of prism} = Al$$

$$\text{Surface area of prism} = 2A + (a + b + c)l.$$

For example, for a prism of length 15 mm and
end face of area 6 mm² and perimeter 12 mm,

the volume of the prism $= 6 \text{ mm}^2 \times 15 \text{ mm} = 90 \text{ mm}^3$,

the surface area of the prism $= 2 \times 6 \text{ mm}^2 + 12 \text{ mm} \times 15 \text{ mm}$
$$= 12 \text{ mm}^2 + 180 \text{ mm}^2$$
$$= 192 \text{ mm}^2.$$

Fig. 12.3

12.3 A CUBOID

(A rectangular block)

$$\text{Volume of a cuboid} = (\text{area of end face}) \times \text{length}$$
$$= abc.$$

$$\text{Surface area of a cuboid} = (2 \times \text{area of end face}) + (\text{perimeter of end face} \times \text{length})$$
$$= 2ab + 2bc + 2ac = 2(ab + bc + ac).$$

For example, for a cuboid with edges, 2 m, $2\frac{1}{2}$ m, and 4 m,

the volume of the cuboid $= 2 \text{ m} \times 2\frac{1}{2} \text{ m} \times 4 \text{ m} = 20 \text{ m}^3$,

the surface area of the cuboid $= 2(2 \text{ m} \times 2\frac{1}{2} \text{ m} + 2\frac{1}{2} \text{ m} \times 4 \text{ m} + 2 \text{ m} \times 4 \text{ m})$
$$= 2(5 \text{ m}^2 + 10 \text{ m}^2 + 8 \text{ m}^2)$$
$$= 2 \times 23 \text{ m}^2 = 46 \text{ m}^2.$$

12.4 A RIGHT CIRCULAR CYLINDER

(This is a special case of a prism)

$$\text{Volume of a cylinder} = (\text{area of base}) \times \text{height}$$
$$= \pi r^2 h.$$

$$\text{Surface area of a cylinder} = (\text{area of two ends}) + (\text{area of curved surface})$$
$$= (2 \times \text{area of end face}) + (\text{perimeter of end face} \times \text{length})$$
$$= 2\pi r^2 + 2\pi rh = 2\pi r(r + h).$$

Fig. 12.4

Fig. 12.5

For example, for a circular cylinder with height 30 cm and radius 14 cm,

the volume of the cylinder $= \pi \times 14^2 \times 30 \text{ cm}^3$

$$= \frac{22}{\not{7}_1} \times {}^2\not{14} \times 14 \times 30 \text{ cm}^3 \quad \text{(taking } \pi \text{ as } \frac{22}{7}\text{)}$$

$$= 18\,480 \text{ cm}^3,$$

the surface area of the cylinder $= (2 \times \pi \times 14^2 \text{ cm}^2) + (2 \times \pi \times 14 \times 30 \text{ cm}^2)$

$$= \left(2 \times \frac{22}{7} \times 14 \times 14 \text{ cm}^2\right) + \left(2 \times \frac{22}{7} \times 14 \times 30\right) \text{cm}^2$$

$$= 2 \times \frac{22}{7} \times 14 \times (14 + 30) \text{ cm}^2 \quad \text{(taking out common factors)}$$

$$= 2 \times \frac{22}{\not{7}_1} \times \not{14}^2 \times 44 \text{ cm}^2$$

$$= 3872 \text{ cm}^2.$$

12.5 A sphere

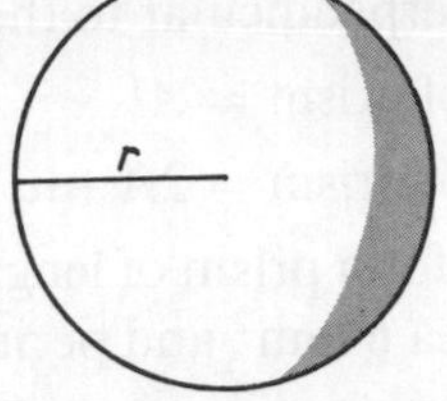

Volume of a sphere $= \frac{4}{3} \times \pi \times (\text{radius})^3$

$$= \frac{4}{3}\pi r^3.$$

Surface area of a sphere $= 4 \times \pi \times (\text{radius})^2$

$$= 4\pi r^2.$$

For example, for a sphere of radius 6 mm,

Fig. 12.6

the volume of the sphere $= \frac{4}{3} \times \pi \times 6^3 \text{ mm}^3$

$$= \frac{4}{\not{3}_1} \times 3.142 \times \not{6}^2 \times 6 \times 6 \text{ mm}^3 \quad \text{(taking } \pi \text{ as } 3.142\text{)}$$

$$= 288 \times 3.142 \text{ mm}^3$$

$$= 904.896 \text{ mm}^3$$

$$= 905 \text{ mm}^3 \text{ to the nearest mm}^3,$$

the surface area of the sphere $= 4 \times \pi \times 6^2 \text{ mm}^2$

$$= 4 \times 3.142 \times 36 \text{ mm}^2$$

$$= 144 \times 3.142 \text{ mm}^2$$

$$= 452.448 \text{ mm}^2$$

$$= 452 \text{ mm}^2 \text{ to the nearest mm}^2.$$

12.6 A pyramid

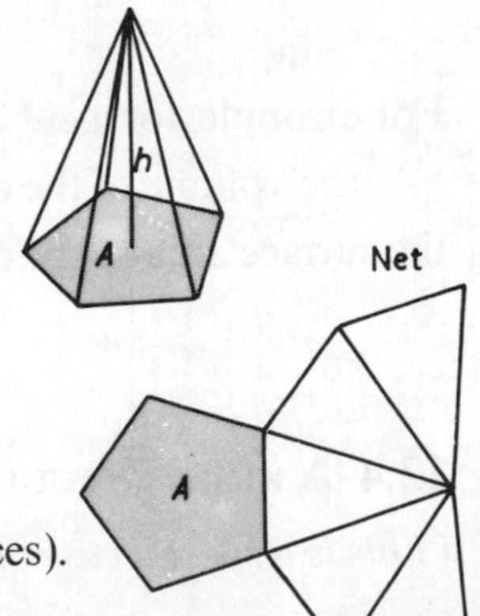

Volume of a pyramid $= \frac{1}{3} \times (\text{base area}) \times \text{height}$

$$= \frac{1}{3}Ah.$$

Surface area of a pyramid $= (\text{area of base}) + (\text{areas of triangular faces}).$

Fig. 12.7

12.7 A right circular cone

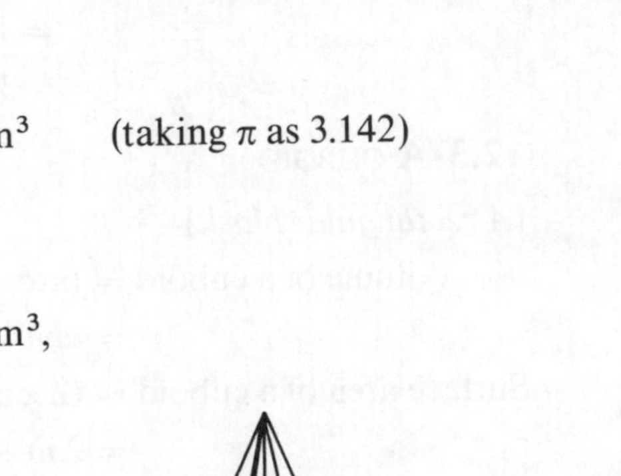

(A cone with a circular base whose apex is directly above the centre of the circle. This is a special case of a pyramid.)

Volume of a cone $= \frac{1}{3} \times (\text{base area}) \times \text{height}$

$$= \frac{1}{3}\pi r^2 h.$$

The surface area of a cone $= (\text{area of base}) + (\text{area of curved surface})$

$$= \pi r^2 + \frac{1}{2}l^2 \times \frac{2\pi r}{l} \quad \text{(See unit 46.4)}$$

$$= \pi r^2 + \pi r l \quad \text{where } l \text{ is the slant height.}$$

Fig. 12.8

For example, for a right circular cone of radius 7 cm, height 24 cm and slant height 25 cm,

$$\text{the volume of the cone} = \frac{1}{3} \times \pi \times 7^2 \times 24 \text{ cm}^3$$

$$= \frac{1}{\cancel{3}_1} \times \frac{22}{\cancel{7}_1} \times \cancel{7}^1 \times 7 \times \cancel{24}^8 \text{ cm}^3 \qquad (\text{taking } \pi \text{ as } \tfrac{22}{7})$$

$$= 1232 \text{ cm}^3,$$

$$\text{the surface area of the cone} = (\pi \times 7^2 \text{ cm}^2) + (\pi \times 7 \times 25 \text{ cm}^2)$$

$$= \left(\frac{22}{\cancel{7}_1} \times \cancel{7}^1 \times 7 \text{ cm}^2\right) + \left(\frac{22}{\cancel{7}_1} \times \cancel{7}^1 \times 25\right) \text{ cm}^2$$

$$= (154 + 550) \text{ cm}^2$$

$$= 704 \text{ cm}^2.$$

13 Ratio, proportion and scale

13.1 RATIO

A **ratio** compares two or more quantities. The ratio of two quantities a and b is written as a to b or $a:b$ or $\frac{a}{b}$. For example, the ratio 5 to 7 can also be written as $5:7$ or $\frac{5}{7}$.

The order in which the comparison is being made is important, *i.e.* $a:b$ is not the same as $b:a$. For example, $5:7 \neq 7:5$.

A ratio is usually given as simply as possible. For example, $27:45$ is $3:5$ in its simplest form.

If the quantities to be compared are given in different units, then they must be converted to the same unit before the ratio can be written correctly. When the quantities are in the same unit, the unit cancels and leaves just a number which is the ratio.

Example
Find the ratio of 400 m to 2 km.

$$\frac{400 \text{ m}}{2 \text{ km}} = \frac{400 \text{ m}}{2000 \text{ m}} = \frac{1}{5}.$$

This ratio can also be written as $1:5$ or 1 to 5. This tells us that the distance 2 km is five times the distance 400 m and the distance 400 m is one fifth the distance 2 km.

Ratios are often used to indicate proportional parts.

Example
Three men, A, B and C hold 120, 200 and 40 shares respectively in a company. If a total dividend of £1800 is paid to the three men in the ratio of their holdings, how much does each receive?

The ratio of the holdings of $A:B:C$ is $120:200:40$, *i.e.* $3:5:1$. There are altogether $9 (=3+5+1)$ equal amounts of money available of which A will receive 3, B will receive 5 and C will receive 1.

$$\text{Therefore } A \text{ receives } \frac{3}{9} \text{ of } £1800 = £600$$

$$B \text{ receives } \frac{5}{9} \text{ of } £1800 = £1000$$

$$C \text{ receives } \frac{1}{9} \text{ of } £1800 = £200.$$

13.2 PROPORTION

Two quantities are in **direct proportion** if an increase (or decrease) in one is matched by an increase (or decrease) in the same ratio, in the other. For example, if one quantity is doubled, the other is doubled also.

Example

Three metres of wood cost £2.25. What is the cost of eight metres?

The amount of wood has been increased in the ratio $8:3$.

Therefore the cost will be increased in the same ratio since the quantities are related by direct proportion.

Hence the cost of 8 metres of wood $= \dfrac{8}{3} \times £2.25$

$$= £6.$$

If an increase (or decrease) in one quantity produces a decrease (or increase) in another, the two quantities are said to be in **inverse proportion**.

Example

If 15 men take eight days to build a boat, how long will it take 12 men to build a similar boat?

The number of men has been reduced in the ratio $12:15$, *i.e.* $4:5$.

However, the time taken to build the boat will be increased in the ratio $5:4$ since the quantities are in inverse proportion.

Hence the time taken for 12 men to build a boat $= \dfrac{5}{4} \times 8$ days

$$= 10 \text{ days}.$$

13.3 SCALE

If a map has a **scale** of $1:25\,000$ this means that 1 cm on the map represents a distance of $25\,000$ cm or 0.25 km on the ground. This scale can also be written as the **representative fraction** $\dfrac{1}{25\,000}$.

Sometimes the scale of a map is given as, for example, 1 cm represents 1 km.

Since 1 km $= 1000$ m $= 100\,000$ cm,

1 cm to 1 km is the same scale as $1:100\,000$.

Example

The scale of a map is $1:20\,000$. Find:

(a) the actual length of a field which measures 2.4 cm on the map;

(b) the distance on the map between two towns which are 5 km apart.

(a) Length of the field $= 2.4 \times 20\,000$ cm $= 48\,000$ cm $= 480$ m

(b) Distance between the towns on the map $= 5 \times \dfrac{1}{20\,000}$ km $= 25$ cm.

Scale is also used in the construction of scale models.

Example

A model aircraft is built to a scale of 1 to 10. If the length of the actual aircraft is 27 m what is the length of the model? If the wing area of the model is 1.96 m² what is the wing area of the actual aircraft? If the volume of the hold in the full size aircraft is 164 m³ what is the volume of the hold in the model?

A model aircraft built to a scale of 1 to 10 means that all linear dimensions in the model are $\frac{1}{10}$ those in the actual aircraft.

Therefore, the length of the model is $\frac{1}{10}$ of 27 m $= 2.7$ m.

Since calculations of areas require squares of linear dimensions, the factor by which areas are reduced in the model is $\left(\dfrac{1}{10}\right)^2 = \dfrac{1}{100}$.

Therefore, since the wing area of the model is 1.96 m²,

the wing area of the actual aircraft is 100×1.96 m² $= 196$ m².

Further, since volumes require the cube of linear dimensions, the factor by which volumes are reduced in the model is

$$\left(\dfrac{1}{10}\right)^3 = \dfrac{1}{1000}.$$

Hence, since the volume of the hold in the aircraft is 164 m³,

the volume of the hold in the model is $\dfrac{164}{1000}$ m³,

$$= 0.164 \text{ m}^3,$$
$$= 1.64 \times 10^5 \text{ cm}^3.$$

The ideas contained in this example are very important and should be understood fully. Many questions are set which require a detailed understanding of the ideas concerning the reductions of lengths, areas and volumes for given scale factors (see unit 36.1).

14 Percentages

A fraction whose denominator is 100 is called a **percentage**.

For example, $\dfrac{50}{100}$ is called 50 per cent and written 50%,

$\dfrac{100}{100} (= 1)$ is called 100 per cent and written 100%.

Percentages are used in the business world to describe rates of interest, profits, *etc*. They make comparisons between different rates of interest easy.

To change a fraction or decimal to a percentage, multiply it by 100%.

Example

Change (a) $\dfrac{4}{5}$ *and (b)* 0.791 *to percentages.*

(a) $\dfrac{4}{5} = \dfrac{4}{5} \times 100\% = 80\%.$ (b) $0.791 = 0.791 \times 100\% = 79.1\%.$

To change a percentage to a fraction or decimal, write it as a fraction whose denominator is 100.

Example

Change 45% to (a) a decimal, (b) a fraction in its lowest terms.

(a) $45\% = \dfrac{45}{100} = 0.45.$ (b) $45\% = \dfrac{45}{100} = \dfrac{9}{20}.$

Note: It is worth remembering the following:

$$\frac{1}{4} = 25\% \qquad \frac{1}{2} = 50\% \qquad \frac{3}{4} = 75\% \qquad \frac{1}{3} = 33\frac{1}{3}\% \qquad \frac{2}{3} = 66\frac{2}{3}\%$$

To express one quantity as a percentage of another, first write one as a fraction of the other, then change the fraction to a percentage.

Example

Express 7 as a percentage of 20.

7 as a percentage of 20 is $\dfrac{7}{20} \times 100\%$

$$= 35\%.$$

If the quantities are given in different units, then they must be converted to the same unit before the calculation can be done.

Example

Express 5 cm as a percentage of 2 m.

First change 2 m to 200 cm.

So 5 cm as a percentage of 200 cm is $\dfrac{5}{200} \times 100\%$

$$= 2.5\%.$$

When finding a percentage of a given quantity, write the percentage as a fraction first.

Example

In a school of 300 children 7% are absent. How many children are absent?

$$7\% \text{ of } 300 = \frac{7}{100} \times 300 = 21.$$

So 21 children are absent.

Many taxes, such as Value Added Tax (VAT) and Income Tax, are given as a percentage of the amount to be taxed.

Example

The price of a meal is £5 + 15% VAT. What is the total cost?

$$15\% \text{ of } £5 = \frac{15}{100} \times £5 = £0.75.$$

So the total cost is £5 + £0.75 = £5.75.

14.1 PERCENTAGE CHANGES

We can increase or decrease quantities by a given percentage. For example, if we begin with a certain amount (100%) and increase it by 5% we end up with 105% of the original. If we begin with the same quantity (100%) and decrease it by 5% we end up with 95% of the original.

Example

(a) Increase £30 by 7%. (b) Decrease £30 by 7%.

The amount we start with is £30, *i.e.* 100%.

Remembering that 1% is $\dfrac{1}{100}$, we have 1% of £30 which is $\dfrac{£30}{100}$.

(a) 107% of £30 is $107 \times \dfrac{£30}{100}$ (107% is 7% more than the original 100%)

$$= \frac{£321}{10}$$

$$= £32.10.$$

(b) 93% of £30 is $93 \times \dfrac{£30}{100}$ (93% is 7% less than the original 100%)

$$= \frac{£279}{10}$$

$$= £27.90.$$

14.2 PROFIT AND LOSS

In business, the difference between the price for which an article is sold (the **selling price**) and the price which was paid for it (the **cost price**) is called the **profit**. A negative profit is called a **loss**.

The profit is usually expressed as a percentage of the cost price and is given by

$$\text{percentage profit} = \frac{\text{selling price} - \text{cost price}}{\text{cost price}} \times 100\%.$$

Example

A shopkeeper buys a box of oranges for £6 and sells them for £7.50. Find his profit as a percentage of his cost price.

$$\text{Profit} = £7.50 - £6 = £1.50$$

$$\text{Percentage profit} = \frac{1.5}{6} \times 100\%$$

$$= \frac{1}{4} \times 100\%$$

$$= 25\%.$$

To work out the selling price for an article, a shopkeeper adds the profit he needs to the cost price of the article. The cost price is always taken to be 100% and the selling price is a percentage increase on the basic cost.

Example
An antique dealer wishes to make a profit of 25% when he sells a table which cost him £900. What must his selling price be?

Let cost price be $100\% = £900$

therefore $1\% = \dfrac{£900}{100}$

and selling price is $125\% = 125 \times \dfrac{£900}{100}$

$= £1125.$

Example
A wine merchant sells a case of wine for £80 and makes a profit of $33\frac{1}{3}\%$. How much did the merchant pay for the wine?

Let selling price be $133\frac{1}{3}\% = £80$

therefore $1\% = \dfrac{£80}{133\frac{1}{3}}$

and cost price is $100\% = 100 \times \dfrac{£80}{133\frac{1}{3}}$

$= 100 \times \dfrac{£240}{400}$

$= £60.$

14.3 SIMPLE INTEREST

If you borrow money from a bank or a building society you will be charged interest on the loan. The interest will be a percentage (the **rate**) of the sum you have borrowed (the **principal**). Similarly, if you deposit money you will be paid interest. The rate of interest is usually given as a percentage per annum (p.a.).

If the interest is paid or withdrawn each year, *i.e.* the principal remains the same, the interest is called **simple interest (SI)**.

If the principal is £P, the time of the loan or investment is T years and the interest rate is $R\%$, then

$$SI = \frac{P \times T \times R}{100}$$

If we know three of the quantities P, T, R or SI this formula enables us to find the fourth.

Another quantity is the **amount** which is the Principal + SI.

Example
Find the amount if £350 is invested for three years at 5%.

$$SI = \frac{350 \times 3 \times 5}{100}$$
$$= £52.50$$

therefore, amount $= £350 + £52.50$
$= £402.50.$

Example
Find the time taken for £300 to become £384 if the rate of interest p.a. is 7%.

Interest $= £384 - £300 = £84$

therefore $£84 = \dfrac{£300 \times T \times 7}{100}$

$84 = 21T$

$\dfrac{84}{21} = T$

therefore $T = 4$ years.

14.4 COMPOUND INTEREST

It is more usual for the interest gained on a deposit account during the first year to be added to the amount originally invested in order to produce a larger principal for the beginning of the second year. This process is repeated each year with the new principal and is called **compound interest (CI)**.

Example

Find the compound interest on £3000 at 6% for three years.

Principal at the beginning of the 1st year $P_1 = £3000$.

Interest for the 1st year, $I_1 = \dfrac{6}{100} \times £3000 = £180$.

Principal at the beginning of the 2nd year $P_2 = £3000 + £180 = £3180$.

Interest for the 2nd year, $I_2 = \dfrac{6}{100} \times £3180 = £190.80$.

Principal at the beginning of the 3rd year $P_3 = £3180 + £190.80 = £3370.80$.

Interest for the 3rd year, $I_3 = \dfrac{6}{100} \times £3370.80 = £202.25$ (to the nearest penny).

Total interest $= I_1 + I_2 + I_3 = £573.05$ (to the nearest penny).

15 Money

15.1 NOTATION

In Britain the basic unit of currency is the pound sterling (£).

$$£1 = 100 \text{ pence (p)}.$$

There are two ways to write amounts of money correctly: using the £ sign only or the p sign only. Do not use both at the same time!

For example, six pounds fifty nine pence $\rightarrow$ £6.59 or 659p

forty seven pence $\rightarrow$ £0.47 or 47p

five pence $\rightarrow$ £0.05 or 5p.

15.2 OPERATIONS

The methods used to add, subtract, multiply and divide amounts of money are basically the same as those used with decimal numbers (see unit 5.3).

Example

Evaluate (i) £4.82 + £7.68 + £5.14;   (ii) £8.84 − £7.52;

(iii) £4.67 × 6;   (iv) £69.33 ÷ 3.

(i)
```
   £4.82
   £7.68
 + £5.14
  _____
  £17.64
```

(ii)
```
   £8.84
 − £7.52
  _____
   £1.31
```

(iii)
```
   £4.67
   ×   6
  _____
  £28.02
```

(iv) £69.33 ÷ 3 = £23.11

Money questions are often set in 'real life' situations. Some of the most common are given below.

15.3 HOUSEHOLD BILLS

Three major household bills which are often paid quarterly, *i.e.* every thirteen weeks, are gas, electricity and telephone bills. They all consist of a fixed charge (called the standing charge on gas and electricity bills and the rental on telephone bills) and a charge based on the number of units used. There is no Value Added Tax (VAT) on gas and electricity (they are considered to be essentials) but VAT is payable on telephone bills.

Example

During one quarter a family used 757 units of 'day time' electricity at 5.87p per unit and 789 units of 'night time' electricity at 2.18p per unit. If the standing charge was £9.25, what was their total electricity bill (to the nearest penny) for that quarter?

757 units at 5.87p per unit → 757 × 5.87p = £44.44

789 units at 2.18p per unit → 789 × 2.18p = £17.20

Standing charge   £9.25

Total bill   £70.89

15.4 RATES

Rates are a tax on property such as houses, shops, etc., and are paid to local councils. They are used to help to pay for local services such as education, waste disposal, libraries, etc.

Every property is given a Rateable Value which depends on such factors as the amount of land, the number of rooms, its condition, the facilities, etc. Each council fixes its local rate or rate in the £, dependent on the amount of money it needs to raise.

Rates can be calculated using:

$$\text{rates due} = \text{rateable value} \times \text{rate in the £.}$$

This gives:

$$\text{rateable value} = \frac{\text{rates due}}{\text{rate in the £}} \text{ and } \text{rate in the £} = \frac{\text{rates due}}{\text{rateable value}}.$$

Water rates are calculated in the same way but they are paid to the local water authority.

Example

Calculate the rates due on a semi-detached house whose rateable value is £225 if the local rate is 137p in the £. What is the water rate in the £ if the water rates due on the same house are £58.50?

Rates due = rateable value × rate in the £

     =   225   ×   137p

     = £308.25.

$$\text{Water rate in the £} = \frac{\text{water rates due}}{\text{rateable value}}$$

$$= \frac{£58.50}{225}$$

$$= 26p$$

15.5 WAGES AND SALARIES

Wages are usually paid weekly and may vary from week to week depending upon the amount of work done.

Some employees are paid 'by the hour': their wages depend on the number of hours worked and the rate of pay per hour. There is usually a basic working week of a fixed number of hours and overtime is usually paid at a higher rate.

Some employees are on 'piecework': their wages depend on the number of 'pieces' they make or assemble and the rate of pay for each piece. There may be a 'bonus scheme' for making more than a fixed number of 'pieces'.

Some employees are paid a basic weekly wage plus commission which is usually a percentage of the value of the goods they have sold during the week.

Example

Mr Brown is paid £3.50 per hour for a basic 37-hour week and overtime at time and a half. What is his wage if he works 43 hours in a week?

Basic wage: 37 hours at £3.50 per hour → 37 × £3.50

= £129.50

Overtime: He works (43 − 37) = 6 hours overtime.

He is paid 'time and a half' *i.e.* $1\frac{1}{2}$ × £3.50

= £5.25 per hour

So 6 hours at £5.25 per hour → 6 × £5.25

= £31.50

Total wage = basic wage + overtime

= £129.50 + £31.50 = £161

A salary is the fixed amount which an employee is paid each year (per annum) and is usually paid in 12 equal monthly instalments.

Example
Mrs White's salary is £10 500 per annum. What is she paid monthly?

Monthly payment = £10 500 ÷ 12

= £875

15.6 INCOME TAX

The Inland Revenue collects income tax for the government from everyone who has an income which is more than a specified minimum amount. It is used to pay for such items as the National Health Service, the armed forces, the civil service, etc. Most people have this tax deducted from their pay weekly or monthly by their employer: this is called the PAYE (Pay As You Earn) system. Self-employed people receive tax bills which they have to pay direct to the Inland Revenue.

Income Tax is not payable on the total (or gross) income: various allowances are deducted to obtain the taxable income:

taxable income = (gross income) − (allowances).

The amount of tax to be paid is calculated from the taxable income using a graduated scale of income tax rates which are usually expressed as percentages of the taxable income or as a number of 'pence in the £'. The allowances and income tax rates can be varied by the Chancellor of the Exchequer.

Example
On a new income tax scheme, tax is levied at 30% on the first £9000 of taxable income and 40% on the remainder. Mr Smith has a gross income of £13 810 and total allowances of £2310. Calculate the amount he pays in income tax under this new scheme.

Taxable income = £13 810 − £2310 = £11 500.

Tax paid: 30% of £9000 = £2700
40% of £2500 = £1000
Total tax paid   £3700

---

16 Averages

There are three important types of **average**: the **mean**, the **mode** and the **median**.

Note: If a question asks you to find the average of a set of numbers and does not state which one, it usually implies you are to find the mean.

16.1 THE MEAN (also called the **arithmetic mean**)

To find the mean of a set of quantities we find their total and divide it by the number of quantities:

$$\text{arithmetic mean} = \frac{\text{total}}{\text{number of quantities}}.$$

Example

Find the mean of the following amounts of money:

   5p,   12p,   9p,   11p,   8p,   10p,   8p.

      Total amount of money $= (5+12+9+11+8+10+8)\text{p} = 63\text{p}.$

Number of sums of money $= 7.$

$$\text{Mean sum of money} = \frac{63\text{p}}{7} = 9\text{p}.$$

If the mean is known, the sum can be found provided we know the number of quantities.

Example

A cricketer has a mean score of 34 runs for his first eight innings of the season. How many runs must he score in his ninth innings in order to increase his mean score to 37?

      Total runs scored in first eight innings $= 8 \times 34 = 272$ runs.

Total runs which must be scored in first nine innings $= 9 \times 37 = 333$ runs.

      The cricketer must score $333 - 272 = 61$ runs in the ninth innings to increase his mean score to 37.

When we are required to find the mean of a set of quantities which do not differ a great deal we can estimate or guess a value for the mean. We usually choose one of the quantities to be the **guessed mean**. Subtracting the guessed value from each quantity then gives us easier numbers to deal with.

Example

Find the mean height (in cm) of a set of 15 boys having the following heights (in cm): 147, 138, 140, 152, 143, 141, 139, 146, 142, 141, 143, 140, 151, 137, 145.

If we guess the mean height to be 141 cm and subtract this from each height we have:

height (cm)	difference from guessed mean 141 cm	
147	$+6$	
138		-3
140		-1
152	$+11$	
143	$+2$	
141	0	
139		-2
146	$+5$	
142	$+1$	
141	0	
143	$+2$	
140		-1
151	$+10$	
137		-4
145	$+4$	
Total	$+41$ $+$	$-11 = +30$

$$\text{The mean height} = \text{guessed mean} + \frac{\text{sum of the differences}}{\text{total number of values}}$$

$$= 141 + \frac{30}{15}\,\text{cm}$$

$$= 141 + 2\,\text{cm}$$

$$= 143\,\text{cm}.$$

The number of times a quantity occurs in a set is called its **frequency**.

When a set of quantities, together with their frequencies, are listed as a table, the table is called a **frequency distribution**.

To find the mean of a set of quantities, some of which are repeated, we can write them as a frequency distribution. If the quantities are closely grouped we can subtract a guessed mean from each one in order to use easier numbers. However, this time, each difference must be multiplied by its frequency in order to find the sum of the differences.

Example

The following are the weights (in kg) of 10 bags of potatoes: 131, 133, 134, 135, 134, 132, 131, 134, 132, 130. *Find the mean weight (in kg).*

This time we shall guess the mean to be 133 kg.

Weight (kg)	frequency (f)	difference (d) from guessed mean of 133 kg	$f \times d$
130	1	-3	-3
131	2	-2	-4
132	2	-1	-2
133	1	0	0
134	3	$+1$	$+3$
135	1	$+2$	$+2$
Total	10		$-9 + +5 = -4$

The mean weight is $133 + \dfrac{-4}{10}$ kg

$$= 132.6 \text{ kg}.$$

16.2 THE MODE

The quantity which occurs most often in a frequency distribution is called the **mode**.

In the above example, the **modal weight** is 134 kg since more bags of potatoes have this weight than any other.

This is a useful average for a manufacturer to consider when he is supplying a particular market. For example, if a car manufacturer knows that blue is the most popular colour he will produce more blue cars than any other colour. (To find the mode of a frequency distribution, see unit 47.4.)

16.3 THE MEDIAN

The **median** of a set of quantities is the middle one when they are placed in order of size.

Example

Find the median length of 8 m, 11 m, 6 m, 9 m, 14 m, 8 m, 10 m.

Rearrange in order: 6 m,　　8 m,　　8 m,　　9 m,　　10 m,　　11 m,　　14 m.

　　　　　　　　　　　　　　　　　　　　↑

　　　　　　　　　　　　　　　middle value

So 9 m is the median length.

In the above example there was an odd number of quantities. If the number of quantities is even then there will be two middle values and the median is the mean of these two.

Example

Find the median of £16, £31, £10, £19, £8, £25, £13, £15.

Rearrange in order: £8, £10, £13, £15, £16, £19, £25, £31.

The number of quantities (eight) is even.

Hence, the median is $\dfrac{£15 + £16}{2}$ (the mean of the two middle values)

$$= £15.50.$$

16.4 AVERAGE SPEED

A common average which occurs in questions is the **average speed** for a journey.

$$\text{Average speed} = \frac{\text{total distance travelled}}{\text{total time taken}}.$$

Care must be taken to be consistent with the units. For example, if the distance is in metres (m) and the time is in seconds (s), then the speed will be in metres per second (m/s or ms^{-1}).

Often the speeds over separate parts of a journey are given. In this case it is necessary to calculate the total distance travelled and the total time taken for the journey in order to find the average speed.

Example

A car travels for 50 minutes at 54 km h⁻¹ and then for 40 minutes at 42 km h⁻¹. Find its average speed for the whole journey.

Distance travelled = speed × time.

So the distance travelled in 50 minutes ($=\frac{5}{6}$ hour) at 54 km h⁻¹

$$= 54 \times \frac{5}{6} \text{ km} = 45 \text{ km}.$$

The distance travelled in 40 minutes ($=\frac{4}{6}$ hour) at 42 km h⁻¹

$$= 42 \times \frac{4}{6} \text{ km} = 28 \text{ km}.$$

∴ total distance travelled $= 45 \text{ km} + 28 \text{ km} = 73 \text{ km}$

and total time taken $= \frac{5}{6} \text{ hour} + \frac{4}{6} \text{ hour} = \frac{9}{6} \text{ h} = \frac{3}{2} \text{ h}.$

So the average speed for the whole journey $= \frac{73}{\frac{3}{2}} \text{ km h}^{-1}$

$$= 48\frac{2}{3} \text{ km h}^{-1}.$$

17 Symmetry

17.1 LINE SYMMETRY

A plane shape is said to have **line symmetry** if folding about a line places one half of the shape exactly in contact with the other half.

The line about which the shape is folded is called an **axis of symmetry**. For example, in Fig. 17.1 the dotted lines are axes of symmetry for (*i*) a square (four axes of symmetry), (*ii*) a rectangle (two axes of symmetry), (*iii*) an isosceles triangle (one axis of symmetry).

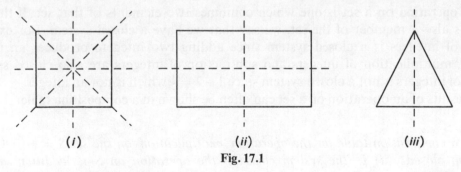

(*i*) (*ii*) (*iii*)

Fig. 17.1

If a mirror is placed along an axis of symmetry, the half shape, together with its reflection, will appear to be the full shape.

17.2 ROTATIONAL SYMMETRY

Figure 17.2 shows (*i*) a square, (*ii*) a rectangle, (*iii*) an equilateral triangle. The centre of each shape is marked *O*.

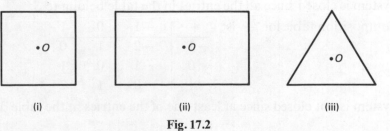

(i) (ii) (iii)

Fig. 17.2

If the square is rotated about O through one of the four angles (90°, 180°, 270°, 360°) it will not appear to have been moved. We say a square has **rotational symmetry** of **order** 4.

If the rectangle is rotated through 180° or 360° about O its position will appear to be the same. We say a rectangle has rotational symmetry of order 2.

The equilateral triangle can be rotated about O through one of three angles (120°, 240°, 360°) without it appearing to have moved. It has rotational symmetry of order 3.

Every plane shape has rotational symmetry of order 1 since rotation through 360° will bring it back to its original position.

17.3 POINT SYMMETRY

A plane shape has **point symmetry** if it appears to be the same after a rotation through 180° about the centre of rotation.

For example, in Fig. 17.3 if the figure is rotated through 180° about O it will look the same before and after rotation.
The figure has point symmetry.

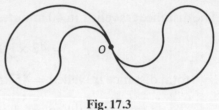

Fig. 17.3

If a plane shape has rotational symmetry of order n, where n is an even integer, it will also have point symmetry. For example, a square (order 4) and a rectangle (order 2) each have point symmetry.

17.4 PLANE SYMMETRY

In Fig. 17.4, the square pyramid has a **plane of symmetry**.

Suppose the plane is a mirror which slices the pyramid in half, as shown.

Then looking at half the pyramid and its reflection is like looking at the full pyramid.

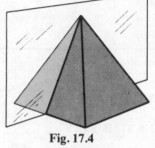

Fig. 17.4

18 Composition tables

A **binary operation** on a set is one which combines two elements of that set. If the third element is also a member of the set, we say that we have a **closed system**. For example, addition of integers is a closed system since adding two integers produces an integer. Similarly, multiplication of integers and subtraction of integers are also closed systems. Division of integers is not a closed system since $1 \div 2 = \frac{1}{2}$ which is not an integer.

The results of an operation on a set can often be shown in a **composition table**.

Example
(*i*) *Make a composition table for the operation 'multiplication' on the set* $S = \{-1, 0, 1\}$. *Is the system closed?* (*ii*) *Is the system closed if the operation on* S *is 'addition' and not 'multiplication'?*

(*i*) The composition table for '×' is:

×	−1	0	1
−1	1	0	−1
0	0	0	0
1	−1	0	1

The system is closed since all the entries in the table belong to S.

(*ii*) The composition table for '+' is:

+	−1	0	1
−1	−2	−1	0
0	−1	0	1
1	0	1	2

The system is not closed since at least one of the entries in the table does not belong to S.

18.1 MODULAR ARITHMETIC

In arithmetic **modulo n**, where n is a positive integer, every integer is congruent to one of the numbers $0, 1, 2, \ldots, (n-1)$. To find the number congruent to a given integer in modulo n, divide the integer by n and write down the remainder. For example, $51 \equiv 3 \bmod 4$ since 3 is the remainder when 51 is divided by 4.

Addition, subtraction, multiplication and division can be carried out in any modulus. For calculations in arithmetic **mod n**, a clock face, with the numbers $0, 1, 2, \ldots, (n-1)$ equally spaced around it, is sometimes helpful.

Modular arithmetic is perhaps best explained by means of an example.

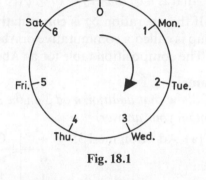

An explorer sets out on a Sunday on a journey which will take him 17 days. We can use the special clock face shown in Fig. 18.1 to find the day on which he arrives.

Starting on Sunday (day 0) and moving in a clockwise direction for 17 days, we find that he arrives on a Wednesday (day 3).

We can write this as,

$$0 + 17 \equiv 3 \bmod 7 \text{ (mod 7 because there are seven days in a week)}$$

and read it as '$0 + 17$ is congruent to 3 mod 7'.

Similarly, a journey of 40 days beginning on a Thursday (day 4) will end on a Tuesday (day 2) since,

$$4 + 40 \equiv 2 \bmod 7.$$

A quicker way to find the finishing day is simply to write down the remainder after dividing 44 ($= 4 + 40$) by 7, *i.e.* 2.

These are examples in arithmetic **modulo 7**. In this arithmetic, every integer is congruent to one of the numbers 0, 1, 2, 3, 4, 5, 6. For example, $10 \equiv 3 \bmod 7$ since 3 is the remainder when 10 is divided by 7. Arithmetic modulo 7 is an example of a **finite arithmetic**, so called because it uses a finite number of elements.

There are many other finite arithmetics. We can use composition tables to solve equations in finite arithmetics.

Example

Make a composition table for multiplication mod 4 on the set $S = \{0, 1, 2, 3\}$. Is the system closed? Use your table to write down the solution set for each of the equations, (i) $2x = 2$, (ii) $2 \div x = 3$, (iii) $3 \div x = 2$, where $x \in S$.

In arithmetic mod 4 every integer will be congruent to one of the numbers 0, 1, 2, 3. For example, $2 \times 3 = 6$ and $6 \equiv 2 \bmod 4$.

Multiplication mod 4:

$\times$	0	1	2	3
0	0	0	0	0
1	0	1	2	3
2	0	2	0	2
3	0	3	2	1

Since each of the entries in the table is a member of S, the system is closed.

  (i) To solve $2x = 2$,
     from the table, $2 \times 1 = 2$ and $2 \times 3 = 2$,
     hence, the solution set is $\{1, 3\}$

 (ii) $2 \div x = 3 \Rightarrow 2 = 3 \times x$,
     hence, the solution set is $\{2\}$

(iii) $3 \div x = 2 \Rightarrow 3 = 2 \times x$,
     from the table we see that there is no x such that $2 \times x = 3$,
     hence, the solution set is $\{\ \}$ or ϕ.

18.2 Groups

A set S together with a binary operation $\otimes$ forms a **group** if all the following are true:

(*i*) S is closed with respect to $\otimes$,
that is $a \otimes b = c$ for all $a, b, c \in S$;

(*ii*) there exists a unique identity element $e \in S$,
such that $e \otimes a = a \otimes e = a$ for all $a \in S$;

(*iii*) each element $a \in S$ has a unique inverse $a^{-1} \in S$,
such that $a \otimes a^{-1} = a^{-1} \otimes a = e$;

(*iv*) the operation $\otimes$ is associative,
that is $a \otimes (b \otimes c) = (a \otimes b) \otimes c$ for all $a, b, c \in S$.

If the operation $\otimes$ is **commutative** (see unit 2.2) for all elements of the group, then the group is called a commutative or **Abelian** group. Not all groups are commutative groups.

The composition table for an Abelian group is symmetrical about the leading diagonal.

Example

(**a**) *Show that addition mod 3 on the set $S = \{0, 1, 2\}$ forms a group.* (**b**) *Is the group Abelian? Explain your answer.*

(**a**) Addition mod 3:

+	0	1	2
0	0	1	2
1	1	2	0
2	2	0	1

leading diagonal

(*i*)   The system is closed since every entry in the table belongs to S.

(*ii*) Adding 0 to each element of S does not alter that element, therefore 0 is the unique identity element.

(*iii*) In each row and column of the table, 0 appears once and once only. Hence each element has a unique inverse,
e.g. $1 + 2 = 2 + 1 = 0$, so 2 is the inverse of 1 and 1 is the inverse of 2;
$0 + 0 = 0$, so 0 is its own inverse.

(*iv*) $(0 + 1) + 2 = 1 + 2 = 0$
$0 + (1 + 2) = 0 + 0 = 0$
This demonstrates associativity for some elements. (It would take too long to show that the system is associative for all possible combinations.)

(**b**) Since the composition table is symmetrical about the leading diagonal (the line of elements from the top left to bottom right), the group is Abelian.
The operation 'addition mod 3' on the set S is commutative for all elements of S, *e.g.* $1 + 2 = 2 + 1$.

18.3 Cyclic groups

If all the elements of a group can be written as powers of a single element, the group is called a **cyclic** group.

For example, consider the group of rotations of the equilateral triangle. If an equilateral triangle is rotated anti-clockwise through 120° about its centre in its own plane, it will not appear to have moved (Fig. 18.2). Call this rotation R_1.

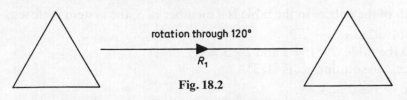

Fig. 18.2

Also, R_2 is an anti-clockwise rotation through 240° and R_3 is an anti-clockwise rotation through 360°. For any of these rotations the triangle will not appear to have moved.

The set $S = \{R_1, R_2, R_3\}$ together with the operation $\circledast$ meaning 'followed by' forms a group. (For example $R_1 \circledast R_2$ means do R_2 followed by R_1. The result is R_3.)

The composition table for S and 'followed by' is:

⊛	R_1	R_2	R_3	1st rotation
R_1	R_2	R_3	R_1	
R_2	R_3	R_1	R_2	
R_3	R_1	R_2	R_3	

If the four conditions for a group are checked, they will be found to be satisfied. For this group, $R_1 ⊛ R_1 = R_2$ and $R_1 ⊛ R_1 ⊛ R_1 = R_3$. If we therefore write

$$R_1^2 = R_1 ⊛ R_1 \quad (= R_2)$$
$$\text{and} \quad R_1^3 = R_1 ⊛ R_1 ⊛ R_1 \quad (= R_3)$$

we can rewrite the elements of the group as R_1, R_1^2, R_1^3.

The group table can then be rewritten as:

⊛	R_1	R_1^2	R_1^3
R_1	R_1^2	R_1^3	R_1
R_1^2	R_1^3	R_1	R_1^2
R_1^3	R_1	R_1^2	R_1^3

i.e. with all the elements written as powers of R_1. So, the group is a cyclic group.

18.4 ISOMORPHIC GROUPS

Two groups are said to be **isomorphic** if their composition tables have the same pattern.

Example
By compiling two composition tables, show that the group formed by addition mod 3 on the set $\{1, 2, 0\}$ *is isomorphic to the group of rotations of the equilateral triangle.*

Addition mod 3:

+	1	2	0
1	2	0	1
2	0	1	2
0	1	2	0

⊛	R_1	R_2	R_3	1st rotation
R_1	R_2	R_3	R_1	
R_2	R_3	R_1	R_2	
R_3	R_1	R_2	R_3	

If R_1, R_2, R_3 are replaced by 1, 2, 0 respectively, then the second composition table is the same as the first. Hence each table has the same pattern and so the two groups are isomorphic.

---

19 Simple algebra

19.1 NOTATION

In **algebra**, where letters are used to represent numbers (sometimes unknown), the basic laws of arithmetic and rules of signs also apply (see units 2.2 and 2.3). For example,

	In arithmetic	In algebra
Commutative laws:		
+	$3 + 5 = 5 + 3$	$a + b = b + a$
×	$3 \times 5 = 5 \times 3$	$ab = ba$
Associative laws:		
+	$(3 + 5) + 2 = 3 + (5 + 2)$	$(a + b) + c = a + (b + c)$
×	$(3 \times 5) \times 2 = 3 \times (5 \times 2)$	$(a + b)c = a(bc)$
Distributive laws (× over +):		
left	$3 \times (5 + 2) = 3 \times 5 + 3 \times 2$	$a(b + c) = ab + ac$
right	$(3 + 5) \times 2 = 3 \times 2 + 5 \times 2$	$(a + b)c = ac + bc$

An **algebraic expression** is a set of letters and numbers combined by at least one of the operations $+, -, \times, \div$. For example, $6x + 5 - 3y$, $2ab^3c^4$, $\dfrac{x^2 - 1}{x + 2}$, are all expressions.

The **terms** of an expression are those parts of it which are connected by plus ($+$) or minus ($-$) signs. For example, the terms of the expression $2xy + 3x^2 - 7x^2y^3$ are $2xy$, $3x^2$ and $7x^2y^3$. Note that $2xy$, for instance, is only one term, x and y are not separate terms here.

When letters are used to represent different numbers, they are called **variables**. Letters which have fixed values are called **constants**. For example, in the expression $\frac{1}{3}\pi r^2 h$, r and h are variables but $\frac{1}{3}$ and π are constants.

A **coefficient** is a number placed before, and thus multiplying, a letter or group of letters. For example, in the expression $9x^2 - 4x + 2$, 9 is the coefficient of x^2 and -4 is the coefficient of x. Note that $+2$ is the constant term.

It is important that the meaning(s) of the 'shorthand' we use in algebra are known and understood. For example,

a	means	$1 \times a$ or $1a$
$-a$	means	$-1 \times a$ or $-1a$
$3a$	means	$a + a + a$ or $3 \times a$
$\dfrac{a}{3}$	means	$a \div 3$ or $\frac{1}{3}$ of a
ab	means	$a \times b$
$2ab$	means	$ab + ab$ or $2 \times ab$ or $2 \times a \times b$
a^3	means	$a \times a \times a$
$3a^2$	means	$a^2 + a^2 + a^2$ or $3 \times a^2$ or $3 \times a \times a$
$(3a)^2$	means	$3a \times 3a$ or $3 \times a \times 3 \times a$
$3ab^2$	means	$ab^2 + ab^2 + ab^2$ or $3 \times ab^2$ or $3 \times a \times b \times b$
$a^{\frac{1}{3}}$	means	$\sqrt[3]{a}$

19.2 SIMPLIFICATION

Expressions may be simplified using the four basic operations of addition, subtraction, multiplication and division. Since the terms may be positive ($+$) or negative ($-$), the rules for combining directed numbers will apply (see unit 2.3).

Addition and subtraction

Only **like terms** can be added or subtracted and written as a single term. This is often called **collecting together like terms**.

Like terms are numerical multiples of the same algebraic 'quantity'. For example, $7x$, $5x$ and $-3x$ are like terms. When looking for like terms, remember that the order in which the letters are written in a term is not important. For example, $3ab^2c$, $-5b^2ca$ and $6cab^2$ are like terms also. However, letters are usually written in alphabetical order in answers. For example, ab^2c rather than b^2ca.

Example

Simplify: (i) $-3a^2 + 9a^2 - 11a^2 - 5a^2$ (ii) $4bac + 11cab - 2bca$

(i) $-3a^2 + 9a^2 - 11a^2 - 5a^2 = -10a^2$ (ii) $4bac + 11cab - 2bca = 13abc$

Unlike terms cannot be collected together and written as a single term. For example, $3x - 7y$ cannot be simplified and $5x + 3x^2 - 9x^4$ is in its simplest form.

There are often several different sets of like terms in an expression. Each set can be simplified separately to give an expression in its simplest form.

Example

Simplify: (i) $7x + 3y - 6y + 2x - y$ (ii) $3xy^2 + 2x^2y - 4y^2x + 6yx^2$

(i) $7x + 3y - 6y + 2x - y$ (ii) $3xy^2 + 2x^2y - 4y^2x + 6yx^2$

    $= 7x + 2x + 3y - 6y - y$ $= 3xy^2 - 4xy^2 + 2x^2y + 6x^2y$

    $= 9x - 4y$ $= -xy^2 + 8x^2y$

Multiplication and division

When multiplying or dividing expressions containing the same letter(s), the basic rules of indices apply (see unit 31.1).

Remember that: $a \times b$ is written as ab,

$$a \div b \text{ is written as } \frac{a}{b}.$$

Example

Simplify: (i) $2ab(-3bc)$ (ii) $6mn^2 \times 5m^3n^4$ (iii) $8a^3b^2 \div 4ab^3$

(i) $2ab \times (-3bc)$ (ii) $6mn^2 \times 5m^3n^4$ (iii) $8a^3b^2 \div 4ab^3$

    $= -6ab^2c$ $= 30m^4n^6$ $= \dfrac{8a^3b^2}{4ab^3} = \dfrac{2a^2}{b}$

The rules for dealing with algebraic fractions are given in unit 28.

19.3 SUBSTITUTION

Substitution is the replacing of letters in an algebraic expression by given values to obtain a numerical value for that expression.

Example

If $x = 2$ and $y = 5$, find the values of: (i) x^3 (ii) $3xy$ (iii) $(4y)^2$

(i) $x^3 = x \times x \times x$ (ii) $3xy = 3 \times x \times y$ (iii) $(4y)^2 = 4 \times y \times 4 \times y$

      $= 2 \times 2 \times 2$ $= 3 \times 2 \times 5$ $= 4 \times 5 \times 4 \times 5$

      $= 8$ $= 30$ $= 400$

It is important to remember the rules for dealing with signs (see unit 2.3). Special care is needed when negative $(-)$ numbers are involved. Do not try to do too much in each step. Remember also that 'multiplication by zero' gives zero.

Example

If $a = 2$, $b = -1$, $c = -3$ and $d = 0$, evaluate the following:

(i) $a-b-c$ (ii) acd (iii) $3a^2 - 2bc + d$

(i) $a-b-c$ (ii) acd (iii) $3a^2 - 2bc + d$

   $= 2-(-1)-(-3)$ $= 2 \times (-3) \times 0$ $= (3 \times 2 \times 2) - (2 \times -1 \times -3) + 0$

   $= 6$ $= 0$ $= 12 - 6$

                                            $= 6$

It is usually easier to substitute values into an expression before simplifying rather than vice versa.

Example

Evaluate the expression $2x^3 - 5x^2$ when $x = -1$.

$2x^3 - 5x^2 = 2 \times (-1)^3 - 5 \times (-1)^2$

            $= 2 \times (-1) - 5 \times (+1)$ *since* $(-1)^3 = -1 \times -1 \times -1 = -1$

            $= -2 - 5$ *and* $(-1)^2 = -1 \times -1 = +1$

            $= -7$

19.4 BRACKETS

Brackets are used to group terms together. They may be removed, or expanded, by using the distributive laws (see unit 2.2).

To remove brackets, multiply the term 'outside' the bracket by each of the terms inside the bracket. For example, $a(b+c) = ab + ac$.

Care must be taken with the signs when removing brackets. Remember the rules for signs when multiplying (see unit 2.3). A $(-)$ sign 'outside' a bracket changes all the signs inside the bracket. For example, $-(a-b) = -a + b$.

Example

Remove the brackets in (i) $-3(2x-5)$ (ii) $2x^2(x^3 + 2xy - y^2)$

(i) $-3(2x-5)$ (ii) $2x^2(x^3 + 2xy - y^2)$

   $= -6x + 15$ $= 2x^5 + 4x^3y - 2x^2y^2$

When simplifying expressions containing brackets, first remove the brackets and then collect the terms together. Do not try to do both in one step.

Example

Simplify: (i) $5a + 2(2a - 3) + 4$ (ii) $12b - (5 + b) - 6$

  (i) $5a + 2(2a - 3) + 4$ (ii) $12b - (5 + b) - 6$

       $= 5a + 4a - 6 + 4$ $= 12b - 5 - b - 6$

       $= 9a - 2$ $= 11b - 11$

The product of two brackets is found by multiplying each term in the second bracket separately by each term in the first bracket. After the brackets have been removed, the expression is simplified by collecting any like terms together.

Example

Expand: (i) $(x + 2)(3x - 5)$ (ii) $(a - b)(a^2 + ab + b^2)$

  (i) $(x + 2)(3x - 5) = x(3x - 5) + 2(3x - 5)$

                  $= 3x^2 - 5x + 6x - 10$

                  $= 3x^2 + x - 10$

  (ii) $(a - b)(a^2 + ab + b^2) = a(a^2 + ab + b^2) - b(a^2 + ab + b^2)$

                     $= a^3 + a^2 b + ab^2 - a^2 b - ab^2 - b^3$

                     $= a^3 + a^2 b - a^2 b + ab^2 - ab^2 - b^3$

                     $= a^3 - b^3$

Three important expansions are:

$$(a + b)^2 = (a + b)(a + b) = a^2 + 2ab + b^2$$

$$(a - b)^2 = (a - b)(a - b) = a^2 - 2ab + b^2$$

$$(a + b)(a - b) = a^2 - b^2$$

Learn these three expansions, taking careful note of the signs.

If there are brackets enclosed by brackets, then the 'inside' brackets are removed first. It is safer to keep each step separate.

Example

Expand $2a[(a + 2b) + 3(2a - b)]$.

   $2a[(a + 2b) + 3(2a - b)] = 2a[a + 2b + 6a - 3b]$

                       $= 2a[a + 6a + 2b - 3b]$

                       $= 2a[7a - b]$

                       $= 14a^2 - 2ab$

19.5 FORMING EXPRESSIONS

Verbal statements in mathematics can often be written as algebraic expressions. For example, if n represents an unknown number, then:

   '3 more than the number' is written as $n + 3$

   '7 less than the number' is written as $n - 7$

   '5 times the number' is written as $5n$

   'a quarter of the number' is written as $\dfrac{n}{4}$

   'the number subtracted from 2' is written as $2 - n$

   '6 divided by the number' is written as $\dfrac{6}{n}$

   'y more than the number' is written as $n + y$

   'y times the number' is written as ny or yn.

Note: Any letter may be used to represent the unknown number in expressions.

It is often useful, when trying to form algebraic expressions from given descriptions, to work out (usually mentally) how an equivalent problem in arithmetic would be solved. This can also be used as a check.

Example

A student buys x books at £a each and y books at £b each. Write an expression for the average cost of these books.

Cost of x books at £a each is £xa.

Cost of y books at £b each is £yb.

Total cost of books bought is £$(xa+yb)$.

Total number of books bought is $(x+y)$.

$$\text{Average cost of these books} = \frac{\text{Total cost of books}}{\text{Total number of books}} = \frac{£(xa+yb)}{(x+y)}.$$

Care must be taken to be consistent with the units used when answering these questions. Always state clearly the units used at each stage in the answer.

Example

A field is shown on a map as a rectangle x centimetres long and y millimetres wide. The scale of the map is 'a centimetres represent 1 kilometre'. Write an expression for the area of the actual field in square metres.

Since 1 millimetre $= \dfrac{1}{10}$ centimetre

y millimetres $= \dfrac{y}{10}$ centimetres

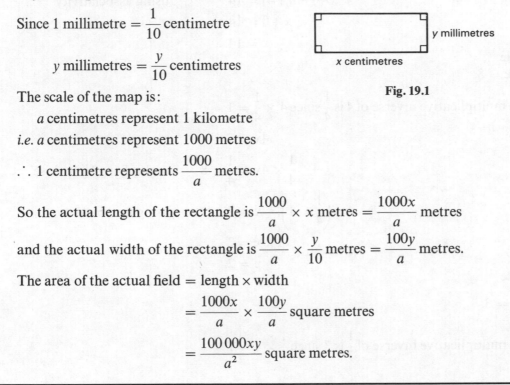

x centimetres

y millimetres

Fig. 19.1

The scale of the map is:

a centimetres represent 1 kilometre

i.e. a centimetres represent 1000 metres

∴ 1 centimetre represents $\dfrac{1000}{a}$ metres.

So the actual length of the rectangle is $\dfrac{1000}{a} \times x$ metres $= \dfrac{1000x}{a}$ metres

and the actual width of the rectangle is $\dfrac{1000}{a} \times \dfrac{y}{10}$ metres $= \dfrac{100y}{a}$ metres.

The area of the actual field $=$ length $\times$ width

$$= \frac{1000x}{a} \times \frac{100y}{a} \text{ square metres}$$

$$= \frac{100\,000xy}{a^2} \text{ square metres}.$$

20 Linear equations

A **linear equation** in one unknown has no squares or higher power of the unknown. For example, $x+5 = 3$, $2x = 9$, $3-5x = 7$ are linear equations.

The **solution** of an equation is the value of the unknown which 'satisfies' it, *i.e.* which, when substituted into the equation, makes the left- and right-hand side equal to the same number. A linear equation in one unknown has only one solution.

Remember: an equation remains unaltered if:

 (*i*) the same number is added to or subtracted from each side;

(*ii*) each side is multiplied or divided by the same number (not zero).

These are used in solving equations.

20.1 SIMPLE EQUATIONS

The following examples illustrate the solution of simple linear equations involving addition, subtraction, multiplication and division.

Example

Solve $x + 3 = 7$.

The additive inverse of 3 is -3 since $3 + -3 = 0$

$$x + 3 = 7$$
$$(x + 3) + -3 = 7 + -3 \qquad \text{adding inverse}$$
$$x + (3 + -3) = 4 \qquad \text{using associativity}$$
$$x + 0 = 4$$
$$x = 4.$$

Example

Solve $x - 4 = 10$.

The additive inverse of -4 is 4 since $-4 + 4 = 0$

$$x - 4 = 10$$
$$x + -4 = 10 \qquad \text{rewriting}$$
$$(x + -4) + 4 = 10 + 4 \qquad \text{adding inverse}$$
$$x + (-4 + 4) = 14 \qquad \text{using associativity}$$
$$x + 0 = 14$$
$$x = 14.$$

Example

Solve $4x = 8$.

The multiplicative inverse of 4 is $\dfrac{1}{4}$ since $4 \times \dfrac{1}{4} = 1$

$$4x = 8$$
$$\frac{1}{4} \times 4x = \frac{1}{4} \times 8 \qquad \text{multiplying by inverse}$$
$$\left(\frac{1}{4} \times 4\right) \times x = 2 \qquad \text{using associativity}$$
$$1 \times x = 2$$
$$x = 2.$$

Example

Solve $\dfrac{x}{7} = 3$.

The multiplicative inverse of $\dfrac{1}{7}$ is 7 since $\dfrac{1}{7} \times 7 = 1$

$$\frac{x}{7} = 3$$
$$7 \times \frac{x}{7} = 7 \times 3$$
$$\left(7 \times \frac{1}{7}\right) \times x = 21$$
$$1 \times x = 21$$
$$x = 21.$$

The above methods are time consuming and short cuts may be taken if you are fully aware of what is happening. The following examples use shorter methods.

Example

Solve $2x + 5 = 11$.

$$2x + 5 = 11$$
$$2x = 11 - 5$$
$$2x = 6$$
$$x = 6 \times \tfrac{1}{2}$$
$$x = 3.$$

Some equations have the unknown quantity on both sides of the equals sign. In equations of this kind, group all the terms containing the unknown on one side of the equation and the other terms on the other side.

Example

Solve (a) $3x + 4 = 7 - 2x$ *(b)* $3 - 2x = 7x + 12$.

$$(a) \quad 3x + 4 = 7 - 2x$$
$$3x + 2x = 7 - 4$$
$$5x = 3$$
$$x = \frac{3}{5}.$$

$$(b) \quad 3 - 2x = 7x + 12$$
$$3 - 12 = 7x + 2x$$
$$-9 = 9x$$
$$-1 = x$$
$$x = -1.$$

Notice that in part (*b*) of this example the *x*'s were gathered on the right of the equation. This was so that we would have a positive (+) term in *x*. If we had gathered the *x*'s on the left, the term would have become $-9x$ which is not as easy to deal with later on.

20.2 EQUATIONS INVOLVING BRACKETS

There are two things to remember before you attempt to solve an equation with brackets:

(*i*) remove the brackets, remembering that everything inside the bracket must be multiplied by the number outside the bracket (see unit 19);

(*ii*) watch the signs (see unit 2.3).

Example

Solve $2(x + 5) = 5(x - 7)$.

$$2(x + 5) = 5(x - 7)$$
$$2x + 10 = 5x - 35$$
$$10 + 35 = 5x - 2x$$
$$45 = 3x$$
$$15 = x$$
$$x = 15.$$

Example

Solve $2(x - 1) - 3(2x - 1) = x + 6$.

$$2(x - 1) - 3(2x - 1) = x + 6$$
$$2x - 2 - 6x + 3 = x + 6$$
$$-2 + 3 - 6 = x + 6x - 2x$$
$$-5 = 5x$$
$$-1 = x$$
$$x = -1.$$

Study these examples carefully and make sure you understand why the signs are as given, especially in the second line where the brackets have been removed.

20.3 EQUATIONS INVOLVING FRACTIONS

The safest way to deal with equations involving fractions is to clear the fractions first by multiplying throughout by the LCM (see unit 2.5) of the denominators.

Example

Solve $\dfrac{x - 1}{2} - \dfrac{2x + 1}{3} = \dfrac{x}{4}$.

The LCM of 2, 3 and 4 is 12. Multiply each term by 12.

$$\frac{12(x-1)}{2} - \frac{12(2x+1)}{3} = \frac{12x}{4}$$

$$6(x-1) - 4(2x+1) = 3x$$

$$6x - 6 - 8x - 4 = 3x$$

$$-6 - 4 = 3x + 8x - 6x$$

$$-10 = 5x$$

$$-2 = x$$

$$x = -2.$$

21 Relations and functions

21.1 RELATIONS

A **relation** is a connection between two sets. In the statement 'John is the brother of Ann', the relation is 'is the brother of' and John $\in$ {boys} and Ann $\in$ {girls}. In Mathematics the quantities connected by relations are often numbers.

Figure 21.1 shows four arrow diagrams illustrating the four different types of relations. Above each is written the type of relation and below each is written the meaning of the arrow.

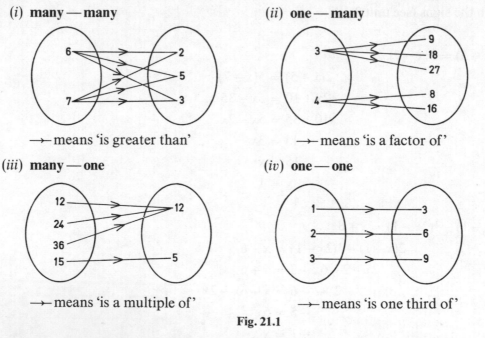

(i) **many — many**

$\longrightarrow$ means 'is greater than'

(ii) **one — many**

$\longrightarrow$ means 'is a factor of'

(iii) **many — one**

$\longrightarrow$ means 'is a multiple of'

(iv) **one — one**

$\longrightarrow$ means 'is one third of'

Fig. 21.1

21.2 FUNCTIONS (OR MAPPINGS)

The words function and mapping have the same meaning. A **function** or **mapping**:

(a) is a *many — one* or *one — one* relation between two sets X and Y;

(b) relates every member of X, to one and only one member of Y.

The **domain** of the function is X.

The **range** of the function is that subset of Y (the **image set**) which consists of all possible images of members of X.

Sometimes Y may contain members which are not images of members of X.

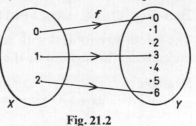

Fig. 21.2

For example, for the mapping f and the two sets X and Y shown in Fig. 21.2, the domain is $\{0, 1, 2\}$ and the range is $\{0, 3, 6\}$.

There are various ways of describing a function. The most usual ones are:

(*i*) mapping diagrams

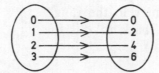

(*ii*) sets of ordered pairs, *e.g.*, $\{(0,0), (1,2), (2,4), (3,6)\}$

(*iii*) algebraic relations, *e.g.*, $y = 2x$

(*iv*) Cartesian graphs (see unit 22.1).

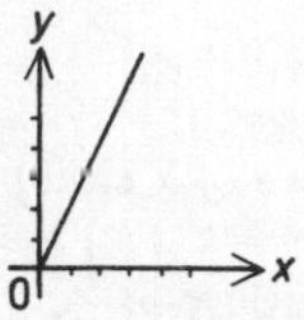

These all represent the same function, written, $f: x \rightarrow 2x$. This is read as, 'f maps x into $2x$'.

In general, a function f, relating two sets X and Y can be illustrated by a mapping diagram (Fig. 21.3).

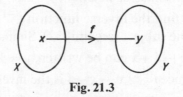

Fig. 21.3

Figure 21.3 shows $f: x \rightarrow y$ (f maps x into y).

Since every member x of X is mapped into Y the function can also be written $f: X \rightarrow Y$.

f is called the function, and the image of x, written $f(x)$, is called the value of the function at x. So y and $f(x)$ are the same member of Y.

Example

Functions f and g are defined by

$f: x \rightarrow x+1, for\ -1 \leqslant x \leqslant 2,$

$g: x \rightarrow 2x^2,\ for\ -2 \leqslant x \leqslant 2.$

Calculate the ranges of the functions f and g.

The end points of the domain do not necessarily give the end points of the range. Therefore, it is safer to draw a sketch of the Cartesian graph of each function over its domain.

Over the given domain, $-1 \leqslant x \leqslant 2$, f is linear and continuous (*i.e.* a straight line without gaps).

When $x = -1, f(x) = -1 + 1 = 0.$

When $x = 2, f(x) = 2 + 1 = 3.$

Hence the range of f is $0 \leqslant y \leqslant 3.$

Figure 21.4 shows the Cartesian graph of f over the given domain.

Fig. 21.4

Over the given domain, $-2 \leqslant x \leqslant 2$, g is quadratic and continuous. (The graph of a quadratic is a parabola (see unit 30).)

When $x = 0, g(x) = 2.0^2 = 0.$

When $x = -2, g(x) = 2.(-2)^2 = 8.$

When $x = 2, g(x) = 2.(2)^2 = 8.$

Hence the range of g is $0 \leqslant y \leqslant 8.$

Figure 21.5 shows the Cartesian graph of g over the given domain.

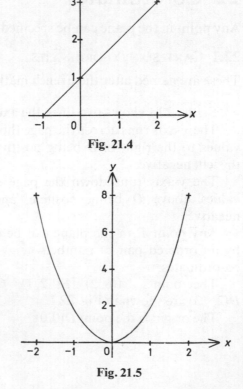

Fig. 21.5

21.3 INVERSE FUNCTIONS

If a function f is one–one and maps an element x in the domain to an element y in the range, then the function that maps y back to x is the **inverse** of f, written f^{-1} (Fig. 21.6).

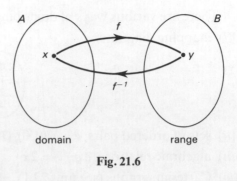

domain   range

Fig. 21.6

Example

Functions f, g and h are defined for all values of x except $x = 0$ and -1 by

$$f: x \rightarrow 1 + x, \qquad g: x \rightarrow \frac{1}{x}, \qquad h: x \rightarrow \frac{x}{1+x}.$$

Define the inverse functions f^{-1}, g^{-1}, h^{-1}.

To find the inverse function f^{-1} we write $y = f(x)$ and transform the equation to make x the subject (see unit 32). Similarly for g and h.

$f: x \rightarrow 1 + x$ can be written, $y = 1 + x \Rightarrow x = y - 1$.

Hence $f^{-1}: x \rightarrow x - 1$ is the inverse of f.

$g: x \rightarrow \dfrac{1}{x}$ can be written $y = \dfrac{1}{x} \Rightarrow x = \dfrac{1}{y}$.

Hence $g^{-1}: x \rightarrow \dfrac{1}{x}$ is the inverse of g. (Notice that g is its own inverse.)

$h: x \rightarrow \dfrac{x}{1+x}$ can be written $y = \dfrac{x}{1+x} \Rightarrow x = \dfrac{y}{1-y}$.

Hence $h^{-1}: x \rightarrow \dfrac{x}{1-x}$ is the inverse of h.

---

22 Co-ordinates

Any point in the plane can be specified by two **co-ordinates**.

22.1 CARTESIAN CO-ORDINATES

These are named after the French mathematician Rene Descartes (1596–1650).

Figure 22.1 shows two lines, the **axes**, at right angles intersecting at O, the **origin**.

The x-axis runs across the page (horizontal), values to the right of O being positive, and to the left, negative.

The y-axis runs down the page (vertical), values above O being positive, and below, negative.

Any point P in the plane can be described by an ordered pair of numbers (x, y) called its co-ordinates.

The points, $A(6, 2)$, $B(^-2, 1)$, $C(^-2, ^-1)$, $D(2, ^-3)$ are shown in Fig. 22.1.

The origin is the point $O(0, 0)$.

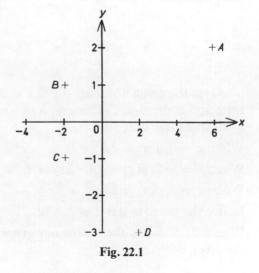

Fig. 22.1

22.2 POLAR CO-ORDINATES

Figure 22.2 shows another way of describing the position of any point in the plane.

Any point *P* in the plane lies on a circle radius *r*, centre *O*.

The angle $\theta°$ is the angle made by *OP* with some fixed line *OX* called the **polar axis** and measured anti-clockwise.

Hence, $(r, \theta°)$ is an ordered pair called the **polar co-ordinates** of *P*.

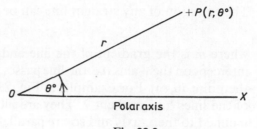

Fig. 22.2

Example

Indicate on a sketch the position of the point P(3, 40°).

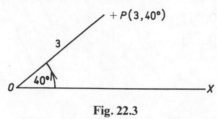

Fig. 22.3

23 The straight line

23.1 THE GRADIENT OF A STRAIGHT LINE

The gradient (or slope) of a straight line is the ratio:

$$\frac{\text{vertical displacement}}{\text{horizontal displacement}}$$

where the displacements are taken between the same two points on the line.

Displacements 'up' ↑ and 'right' → are positive (+),

'down' ↓ and 'left' ← are negative (−).

An 'upwards' sloping line has positive gradient.

A 'downwards' sloping line has negative gradient.

The gradient is equal to the tangent of the angle made by the straight line with the horizontal (see unit 41.1).

For example:

In Fig. 23.1, the straight line passing through $A(^-3, ^-1)$ and $B(1, 2)$ has gradient $\frac{3}{4}$. It has a positive gradient.

Notice that $\tan \alpha = \frac{3}{4}$.

In Fig. 23.2, the straight line passing through $C(2, ^-1)$ and $D(^-2, 2)$ has gradient $\frac{3}{-4}$, i.e. $-\frac{3}{4}$.

It has a negative gradient.

Also $\tan \theta = -\frac{3}{4}$ and θ is an obtuse angle.

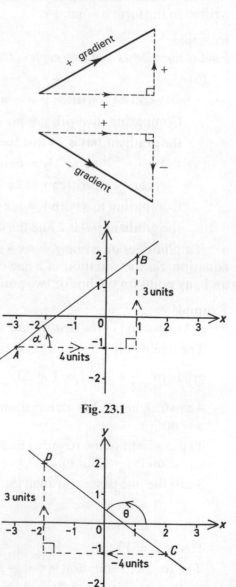

Fig. 23.1

Fig. 23.2

23.2 THE EQUATION OF A STRAIGHT LINE

The equation of any straight line can be written in the form

$$y = mx + c$$

where m is the gradient of the line and c is the intercept on the y-axis (*i.e.* the line passes through the point $(0, c)$). For example, in Fig. 23.3, each of the lines has gradient 2. They are all equally inclined to the x-axis and so are parallel to each other. So the equation of each line is of the form

$$y = 2x + c$$

$y = 2x + 1$ cuts the y-axis at $(0, 1)$.

$y = 2x$ cuts the y-axis at $(0, 0)$.

$y = 2x - 1$ cuts the y-axis at $(0, {}^-1)$.

$y = 2x - 3$ cuts the y-axis at $(0, {}^-3)$.

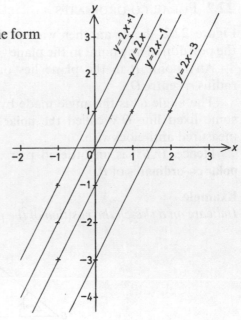

Fig. 23.3

The gradient and intercept of any straight line can be obtained from its equation if it is written in the form $y = mx + c$.

Example

Find the gradients and intercepts of the straight lines (a) $x + y = 5$ *(b)* $3y = 6x - 2$.

    (a) $\qquad\qquad x + y = 5$

        can be rewritten $y = -x + 5$.

        Comparing this with $y = mx + c$

        the gradient (m) is $^-1$ and the intercept (c) is 5.

    (b) $\qquad\qquad 3y = 6x - 2$

        can be rewritten $y = 2x - \frac{2}{3}$.

        Comparing this with $y = mx + c$

        the gradient (m) is 2 and the intercept (c) is $-\frac{2}{3}$.

If a point lies on a line $y = mx + c$, then the x and y values of that point must satisfy the equation. So the equation of a line can be found if we know either the gradient of the line and any point on the line or two points through which the line passes.

Example

Find the equation of the straight line passing through $(5, 3)$ *and* $(3, 7)$.

The line passing through $(5, 3)$ and $(3, 7)$ has gradient $\dfrac{4}{-2} = -2$ (see Fig. 23.4).

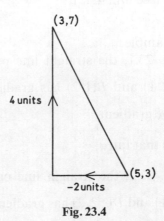

Any straight line has an equation of the form $y = mx + c$.

The gradient of the required line is $^-2$, so its equation is $y = {}^-2x + c$.

Since the line passes through $(5, 3)$, we have

$$3 = {}^-2 \times 5 + c$$
$$3 = {}^-10 + c$$

Hence $c = 13$.

Fig. 23.4

The required equation is $y = -2x + 13$.

Note: The other point $(3, 7)$ could have been used to find c.

24 Simultaneous equations

These two linear equations:

$$2x - y = 10$$
$$x + 3y = 5$$

could each be plotted on the same pair of axes and their point of intersection found. This is true because each is the equation of a straight line and the two lines are not parallel and so meet at a point.

Sets of equations for which there are common solutions are often called **simultaneous equations**.

Simultaneous equations can be solved in several ways. Solution by elimination and substitution are described below. For solution by graphical methods see unit 30 and by matrix methods see unit 26.

24.1 SOLUTION BY ELIMINATION

Linear simultaneous equations are often solved by equalising the coefficients of one of the unknowns and then eliminating that unknown by adding or subtracting the equations. The method is illustrated in the following examples.

Example

Solve the equations $2x - y = 10$ and $x + 3y = 5$ simultaneously.

First, number each equation

$$2x - y = 10 \qquad (1)$$
$$x + 3y = 5 \qquad (2)$$

If we adjust equation (1) by multiplying by 3, then add the two equations together, the term in y will disappear. (Since $-3y + 3y = 0$.)

$$3 \times (1) \qquad 6x - 3y = 30$$
$$(2) \qquad x + 3y = 5.$$
Adding we get $\qquad 7x = 35$
$$x = 5.$$

Substituting this value of x into (1) gives,

$$2 \times 5 - y = 10$$
$$y = 0.$$

Hence, the solution of the equations is $x = 5$, $y = 0$ *or* $(5, 0)$.

Check this by substituting $x = 5$ and $y = 0$ into (2).

LHS $= 5 + (3 \times 0) = 5$, RHS $= 5$, so solution checks.

When we found the value of x ($= 5$) we could have substituted into either (1) or (2) to find y. Always choose the equation which looks easier.

Sometimes the equations are 'mixed up' and need to be rearranged before we start.

Example

Solve the equations $y = 2x + 4$ and $3x = 7 - 5y$ simultaneously.

Rearranging the equations

$$-2x + y = 4 \qquad (1)$$
$$3x + 5y = 7 \qquad (2)$$
$$3 \times (1) \qquad -6x + 3y = 12$$
$$2 \times (2) \qquad 6x + 10y = 14$$
adding $\qquad 13y = 26$
$$y = 2$$

Substituting $y = 2$ into (2) gives,

$$3x + 10 = 7$$
$$3x = -3$$
$$x = -1$$

Hence the solution of the two equations is $x = -1, y = 2$ or $(-1, 2)$.

Check this solution by substituting $x = -1$ and $y = 2$ into (*1*).

Since one term in x is negative and one positive, we adjusted both equations in order to eliminate x by adding the equations together.

If both the terms in x and both the terms in y are positive, it will be necessary to subtract one equation from the other, possibly after adjustment.

24.2 SOLUTION BY SUBSTITUTION

An alternative method is to find an expression for one unknown in terms of the other unknown from one equation and then substitute in the other equation. This method is normally used when one of the pair of simultaneous equations is linear and the other quadratic. In this case it is easier to substitute y (or x) from the linear equation into the quadratic. This gives a quadratic equation in one unknown, which can be solved (see unit 29).

Example

Solve the equations $3x^2 - 4y + 1 = 0$ *and* $2x - y = 1$.

$$3x^2 - 4y + 1 = 0 \qquad (1)$$
$$2x - y = 1 \qquad (2)$$

From (2) $\qquad y = 2x - 1$

Substitute into (*1*) $\quad 3x^2 - 4(2x - 1) + 1 = 0$

or $\quad 3x^2 - 8x + 5 = 0$

i.e. $\quad (3x - 5)(x - 1) = 0$

Solution of this quadratic (see unit 29) gives $x = \dfrac{5}{3}$ or $x = 1$.

Substitute each of these values of x back into (2) giving, when $x = \dfrac{5}{3}, y = \dfrac{7}{3}$

and when $x = 1, y = 1$.

Hence the two solutions are $\left(\dfrac{5}{3}, \dfrac{7}{3}\right)$ and $(1, 1)$.

Check these solutions by substituting into (2).

---

25 Inequalities and linear programming

25.1 INEQUALITIES

Figure 25.1 shows part of a number line.

One number is greater than another if it lies to the right of the other on this number line.

Since 3 is greater than 1 we write $3 > 1$.

Since -3 is less than 1 we write $-3 < 1$.

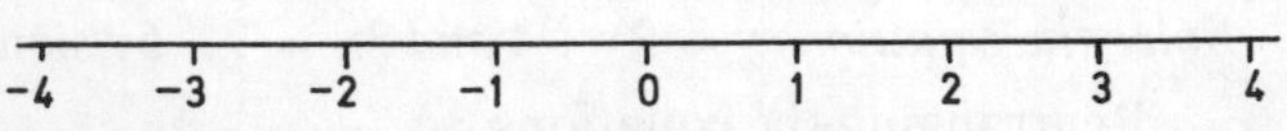

Fig. 25.1

These are called **inequalities**.

An inequality which contains one or more unknown variables is sometimes called an **inequation**. For example, $x < 4, x > {}^-2, 2x + 1 \geqslant 3, y \leqslant 4x^2 - 1$ may be called inequations.

Inequalities can sometimes be combined. For example, if we have a number x where $-2 < x$ and $x < 4$, then we can combine the two inequalities and write $-2 < x < 4$.

25.2 RULES FOR INEQUALITIES

(*i*) The same number may be added to or subtracted from both sides of an inequality.

For example, addition: $5 > -2$ and $5 + 1 > -2 + 1$, i.e. $6 > -1$,

subtraction: $5 > -2$ and $5 - 1 > -2 - 1$, i.e. $4 > -3$.

(*ii*) Multiplying or dividing both sides of an inequality by the same positive number leaves the inequality unaltered.

For example, multiplication: $4 > -6$ and $2 \times 4 > 2 \times -6$, *i.e.* $8 > -12$,
division: $4 > -6$ and $4 \div 2 > -6 \div 2$, *i.e.* $2 > -3$.

(*iii*) Multiplying or dividing both sides of an inequality by the same negative number reverses the sign of the inequality.

For example, multiplication: $9 > 6$ but $-2 \times 9 < -2 \times 6$, *i.e.* $-18 < -12$,
division: $9 > 6$ but $9 \div -3 < 6 \div -3$, *i.e.* $-3 < -2$.

25.3 SOLUTION OF INEQUATIONS

The solution of an inequation is a range (or ranges) of values of the variable.

The solution sets of simple inequations may be illustrated on a number line. For example, if x is a real number and $-3 < x < 2$, this inequality represents a **region** on the real number line. The region is the set $S = \{x : -3 < x < 2\}$. Figure 25.2 shows this region.

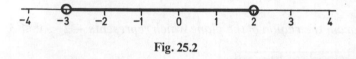

Fig. 25.2

(The open circles at each end show that -3 and 2 do not belong to the region.)

Sometimes one or both end points belong to the set. In this case we fill in the circle(s). For example, $S = \{x : -1 \leqslant x < 3\}$. Here -1 belongs to S, and Fig. 25.3 shows this set S.

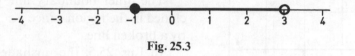

Fig. 25.3

The two sets shown in Figs. 25.2 and 25.3 are infinite sets. However, not all sets of points on a number line are infinite.

For example, we can rewrite $S = \{x : 0 \leqslant x < 5, x$ an integer$\}$ by listing its members, *i.e.* $S = \{0, 1, 2, 3, 4\}$.

Linear inequations in one unknown may be solved by using the rules of inequalities. The following two examples use the rules:

Example
Find the solution set S of integers x if: $1 < x + 3 \leqslant 5$.

It is safer to deal with each inequality separately,

$$1 < x + 3 \qquad\qquad x + 3 \leqslant 5,$$
$$\text{so} \quad 1 - 3 < x, \qquad \text{so} \qquad x \leqslant 5 - 3,$$
$$-2 < x. \qquad\qquad x \leqslant 2.$$

Hence, combining the two inequalities gives $-2 < x \leqslant 2$ and $S = \{-1, 0, 1, 2\}$.

Example
Find the solution set S of integers x if: $1 \leqslant 2 - x \leqslant 4$.

Again, deal with each inequality separately,

$$1 \leqslant 2 - x \qquad\qquad 2 - x \leqslant 4.$$

Multiplying each inequality by -1 reverses the signs,

$$-1 \geqslant x - 2 \qquad\qquad x - 2 \geqslant -4$$
$$\text{so} \quad -1 + 2 \geqslant x \qquad \text{so} \qquad x \geqslant -4 + 2$$
$$1 \geqslant x \qquad\qquad x \geqslant -2.$$

Hence, combining the two inequalities gives $1 \geqslant x \geqslant -2$ or rewriting in reverse order, $-2 \leqslant x \leqslant 1$.

The solution set $S = \{-2, -1, 0, 1\}$.

Linear inequations in two unknowns are best solved graphically.

25.4 GRAPHS OF INEQUALITIES

Inequalities can be used to describe regions of the plane.

On graphs of inequalities it is conventional to shade in the area of the plane which is not included in the inequality. The corresponding equality gives the boundary line. This is drawn as:

(*a*) a continuous line if the inequality is ⩾ or ⩽, *i.e.* it is included in the region;

(*b*) a broken line if the inequality is > or <, *i.e.* it is not included in the region.

A convenient point is chosen to check on which side of the line the inequality applies.

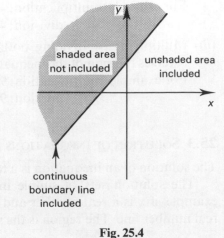

Fig. 25.4

Example

Indicate on a diagram the region of the plane which represents $-2 < y \leqslant 3$.

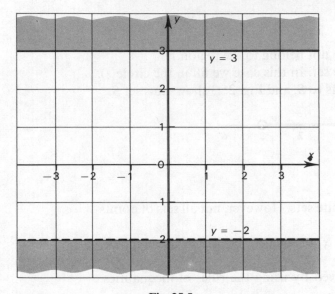

Fig. 25.5

The **boundary** line $y = 3$ is included in the region (since $y \leqslant 3$) and is shown by a continuous line.

The other boundary line $y = -2$ is not included in the region (since $y > -2$) and is shown by a broken line.

In Fig. 25.5, the unshaded area represents the region $-2 < y \leqslant 3$.

In the previous example the required region was an infinite strip. Sometimes the solution set will be a finite region or even a finite set of points.

Example

Find graphically $S = \{(x, y) : x < 3, y \leqslant 4, x + y > 2\}$ *where x and y are integers.*

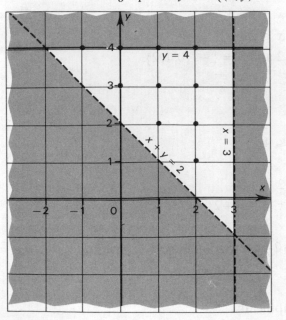

Fig. 25.6

In Fig. 25.6, $x = 3$ and $x + y = 2$ are shown by broken lines and $y = 4$ by a continuous line.

The members of S are indicated by the large dots.

Therefore, $S = \{(-1, 4), (0, 4), (1, 4), (2, 4), (0, 3), (1, 3), (2, 3), (1, 2), (2, 2), (2, 1)\}$.

25.5 LINEAR PROGRAMMING

Linear programming is a method used to solve problems, especially in business management and economics, involving conditions which can be expressed using linear inequalities. For example, a manufacturing industry makes its profits by selling its goods. The cheaper the goods are to produce, the more profit there will be. Many factors govern the cost of production, *e.g.* wages, cost of raw materials and transport. Minimising production costs helps to maximise profits. The factors which contribute to this process can be expressed mathematically as linear relationships in the form of inequalities.

At this level the problems involve only two variables and can be solved graphically. The method used is illustrated in the following example.

Example

A discount store stocks two makes of video-recorder, Tony and Hiscratchi. Both makes of video-recorder are packed in the same size box and the store has room for a maximum of 100 recorders. The store manager knows that Hiscratchi is more popular and so plans to order at least twice as many Hiscratchi video-recorders as Tonys. However, he wants to order at least 10 Tony recorders and not more than 80 Hiscratchi recorders.

Taking x to be the number of Tony video-recorders and y to be the number of Hiscratchi video-recorders which he orders, write down the four inequalities involving x and/or y which satisfy these conditions.

The point (x, y) represents x Tony video-recorders and y Hiscratchi video-recorders. Using a scale of 1 cm to represent 10 video-recorders on each axis, construct and indicate clearly, by shading the unwanted regions, the region in which (x, y) must lie.

The profit on a Tony video-recorder is £30 and on a Hiscratchi recorder is £20. Use your graph to estimate the number of video-recorders of each make that the manager should order to give the maximum possible profit. Calculate this maximum possible profit.

We are given that:

x is the number of Tony video-recorders, and
y is the number of Hiscratchi video-recorders ordered.

The conditions given can be expressed as four inequalities.

(*i*) Since the maximum number of video-recorders which can be stored is 100,

$x + y \leqslant 100$.

(*ii*) Since at least twice as many Hiscratchis are ordered as Tonys,

$y \geqslant 2x$.

(*iii*) Since at least 10 Tony video-recorders are to be ordered,

$x \geqslant 10$.

(*iv*) Since not more than 80 Hiscratchi video-recorders are to be ordered,

$y \leqslant 80$.

Figure 25.7 shows the boundary lines $x + y = 100$, $y = 2x$, $x = 10$ and $y = 80$. The unshaded area represents the region defined by the four inequalities $x + y \leqslant 100$, $y \geqslant 2x$, $x \geqslant 10$, $y \leqslant 80$.

The possible values for (x, y) lie within the unshaded region or on the boundary lines.

As the profit made on each Tony video-recorder sold is £30 and on each Hiscratchi video-recorder sold is £20, the total profit, say £P, made when x Tony video-recorders and y Hiscratchi recorders are sold, will satisfy

$$P = 30x + 20y.$$

Suppose that 20 Tony video-recorders and 60 Hiscratchi video-recorders are sold. The profit will be given by:

$$P = (30 \times 20) + (20 \times 60)$$
$$= 1800.$$

In Fig. 25.7, the line $30x + 20y = 1800$ is shown. This is called a **profit line**. The line representing any other profit would be parallel to this line since only P changes. The maximum possible profit is given by the line parallel to $30x + 20y = 1800$ which makes P

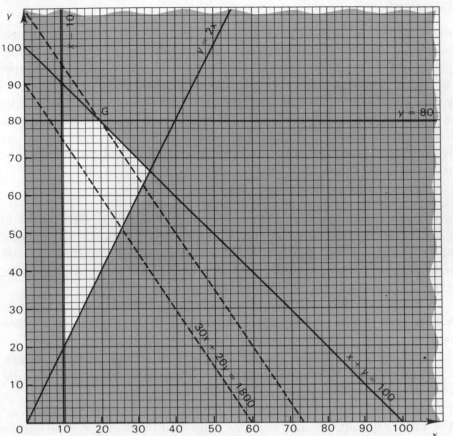

Fig. 25.7

a maximum, *i.e.* the line which is furthest from the origin yet still satisfies the given conditions. From the graph it can be seen that this occurs when the line passes through the point *G* where $x = 20$ and $y = 80$.

So the manager should order 20 Tony video-recorders and 80 Hiscratchi recorders to give the maximum possible profit.

The maximum possible profit is given by:

$$P = (30 \times 20) + (20 \times 80)$$
$$= 2200$$

i.e. £2200 is the maximum possible profit.

26 Matrices

A **matrix** can be thought of as a store of information. For example, the last five matches played by four football teams produced the following results:

	Won	Lost	Drawn
Liverpool	4	0	1
Manchester United	2	1	2
Nottingham Forest	3	0	2
Everton	1	3	1

This information can be written as the matrix: $\begin{pmatrix} 4 & 0 & 1 \\ 2 & 1 & 2 \\ 3 & 0 & 2 \\ 1 & 3 & 1 \end{pmatrix}$

This matrix has 4 **rows** and 3 **columns**. The **order** is 4×3.

The matrix $(5 \quad -1 \quad 4)$ is of order 1×3 and called a **row matrix**.

The matrix $\begin{pmatrix} 4 \\ 9 \end{pmatrix}$ is of order 2×1 and called a **column matrix**.

A **square matrix** is one which has the same number of rows and columns.

The entries in a matrix are called the **elements** of the matrix.

Two matrices are **equal** if and only if they are of the same order and corresponding elements are equal.

For example, $\begin{pmatrix} a & b \\ c & d \end{pmatrix} = \begin{pmatrix} p & q \\ r & s \end{pmatrix}$ if and only if $a = p, b = q, c = r, d = s$.

Matrices are often denoted by capital letters, *e.g. A, B*.

A **zero matrix**, O, is one in which every element is zero.

For example, for 2×2 matrices, $O = \begin{pmatrix} 0 & 0 \\ 0 & 0 \end{pmatrix}$.

A **unit matrix**, I, is a square matrix in which each element in the leading diagonal is 1 and every other element is zero. I is sometimes called an **identity matrix**.

For example, the 2×2 identity matrix $I = \begin{pmatrix} 1 & 0 \\ 0 & 1 \end{pmatrix}$.

(Remember: the leading diagonal is the line of element from the top left to the bottom right.)

26.1 ADDITION OF MATRICES

If two matrices A and B are of the same order, the sum of A and B, *i.e.* $A + B$, is obtained by adding corresponding elements.

For example,

$$\text{if } A = \begin{pmatrix} 2 & 4 \\ -1 & 3 \end{pmatrix} \text{ and } B = \begin{pmatrix} 0 & 1 \\ 8 & 7 \end{pmatrix}$$

$$A + B = \begin{pmatrix} 2+0 & 4+1 \\ -1+8 & 3+7 \end{pmatrix} = \begin{pmatrix} 2 & 5 \\ 7 & 10 \end{pmatrix}.$$

The **addition** of matrices is **commutative**, *i.e.* $A + B = B + A$ for all matrices A and B which can be added together.

The **addition** of matrices is **associative**, *i.e.* $(A + B) + C = A + (B + C)$ for all matrices A, B and C which can be added together.

26.2 SUBTRACTION OF MATRICES

If two matrices A and B are of the same order, to subtract B from A, add the **additive inverse** of B to A, *i.e.* $A - B = A + (-B)$.

The additive inverse of B is the matrix $-B$ such that the sign of each element of B is reversed.

For example,

$$\text{If } A = \begin{pmatrix} -2 & 4 \\ 6 & 9 \end{pmatrix} \text{ and } B = \begin{pmatrix} 3 & -4 \\ -1 & 0 \end{pmatrix}, \text{ then } -B = \begin{pmatrix} -3 & 4 \\ 1 & 0 \end{pmatrix}$$

$$\text{and } A - B = A + (-B) = \begin{pmatrix} -2 & 4 \\ 6 & 9 \end{pmatrix} + \begin{pmatrix} -3 & 4 \\ 1 & 0 \end{pmatrix}$$

$$= \begin{pmatrix} -5 & 8 \\ 7 & 9 \end{pmatrix}.$$

26.3 MULTIPLICATION OF A MATRIX BY A SCALAR

To multiply a matrix by a scalar (real number), multiply each element of the matrix by the scalar.

For example,

$$2 \begin{pmatrix} 3 & 6 \\ -1 & 5 \end{pmatrix} = \begin{pmatrix} 2 \times 3 & 2 \times 6 \\ 2 \times -1 & 2 \times 5 \end{pmatrix} = \begin{pmatrix} 6 & 12 \\ -2 & 10 \end{pmatrix}.$$

26.4 MULTIPLICATION OF TWO MATRICES

Two matrices A and B can be multiplied together if and only if the number of columns of the left-hand matrix equals the number of rows of the right-hand matrix. If this happens, A and B are said to be **compatible**.

For example, if $A = \begin{pmatrix} 1 & 3 & -2 \\ 5 & 0 & 1 \end{pmatrix}$ and $B = \begin{pmatrix} 4 \\ 1 \\ -3 \end{pmatrix}$ then A and B are compatible

since the order of A is 2×3 and the order of B is 3×1. Hence AB can be evaluated, its order being 2×1. However, BA does not exist since A and B are not compatible for multiplication in this order.

To find AB we multiply every row of A by every column of B.
For example,

$$AB = \begin{pmatrix} 1 & 3 & -2 \\ 5 & 0 & 1 \end{pmatrix} \begin{pmatrix} 4 \\ 1 \\ -3 \end{pmatrix} = \begin{pmatrix} (1 \times 4) + (3 \times 1) + (-2 \times -3) \\ (5 \times 4) + (0 \times 1) + (1 \times -3) \end{pmatrix} = \begin{pmatrix} 4 + 3 + 6 \\ 20 + 0 + -3 \end{pmatrix} = \begin{pmatrix} 13 \\ 17 \end{pmatrix}.$$

It is not possible (at this level) to give a general rule for matrix multiplication since the compatible matrices can be of different orders. However, two common types are these:

$$(i) \begin{pmatrix} a & b \\ c & d \end{pmatrix} \begin{pmatrix} x \\ y \end{pmatrix} = \begin{pmatrix} ax + by \\ cx + dy \end{pmatrix} \qquad (ii) \begin{pmatrix} a & b \\ c & d \end{pmatrix} \begin{pmatrix} x & z \\ y & t \end{pmatrix} = \begin{pmatrix} ax + by & az + bt \\ cx + dy & cz + dt \end{pmatrix}.$$

If a matrix of order $p \times q$ and a matrix of order $q \times r$ are multiplied together in that order, the order of the resulting matrix is $p \times r$.

In general, matrix multiplication is not commutative, *i.e.* $AB \neq BA$. However, it is associative, *i.e.* $(AB)C = A(BC)$.

26.5 THE DETERMINANT OF A 2×2 MATRIX

The **determinant** of a 2×2 matrix $A = \begin{pmatrix} a & b \\ c & d \end{pmatrix}$ is the number $ad - bc$.

The determinant of a matrix A is usually written $|A|$ or det A.

For example, if $A = \begin{pmatrix} 2 & 1 \\ 4 & 3 \end{pmatrix}$

$$|A| = (2 \times 3) - (1 \times 4) = 6 - 4 = 2.$$

If the determinant of a matrix is zero, the matrix is said to be **singular**, otherwise it is said to be **non-singular**.

26.6 INVERSE OF A 2×2 MATRIX

Every non-singular 2×2 matrix A has a **multiplicative inverse** A^{-1} such that $AA^{-1} = A^{-1}A = I$, where I is the unit matrix.

If $A = \begin{pmatrix} a & b \\ c & d \end{pmatrix}$ then $A^{-1} = \dfrac{1}{|A|} \begin{pmatrix} d & -b \\ -c & a \end{pmatrix}.$

For example, if $A = \begin{pmatrix} 3 & 2 \\ -5 & 4 \end{pmatrix}$, then $|A| = (3 \times 4) - (2 \times -5) = 12 - -10 = 22$

$$\text{and } A^{-1} = \tfrac{1}{22} \begin{pmatrix} 4 & -2 \\ 5 & 3 \end{pmatrix} = \begin{pmatrix} \frac{4}{22} & -\frac{2}{22} \\ \frac{5}{22} & \frac{3}{22} \end{pmatrix}.$$

$$\text{Hence, } AA^{-1} = \begin{pmatrix} 3 & 2 \\ -5 & 4 \end{pmatrix} \begin{pmatrix} \frac{4}{22} & -\frac{2}{22} \\ \frac{5}{22} & \frac{3}{22} \end{pmatrix}$$

$$= \begin{pmatrix} \frac{22}{22} & 0 \\ 0 & \frac{22}{22} \end{pmatrix} = \begin{pmatrix} 1 & 0 \\ 0 & 1 \end{pmatrix} = I.$$

Clearly, if $|A| = 0$ the matrix A is singular and has no inverse because $\dfrac{1}{0}$ does not exist.

26.7 THE SOLUTION OF TWO SIMULTANEOUS LINEAR EQUATIONS

Two linear equations:

$$ax + by = p$$
$$cx + dy = q$$

where a, b, c, d, p, q are real numbers, can be written in matrix form as:

$$\begin{pmatrix} a & b \\ c & d \end{pmatrix} \begin{pmatrix} x \\ y \end{pmatrix} = \begin{pmatrix} p \\ q \end{pmatrix}$$

and solved simultaneously.

Example

Solve the simultaneous equations $3x - 2y = 17$ and $x + 5y - 51 = 0$.

Rewrite the equations in this form, $\qquad 3x - 2y = 17$

$$x + 5y = 51$$

and now in matrix form, $\begin{pmatrix} 3 & -2 \\ 1 & 5 \end{pmatrix} \begin{pmatrix} x \\ y \end{pmatrix} = \begin{pmatrix} 17 \\ 51 \end{pmatrix}.$

If $A = \begin{pmatrix} 3 & -2 \\ 1 & 5 \end{pmatrix}$ then $|A| = (3 \times 5) - (-2 \times 1) = 15 - -2 = 17$

$$\text{and } A^{-1} = \tfrac{1}{17} \begin{pmatrix} 5 & 2 \\ -1 & 3 \end{pmatrix} = \begin{pmatrix} \frac{5}{15} & \frac{2}{17} \\ \frac{-1}{17} & \frac{3}{17} \end{pmatrix}.$$

Pre-multiply (*i.e.* multiply on the left) the matrix form of the equations by A^{-1},

$$\textit{i.e.} \begin{pmatrix} \frac{5}{17} & \frac{2}{17} \\ \frac{-1}{17} & \frac{3}{17} \end{pmatrix} \begin{pmatrix} 3 & -2 \\ 1 & 5 \end{pmatrix} \begin{pmatrix} x \\ y \end{pmatrix} = \begin{pmatrix} \frac{5}{17} & \frac{2}{17} \\ \frac{-1}{17} & \frac{3}{17} \end{pmatrix} \begin{pmatrix} 17 \\ 51 \end{pmatrix}$$

$$\begin{pmatrix} 1 & 0 \\ 0 & 1 \end{pmatrix} \begin{pmatrix} x \\ y \end{pmatrix} = \begin{pmatrix} 11 \\ 8 \end{pmatrix}$$

$$\begin{pmatrix} x \\ y \end{pmatrix} = \begin{pmatrix} 11 \\ 8 \end{pmatrix}.$$

Therefore $x = 11$ and $y = 8$.

Check: substitute $x = 11$ and $y = 8$ into the original equations:

$$3.11 - 2.8 = 33 - 16 = 17$$
$$1.11 + 5.8 = 11 + 40 = 51.$$

Note: If the product $A^{-1}A$ on the left-hand side does not equal $I = \begin{pmatrix} 1 & 0 \\ 0 & 1 \end{pmatrix}$, you have calculated either A^{-1} or $A^{-1}A$ incorrectly.

---

27 Factorisation

Factorisation may be thought of as the reverse of the expansion of brackets, *i.e.* using the distributive laws 'backwards'. For example,

Since $(x + 2)(3x - 5) = 3x^2 + x - 10$

the factors of $3x^2 + x - 10$ are $(x + 2)$ and $(3x - 5)$.

So when factorising an expression we have to find the **factors** which multiply together to give the original expression. You can always check your factorisation by multiplying the factors.

The most common types of factorisation are described below.

27.1 COMMON OR OBVIOUS FACTOR

Always look for a **common factor** in an expression first. If there is a common factor, the other factor can be found by dividing each term in the original expression by it. The common factor may be more than one term and in this case it is usually written in a bracket. Always check that there is no common factor left in your answer.

Example

Factorise: (i) $ab + a$,   (ii) $3x - 15y$,   (iii) $-4xy - 12yz$,   (iv) $3a^2 + 12a^2b^2 - 6a^3b$,
(v) $2(y - 3) + x(y - 3)$.

  (i) $ab + a = a(b + 1)$.

  (ii) $3x - 15y = 3(x - 5y)$.

  (iii) $-4xy - 12yz = -4y(x + 3z)$.

  (iv) $3a^2 + 12a^2b^2 - 6a^3b = 3a^2(1 + 4b^2 - 2ab)$.

  (v) $2(y - 3) + x(y - 3) = (y - 3)(2 + x)$.

27.2 GROUPING

To factorise an expression containing four terms, try to **group the terms** into two pairs so that each pair has a common factor. If there is a common factor it can be removed from each pair and the other factor found by inspection or division. Take care with the signs when grouping the terms: make sure that the expression is simply rearranged, not altered. However, it is useful to remember that $a - b = -(b - a)$ when looking for common factors of this type.

Example

Factorise: (i) $ac + ad + bc + bd$,   (ii) $ax + bx - ay - by$,   (iii) $3a - 3b + 4bx - 4ax$,
(iv) $3ab^2 - c^2d + 3ad - b^2c^2$.

  (i) $ac + ad + bc + bd = a(c + d) + b(c + d)$

         $= (c + d)(a + b)$.

  (ii) $ax + bx - ay - by = x(a + b) - y(a + b)$

         $= (a + b)(x - y)$.

  (iii) $3a - 3b + 4bx - 4ax = 3(a - b) + 4x(b - a)$

          $= 3(a - b) - 4x(a - b)$ since $(b - a) = -(a - b)$

          $= (a - b)(3 - 4x)$.

  (iv) $3ab^2 - c^2d + 3ad - b^2c^2 = 3ab^2 + 3ad - c^2d - b^2c^2$ (rearranging)

            $= 3a(b^2 + d) - c^2(d + b^2)$

            $= 3a(b^2 + d) - c^2(b^2 + d)$

            $= (b^2 + d)(3a - c)$.

27.3 DIFFERENCE BETWEEN TWO SQUARES

An expression of the form $a^2 - b^2$ is known as the **difference between two squares**, for obvious reasons.

Since $(a + b)(a - b) = a^2 - b^2$

then $a^2 - b^2 = (a + b)(a - b)$.

This enables every expression which can be written as the difference between two squares to be factorised. Each term must be written as a perfect square to find the factors. Remember that 1 is a perfect square, *i.e.* $1 = 1^2$.

Example

Factorise: (i) $9x^2 - 4y^2$,   (ii) $1 - 25a^4$,   (iii) $a^2 - (b - c)^2$.

  (i) $9x^2 - 4y^2 = (3x)^2 - (2y)^2$

       $= (3x + 2y)(3x - 2y)$.

  (ii) $1 - 25a^4 = 1^2 - (5a^2)^2$

      $= (1 + 5a^2)(1 - 5a^2)$.

  (iii) $a^2 - (b - c)^2 = [a + (b - c)][a - (b - c)]$

        $= (a + b - c)(a - b + c)$.

This factorisation can be used to simplify some arithmetical calculations without using a calculator or tables.

Example

Evaluate: (*i*) $1001^2 - 999^2$,   (*ii*) $5.175^2 - 4.825^2$.

   (*i*) $1001^2 - 999^2 = (1001 + 999)(1001 - 999)$
$$= 2000 \times 2$$
$$= 4000.$$

   (*ii*) $5.175^2 - 4.825^2 = (5.175 + 4.825)(5.175 - 4.825)$
$$= 10 \times 0.35$$
$$= 3.5.$$

27.4 TRINOMIALS

A **trinomial** is an expression containing three terms. For example, $a + b - c$, $x^2 + 7x + 20$, $x^4y - 3xy + 5x^2y^2$ are all trinomials.

The most common trinomial to be factorised is a **quadratic expression** of the type $ax^2 + bx + c$ where $a \neq 0$. It is called quadratic because it contains a term in x^2 and no higher power terms in x.

To factorise expressions of this type with $a = 1$,
$$i.e.\ x^2 + bx + c,$$

first change the three terms into four by splitting up the middle term. We do this by finding the factors of c which add up to b.

Example

Factorise: $x^2 + 3x + 2$.

   The factors of 2 which add up to 3 are 1 and 2.

$x^2 + 3x + 2 = x^2 + 1x + 2x + 2$ since $3x = 1x + 2x$
$$= x(x + 1) + 2(x + 1) \quad \text{left distributive law}$$
$$= (x + 2)(x + 1).$$

When using this method it is essential to be careful with the signs.

Example

Factorise: $x^2 + 2x - 15$.

   The factors of -15 which add up to $+2$ are 5 and -3.

$x^2 + 2x - 15 = x^2 + 5x - 3x - 15$
$$= x(x + 5) - 3(x + 5)$$
$$= (x - 3)(x + 5).$$

If the quadratic expression is of the type $ax^2 + bx + c$ $(a \neq 1)$ first find the factors of ac which add up to b.

Example

Factorise: $3x^2 - 17x + 10$.

   The factors of $3 \times 10 = 30$ which add up to -17 are -15 and -2.

$3x^2 - 17x + 10 = 3x^2 - 15x - 2x + 10$
$$= 3x(x - 5) - 2(x - 5)$$
$$= (3x - 2)(x - 5).$$

If the quadratic expression has no middle term (*i.e.* $b = 0$) the difference between two squares may be used to factorise the expression.

27.5 SUM AND DIFFERENCE OF TWO CUBES

The following expansions enable expressions which are either the **sum or difference of two cubes** to be factorised.
$$(a + b)(a^2 - ab + b^2) = a^3 + b^3$$
$$(a - b)(a^2 + ab + b^2) = a^3 - b^3.$$

Each term must be written as a perfect cube to find the factors. Remember that 1 is a perfect cube, *i.e.* $1 = 1^3$.

Example

Factorise: (i) $1 + 64y^3$,   (ii) $8x^6 - 125a^9$.

$$\begin{aligned}
\text{(i)} \quad 1 + 64y^3 &= 1 + (4y)^3 \\
&= [(1) + (4y)][(1)^2 - (1)(4y) + (4y)^2] \\
&= (1 + 4y)(1 - 4y + 16y^2).
\end{aligned}$$

$$\begin{aligned}
\text{(ii)} \quad 8x^6 - 125a^9 &= (2x^2)^3 - (5a^3)^3 \\
&= [(2x^2) - (5a^3)][(2x^2)^2 + (2x)(5a) + (5a^3)^2] \\
&= (2x^2 - 5a^3)(4x^4 + 10a^3x^2 + 25a^6).
\end{aligned}$$

27.6 HARDER FACTORISATION

A single question may involve more than one type of factorisation and/or repeated use of the same type.

Example

Factorise: (i) $\pi R^2 h - \pi r^2 h$,   (ii) $24x^4 - 18x^3 + 3x^2$,   (iii) $p^2 - pq - 3p + 2 + 2q$.

$$\begin{array}{lll}
\text{(i)} \quad \pi R^2 h - \pi r^2 h &= \pi h(R^2 - r^2) & \text{common factor} \\
&= \pi h(R + r)(R - r) & \text{difference between two squares} \\
\text{(ii)} \quad 24x^4 + 18x^3 + 3x^2 &= 3x^2(8x^2 + 6x + 1) & \text{common factor} \\
&= 3x^2(4x + 1)(2x + 1) & \text{trinomial} \\
\text{(iii)} \quad p^2 - pq - 3p + 2 + 2q &= (p^2 - 3p + 2) - pq + 2q & \text{grouping} \\
&= (p - 1)(p - 2) - q(p - 2) & \text{trinomial and common factor} \\
&= (p - 2)(p - 1 - q) & \text{common factor}
\end{array}$$

28 Algebraic fractions

The rules for dealing with algebraic fractions are essentially the same as those for numerical fractions.

28.1 SIMPLIFICATION

The basic rules of indices are used to simplify fractions. Factors common to both numerator and denominator are cancelled.

Example

Simplify: (i) $\dfrac{9lm}{6l^2m}$,   (ii) $\dfrac{x^2y^5}{3xy}$,   (iii) $\dfrac{15c^3d^2}{5c^2d^3}$.

(i) $\dfrac{\overset{3}{9lm}}{\underset{2}{6l^2m}} = \dfrac{3}{2l}$,   (ii) $\dfrac{x^2y^{\overset{4}{5}}}{3xy} = \dfrac{xy^4}{3}$,   (iii) $\dfrac{\overset{3}{15c^3d^2}}{\underset{1}{5c^2d^3}} = \dfrac{3c}{d}$.

28.2 MULTIPLICATION AND DIVISION

Multiplication is performed by first cancelling common factors and then multiplying numerators and denominators separately.

Division is performed by multiplying the first fraction by the inverse of the second.

Example

Evaluate: (i) $\dfrac{3ab}{5c^2d^3} \times \dfrac{15cd^4}{9a^2b^2}$,   (ii) $\dfrac{4l^2m}{5p} \div \dfrac{12lm^2}{20p^2}$.

(i) $\dfrac{\overset{1}{3ab}}{\underset{1}{5c^2d^3}} \times \dfrac{\overset{3}{15cd^4}}{\underset{3}{9a^2b^2}} = \dfrac{d}{cab}$,   (ii) $\dfrac{4l^2m}{5p} \div \dfrac{12lm^2}{20p^2} = \dfrac{\overset{1}{4l^2m}}{\underset{1}{5p}} \times \dfrac{\overset{4}{20p^2}}{\underset{3}{12lm^2}} = \dfrac{4lp}{3m}$.

28.3 ADDITION AND SUBTRACTION

As in arithmetic, fractions with the same denominator may be added or subtracted.

To add or subtract fractions with different denominators a common denominator must first be found.

Example

Evaluate: (i) $\dfrac{4a}{3b} + \dfrac{5b}{2a}$,   (ii) $\dfrac{1}{p} - \dfrac{1}{q}$.

(i) The LCM of the denominators is $3b \times 2a = 6ab$,

hence $\dfrac{4a}{3b} + \dfrac{5b}{2a} = \dfrac{2a \times 4a}{6ab} + \dfrac{3b \times 5b}{6ab} = \dfrac{8a^2}{6ab} + \dfrac{15b^2}{6ab} = \dfrac{8a^2 + 15b^2}{6ab}$.

(ii) The LCM of the denominators is pq,

hence, $\dfrac{1}{p} - \dfrac{1}{q} = \dfrac{q}{pq} - \dfrac{p}{pq} = \dfrac{q-p}{pq}$.

Sometimes it is necessary to factorise the denominators before attempting to find their LCM.

Example

Write as a single fraction in its lowest terms, $\dfrac{2x+3}{x^2-4} + \dfrac{1}{2-x}$.

The denominator of the first fraction is the difference between two squares (see unit 29.1).

i.e. $x^2 - 4 = x^2 - 2^2 = (x+2)(x-2)$

hence $\dfrac{2x+3}{x^2-4} + \dfrac{1}{2-x}$

$= \dfrac{2x+3}{(x+2)(x-2)} - \dfrac{1}{(x-2)}$ (multiplying numerator and denominator of the second fraction by -1).

The LCM of $(x+2)(x-2)$ and $(x-2)$ is $(x+2)(x-2)$

hence $\dfrac{2x+3}{(x+2)(x-2)} - \dfrac{1}{(x-2)} = \dfrac{(2x+3)}{(x+2)(x-2)} - \dfrac{(x+2)}{(x+2)(x-2)}$

$= \dfrac{(2x+3)-(x+2)}{(x+2)(x-2)}$

$= \dfrac{2x+3-x-2}{(x+2)(x-2)}$

$= \dfrac{x+1}{(x+2)(x-2)}$.

The insertion of brackets into expressions of this type should be noted. It is much safer to write out all the steps using the brackets as long as possible. In this way there is less danger of making mistakes.

---

29 Quadratic equations

A quadratic equation in x is an equation which contains x to the power 2 (*i.e.* x^2) but no higher powers of x. For example, $x^2 + 2x - 3 = 0$, $3x^2 = 2$, $x = 3x^2 + 1$, $2x^2 = x$ are all quadratic equations in x.

The general form of a quadratic equation in x is

$$ax^2 + bx + c = 0$$

where a, b and c are real numbers and $a \neq 0$. Any quadratic equation can be rewritten in this form.

In general, a quadratic equation is satisfied by two values of x, but these values may be equal to each other. The solutions of an equation are also called roots.

The three common methods of solving quadratic equations at this level are by factorisation, by formula and by graph. Solution by factorisation and formula are described below. Graphical solution is described in unit 30.

29.1 SOLUTION BY FACTORISATION

This method uses the fact that if the product of two real numbers is zero, then one or other (or both) of the numbers must be zero, *i.e.* if a and b are both real numbers and $ab = 0$, then either $a = 0$ or $b = 0$, or both a and b equal zero. This is a property of the system of real numbers.

Example

Solve: $x(x+4) = 0$.

Since $x(x+4) = 0$

then, either $x = 0$ or $(x+4) = 0$

i.e.   either $x = 0$ or $x = -4$.

To solve a quadratic equation given in the form $ax^2 + bx + c = 0$ by factorisation, first rewrite the quadratic expression $ax^2 + bx + c$ as the product of two factors (see unit 27). The equation can then be solved as shown above. Always check your solutions in the original equation; this check can often be done mentally.

Example

Find the roots of $x^2 - 5x + 6 = 0$.

$$x^2 - 5x + 6 = 0.$$

The factors of $+6$ which add up to -5 are -3 and -2.

So $x^2 - 3x - 2x + 6 = 0$

$x(x-3) - 2(x-3) = 0$

$(x-3)(x-2) = 0.$

Either $(x-3) = 0$ or $(x-2) = 0$

i.e.   either $x = 3$ or $x = 2$.

Check: If $x = 2$, $(2)^2 - 5(2) + 6 = 4 - 10 + 6 = 0$ ✓

If $x = 3$, $(3)^2 - 5(3) + 6 = 9 - 15 + 6 = 0$.   ✓

Sometimes the quadratic equation is not given in the general form $ax^2 + bx + c = 0$. It must be rewritten in this form before the factors can be found.

Example

Solve: $2x^2 = 9x + 5$.

First, rearrange the equation into the form $ax^2 + bx + c = 0$.

$$2x^2 = 9x + 5$$

$2x^2 - 9x - 5 = 0.$

The factors of $2 \times -5 = -10$ which add up to -9 are $+1$ and -10.

So $2x^2 + 1x - 10x - 5 = 0$

$x(2x+1) - 5(2x+1) = 0$

$(2x+1)(x-5) = 0.$

Either $(2x+1) = 0$ or $(x-5) = 0$

i.e.   either $2x = -1$ or $x = 5$

either $x = -\frac{1}{2}$ or $x = 5$.

Sometimes a quadratic expression has no middle term (*i.e.* $b = 0$) and here we use the difference between two squares to solve the equation.

Example

Solve the equation $x^2 = 3$.

$$x^2 = 3.$$

Rearranging gives:

$$x^2 - 3 = 0.$$

By the 'difference between two squares':

$$(x + \sqrt{3})(x - \sqrt{3}) = 0 \qquad i.e. \ a^2 - b^2 = (a + b)(a - b).$$

So either $(x + \sqrt{3}) = 0$ or $(x - \sqrt{3}) = 0$

i.e. either $\qquad x = -\sqrt{3}$ or $3x = +\sqrt{3}$.

29.2 SOLUTION BY FORMULA

The roots of any quadratic equation,

$$ax^2 + bx + c = 0 \qquad \text{(where } a, b, c \text{ are constants, } a \neq 0\text{)}$$

may be found using the formula

$$x = \frac{-b \pm \sqrt{(b^2 - 4ac)}}{2a}.$$

Learn this formula taking careful note of the signs and brackets.

This formula is used when the quadratic expression $ax^2 + bx + c$ has no factors or if you are unable to find them.

When using this formula, rearrange the quadratic equation in the form $ax^2 + bx + c = 0$ first. This makes it easier for you to compare the given equation with the general form to find values for a, b and c. Take care to put the correct sign with each number and remember that 'x^2' means '$1x^2$' and 'x' means '$1x$'. For example, in $x^2 - 2x + 6 = 0$, $a = 1$, $b = -2$ and $c = +6$. Substitute the values for a, b and c in the formula and do the necessary arithmetic. Do not try to do too many steps at once. Questions involving the formula often ask for a specific degree of accuracy in the answer, for example 'correct to three significant figures'. Check that you have given your answer in the required form.

Example

Solve: $3x^2 - 2x = 3$, *giving your answer to two decimal places.*

First, rearrange the equation: $3x^2 - 2x - 3 = 0$

and compare this with $\qquad ax^2 + bx + c = 0$.

So $a = +3$, $b = -2$ and $c = -3$.

Substituting in the formula $x = \dfrac{-b \pm \sqrt{(b^2 - 4ac)}}{2a}$

$$= \frac{-(-2) \pm \sqrt{[(-2)^2 - 4(3)(-3)]}}{2(3)}$$

$$= \frac{+2 \pm \sqrt{(4 + 36)}}{6}$$

$$= \frac{+2 \pm \sqrt{40}}{6}$$

$$= \frac{+2 \pm 6.325}{6} \qquad \text{(from tables)}$$

$$= \frac{8.325}{6} \quad \text{or} \quad \frac{-4.325}{6}$$

$$= 1.39 \quad \text{or} \quad -0.72 \qquad \text{(to 2 decimal places).}$$

30 Algebraic graphs

An algebraic graph is a geometric representation of an algebraic relation. It consists of a set of points whose coordinates satisfy the given algebraic equation.

30.1 COMMON ALGEBRAIC GRAPHS

When drawing graphs, being able to predict the shape of the final graph and knowing some of its features is very helpful. This is a useful check on the points calculated and plotted. Fortunately the form of the given algebraic equation can provide some of this information.

The algebraic graphs drawn at this level are usually of the following standard types.

Straight line

Any equation which can be written in the form

$$y = mx + c \qquad \text{(where } m \text{ and } c \text{ are constants)}$$

gives a straight line graph (see unit 23). For example, $y = 5x - 6$, $7y = 3$, $y = 4x$, $2x - 5y = 2$ are all equations of straight lines.

The sign of m, the gradient, indicates whether the slope of the line is positive or negative (Fig. 30.1).

Fig. 30.1

The value of c, the intercept, tells you where the line cuts the y-axis, *i.e.* the line passes through the point $(0, c)$. An equation of the form

$$y = mx \qquad \text{(where } m \text{ is a constant)}$$

gives a straight line which passes through the origin $(0, 0)$ (Fig. 30.2).

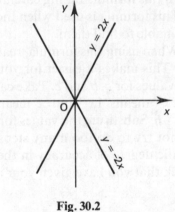

Fig. 30.2

Lines parallel to the axes have simple equations. The equation of the x-axis is $y = 0$. The equation of any line parallel to the x-axis is $y = c$ (where c is a constant) (Fig. 30.3).

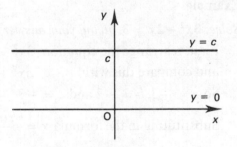

Fig. 30.3

The equation of the y-axis is $x = 0$. The equation of any line parallel to the y-axis is $x = k$ (where k is a constant) (Fig. 30.4).

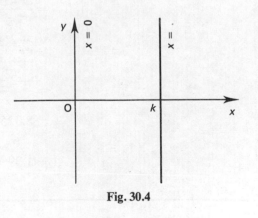

Fig. 30.4

Parabola

The graph of any equation which can be written in the form

$$y = ax^2 + bx + c \quad \text{(where } a, b, c \text{ are constants, } a \neq 0\text{)}$$

is a smooth curve called a parabola. For example, $y = x^2$, $y = 5x^2$, $y = 2x^2 - 1$,
$y = (3x + 1)(x - 5)$,
$y = x^2 - 2x + 7$ are all equations of parabolas.

The sign of the coefficient 'a' indicates which 'way up' the parabola is drawn.

The parabola has a turning point which is a minimum if a is positive, a maximum if a is negative (Fig. 30.5).

The line of symmetry of the parabola always passes through its turning point and is parallel to the y-axis.

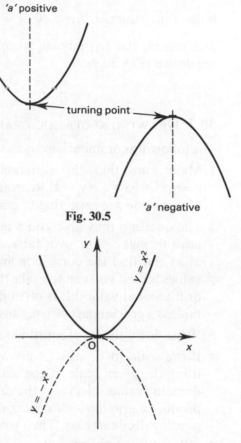

Fig. 30.5

An equation of the form

$$y = ax^2$$

has the origin $(0, 0)$ as its turning point and the y-axis as its line of symmetry (Fig. 30.6).

Fig. 30.6

Cubic

Any function which can be written in the form

$$y = ax^3 + bx^2 + cx + d \quad \text{(where } a, b, c, d \text{ are constants, } a \neq 0\text{)}$$

is called a cubic function in x. For example, $y = x^3$, $y = 3x^3 - 4x$, $y = 2x^3 - 4x^2 + 3x + 7$,
$y = (x - 2)(2x + 1)(3x - 4)$ are all cubic functions in x.

The graph of a cubic function has a characteristic shape which is illustrated below. The sign of the coefficient 'a' indicates which 'way round' the curve is drawn (Fig. 30.7).

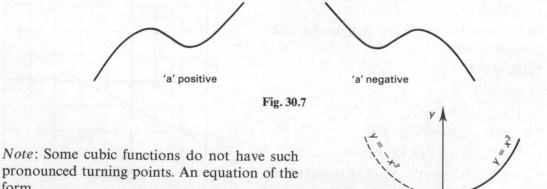

'a' positive   'a' negative

Fig. 30.7

Note: Some cubic functions do not have such pronounced turning points. An equation of the form

$$y = ax^3$$

passes through the origin as shown in Fig. 30.8.

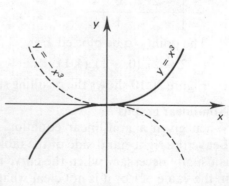

Fig. 30.8

Rectangular hyperbola

The graph of any equation which can be written in the form

$$xy = k \quad \text{(where } k \text{ is constant, } k \neq 0)$$

is a smooth curve called a rectangular hyperbola. For example, $xy = 10$, $y = \dfrac{3}{x}$, $x = \dfrac{1}{y}$ all give rectangular hyperbolae when their graphs are drawn (Fig. 30.9).

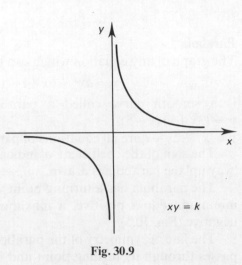

Fig. 30.9

30.2 DRAWING ALGEBRAIC GRAPHS

The following comments apply to the drawing of any algebraic graph.

1 Make sure that the equation is in its standard form, for example $y = mx + c$, $y = ax^2 + bx + c$, $xy = k$. Rearrange it if necessary. This will help you to identify the type of curve you are expecting to draw and will make calculations easier.

2 The question may give you a table of values to use or a table to complete or you may have to make your own table. When calculating values use the given domain (values of x) and find the corresponding values of y using the given equation. Choose simple values for x if you can to make the working easier. Take special care when using negative or fractional values. It is often easier to work in decimals if fractions are involved. This table is a crucial part of your answer: a mistake here will give an incorrect graph.

3 Write down the (x, y) coordinates of the points to be plotted from your table of values.

4 If the scale to be used is given, draw and label the x- and y-axes and number them using the given scale. If the scale is not given, choose suitable scale(s) using the given domain (values of x) and the calculated range (values of y) to help you. Your aim is to produce a graph which 'covers' most of your graph paper and to use a scale which makes plotting decimals easy. Then you can draw and label your axes.

5 Plot the points using the coordinates you have listed. Draw the appropriate smooth curve (straight line, parabola, …) through the points. Label the curve with its equation.

Linear graphs

When given a linear equation to graph, only calculate the values for three points. Two of these points determine the line, the third acts as a check.

Example

Draw the graph of $2y = x - 2$ for $-2 \leqslant x \leqslant 4$.

Rewriting the equation gives

$y = \frac{1}{2}x - 1$.

So the expected graph is a straight line with positive slope.

Table of values:

x	-2	0	4
y	-2	-1	1

The points to be plotted are:

$(-2, -2)$, $(0, -1)$, $(4, 1)$.

Figure 30.10 shows the resulting straight line.

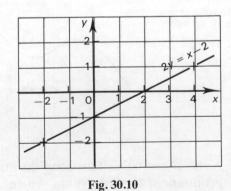

Fig. 30.10

Non-linear graphs

When given a non-linear equation to graph, a more detailed table of values is needed. Leave the right-hand side of the table open in case you need to find any extra points. This is usually necessary when the curve is near a turning point or a large change has occurred in the value of y or it is not clear what is happening to the curve between two points already plotted.

Example

Draw the graph of $y = 4 + 3x - x^2$ for $-2 \leqslant x \leqslant 5$.

From the equation $y = 4 + 3x - x^2$, the expected graph is a $\cap$-shaped parabola. We make a table for all integer values of x lying in the given domain, $-2 \leqslant x \leqslant 5$. Tables of values:

x	-2	-1	0	$+1$	$+2$	$+3$	$+4$	$+5$	Extra point $+1.5$
$-x^2$	-4	-1	0	-1	-4	-9	-16	-25	-2.25
$+3x$	-6	-3	0	$+3$	$+6$	$+9$	$+12$	$+15$	$+4.5$
$+4$	$+4$	$+4$	$+4$	$+4$	$+4$	$+4$	$+4$	$+4$	$+4$
y	-6	0	$+4$	$+6$	$+6$	$+4$	0	-6	$+6.25$

The points to be plotted are:

$(-2, -6), (-1, 0), (0, +4), (+1, +6),$
$(+2, +6), (+3, +4), (+4, 0), (+5, -6).$

To draw the parabola $y = 4 + 3x - x^2$, draw a smooth curve through all plotted points. We can do this because x is continuous throughout the domain. We can see that there is a turning point between $x = 1$ and $x = 2$. So an extra point, with $x = 1.5$, has been found (see table above) and plotted for greater accuracy in drawing. Figure 30.11 shows the resulting parabola.

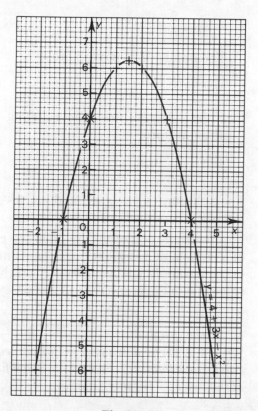

Fig. 30.11

30.3 GRAPHICAL SOLUTION OF EQUATIONS

Algebraic equations may be solved by means of graphs and this is particularly useful if other methods cannot be used. However, the solutions obtained are only approximate.

Intersecting with the x-axis

The graph of the straight line $y = mx + c$ cuts the x-axis ($y = 0$) where $mx + c = 0$. The x-co-ordinate of this point of intersection is the solution of the equation $mx + c = 0$. For example, in Fig. 30.10 the straight line $y = \frac{1}{2}x - 1$ cuts the x-axis at $x = 2$. So $x = 2$ is the solution of $\frac{1}{2}x - 1 = 0$.

The graph of the parabola $y = ax^2 + bx + c$ cuts the x-axis ($y = 0$) in two different points if $b^2 > 4ac$. The x-co-ordinates of these two points are the roots of the quadratic equation $ax^2 + bx + c = 0$. For example, in Fig. 30.11 the parabola $y = 4 + 3x - x^2$ cuts the x-axis at $x = -1$ and $x = +4$. So these are the roots of $4 + 3x - x^2 = 0$. If $b^2 = 4ac$, then the roots of the equation are equal and the parabola will touch the x-axis at one point.

In general a cubic equation will have three solutions which may be found from the points of intersection of its graph with the x-axis.

Intersecting graphs

Many equations are solved graphically by drawing two intersecting graphs.

To solve two simultaneous linear equations graphically, draw the graphs of the two straight lines on the same axes. The point of intersection of the lines gives the value of x

and y which satisfy both equations simultaneously, *i.e.* their solution. You can check your answer by substituting the values into the original equations.

Example
Solve the simultaneous equations $y = x + 2$ and $y = 8 - x$ graphically.

Table of values for $y = x + 2$

x	-2	0	2
y	0	2	4

The points to be plotted are:
$(-2, 0), (0, 2), (2, 4)$.

Table of values for $y = 8 - x$

x	-2	0	8
y	10	8	0

The points to be plotted are:
$(-2, 10), (0, 8), (8, 0)$.

Figure 30.12 shows the resulting straight lines.

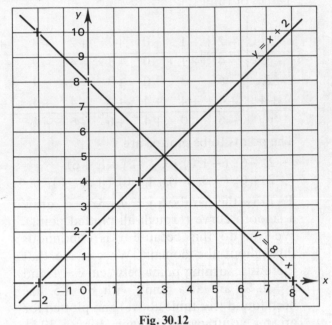

Fig. 30.12

The solution of $y = x + 2$ and $y = 8 - x$ is $x = 3$, $y = 5$, the co-ordinates of the point of intersection of the lines.

Quadratic equations are often solved graphically by finding the point(s) of intersection of a curve and a straight line. For example, $ax^2 + bx + c = k$ can be solved from the graphs of the parabola $y = ax^2 + bx + c$ and the straight line $y = k$; $ax^2 + bx + c = Mx + C$ can be solved from the graphs of $y = ax^2 + bx + c$ and $y = Mx + C$.

Example
Draw the graph of $y = x^2 - x - 2$ for $-2 \leqslant x \leqslant 4$. On the same axes draw the straight line $y = x + 3$. Write down and simplify an equation which is satisfied by the values of x where the two graphs intersect. From your graph find the approximate value (correct to 1 decimal place) of the two roots of this equation.

Table of values for $y = x^2 - x - 2$

x	-2	-1	0	1	2	3	4	Extra point 0.5
x^2	4	1	0	1	4	9	16	0.25
$-x$	2	1	0	-1	-2	-3	-4	-0.5
-2	-2	-2	-2	-2	-2	-2	-2	-2
y	4	0	-2	-2	0	4	10	-2.25

The points to be plotted for the parabola are:

$(-2, 4), (-1, 0), (0, -2), (1, -2), (2, 0), (3, 4),$
$(4, 10), (0.5, -2.25)$.

Table of values for $y = x + 3$

x	-2	0	2
y	1	3	5

The points to be plotted for the straight line are:

$(-2, 1), (0, 3), (2, 5)$.

Figure 30.13 shows the resulting parabola and straight line.

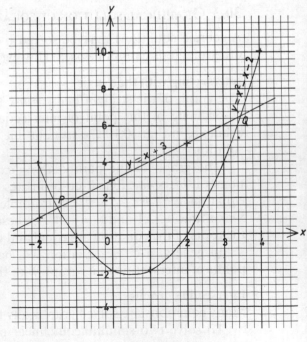

Fig. 30.13

At the points of intersection of the two graphs, the values of y are the same. So where $y = x^2 - x - 2$ and $y = x + 3$ intersect,

$$x^2 - x - 2 = x + 3$$

i.e. $x^2 - 2x - 5 = 0$ is the required equation.

The solutions of this equation are the x-co-ordinates of the points of intersection P and Q.

From the graph the roots of $x^2 - 2x - 5 = 0$ are

$$x = -1.5 \text{ or } x = 3.5 \quad \text{(correct to 1 dp)}.$$

Sometimes it is necessary to find the equation of the straight line which has to be drawn on a graph to give the solutions of an equation.

Example

If the graph of $y = \dfrac{3}{x}$ is drawn, find the equation of the straight line which has to be drawn on the same axes in order to find the approximate solutions of the equation $x^2 + x - 3 = 0$.

First rearrange the equation to be solved so that a $\dfrac{3}{x}$ term appears.

Since $\quad x^2 + x - 3 = 0$

we have $\quad x^2 + x = 3$

or $\quad \dfrac{x^2 + x}{x} = \dfrac{3}{x} \quad (x \neq 0)$

i.e. $\quad x + 1 = \dfrac{3}{x}.$

The line which must be drawn on the same axes is $y = x + 1$.

The x-co-ordinates of the points of intersection of $y = \dfrac{3}{x}$ and $y = x + 1$ will be the solutions of $x^2 + x - 3 = 0$.

Graphical solutions of equations which contain higher powers of x can be found using similar methods to those shown. For example, the approximate solutions of $x^3 - x - 2 = 0$ can be found by drawing the graphs of $y = x^3$ and $y = x + 2$. This is because the equation $x^3 - x - 2 = 0$ can be rearranged as $x^3 = x + 2$.

---

31 Indices and logarithms

31.1 INDICES

When we write $a \times a = a^2$, $b \times b \times b = b^3$ we are using **index notation**. The numerals ^{2} and ^{3} are called **indices**.

Another word we can use instead of index is **'power'**. We read a^5 as 'a to the power 5' where ^{5} is the index and a is called the **base**.

Basic rules of indices

1 To multiply two numbers with the same base, add the indices:

$$x^m + x^n = x^{m+n}.$$

For example, $\qquad x^2 \times x^3 = x^{2+3} = x^5$

since $\qquad x^2 \times x^3 = x \times x \times x \times x \times x = x^5.$

2 To divide two numbers with the same base, subtract the indices:

$$x^m \div x^n = x^{m-n}.$$

For example, $\qquad y^5 \div y^2 = y^{5-2} = y^3$

since $\qquad y^5 \div y^2 = \dfrac{y \times y \times y \times y \times y}{y \times y} = y^3.$

3 Any base raised to the power 0 is 1, *i.e.* $x^0 = 1$.

For example, $\left.\begin{array}{l} r^b \div r^b = r^{b-b} = r^0 \\ \\ r^b \div r^b = \dfrac{r^b}{r^b} = 1 \end{array}\right\}$ so $r^0 = 1$.

but

4 Negative indices: $p^{-n} = \dfrac{1}{p^n}$.

For example, $\left.\begin{array}{l} p^3 \div p^5 = p^{3-5} = p^{-2} \\ \\ p^3 \div p^5 = \dfrac{p \times p \times p}{p \times p \times p \times p \times p} = \dfrac{1}{p^2} \end{array}\right\}$ so $p^{-2} = \dfrac{1}{p^2}$.

but

5 To raise a number written in index notation to a power, multiply the indices:

$$(x^m)^n = x^{m \times n}.$$

For example, $(x^2)^3 = x^{2 \times 3} = x^6$

since $(x^2)^3 = x^2 \times x^2 \times x^2 = x^6.$

6 To find the *n*th root of a number, written in index notation, divide the index by *n*:

$$\sqrt[n]{x^m} = x^{\frac{m}{n}}.$$

For example, $\sqrt[3]{y^6} = y^{\frac{6}{3}} = y^2$

since $\sqrt[3]{y^6} = \sqrt[3]{[(y \times y)(y \times y)(y \times y)]} = y^2.$

7 Fractional indices: $p^{\frac{1}{n}} = \sqrt[n]{p}$.

For example, $8^{\frac{1}{3}} = \sqrt[3]{8} = 2.$

31.2 LOGARITHMS

Logarithm is yet another word for power or index. However, this word is normally used when we replace the operations of multiplication and division by the easier ones of addition and subtraction in arithmetic. We can do this if we write the numbers we are dealing with in index notation using the same base.

Example
Work out 128×16 *by writing the numbers in index notation using* 2 *as the base.*

$$128 = 2^7 \text{ and } 16 = 2^4$$
$$\text{so } 128 \times 16 = 2^7 \times 2^4 = 2^{11} = 2048.$$

In this example, 7 and 4 are the logarithms of 128 and 16 to the base 2.

Common logarithms
If we use a small number such as 2 or 3 as the base, the logarithms get very big very quickly. The base which is commonly used is 10 and the indices are then called **common logarithms**.

For example, $100 = 10^2$ so 2 is called the common logarithm of 100.

Another way to say that is: $\log_{10} 100 = 2$, where **log** is short for logarithm.

Not all common logarithms are whole numbers, *e.g.* $\log_{10} 2 = 0.3010$ and $\log_{10} 3 = 0.4771$, both logarithms written to 4 significant figures.

Example
If $\log_{10} 2 = 0.3$ *and* $\log_{10} 3 = 0.5$ *both written to 1 sf, find (a)* $\log_{10} 6$*, (b)* $\log_{10} 1.5$*, (c)* $\log_{10} 16$ *and (d)* $\log_{10} 2.25$*. Do not use tables.*

Since $\log_{10} 2 = 0.3$ and $\log_{10} 3 = 0.5$ we can write

$$2 = 10^{0.3} \quad \text{and} \quad 3 = 10^{0.5}.$$

(*a*) $6 = 2 \times 3 = 10^{0.3} \times 10^{0.5} = 10^{0.8}.$

Hence $\log_{10} 6 = 0.8$.

(*b*) $1.5 = \dfrac{3}{2} = \dfrac{10^{0.5}}{10^{0.3}} = 10^{0.5} \div 10^{0.3} = 10^{0.2}.$

Hence $\log_{10} 1.5 = 0.2$.

(*c*) $16 = 2^4 = (10^{0.3})^4 = 10^{4 \times 0.3} = 10^{1.2}.$

Hence $\log_{10} 16 = 1.2$.

(d) $2.25 = \dfrac{9}{4} = 3^2 \div 2^2 = (10^{0.5})^2 \div (10^{0.3})^2 = 10^1 \div 10^{0.6} = 10^{0.4}$.

Hence $\log_{10} 2.25 = 0.4$.

31.3 LOGARITHM AND ANTILOGARITHM TABLES

The common logarithms of all numbers written to 4 sf and lying between 1 and 10 have been listed in tables. Since any number can be written in standard form, these tables can be used to give us the logarithm of any number written to 4 sf.

Note: If you use three-figure tables, ignore the fourth significant figure in the following examples.

Example
Write the number 147.5 in standard form and hence find its logarithm using tables.

$$147.5 = 10^2 \times 1.475$$
$$= 10^2 \times 10^{0.1687} \quad \text{(from tables, } \log_{10} 1.475 = 0.1687\text{)}$$
$$= 10^{2.1687} \quad \text{(adding indices)}$$

Hence $\log_{10} 147.5 = 2.1687$.

The whole-number part of a logarithm is the **characteristic** and the decimal part is the **mantissa**. In the above example the characteristic is 2 and the mantissa is 0.1687.

Logarithms of **numbers less than one** are found in a similar way to those for numbers bigger than one. The exception is the way in which they are usually written.

Example
Express 0.3629 in index notation.
$$0.3629 = 10^{-1} \times 10^{0.5598}$$
$$= 10^{-1+0.5598}$$
$$= 10^{\bar{1}.5598}$$

where $\bar{1}.5598 = -1 + 0.5598$.

When the logarithm has a **negative characteristic** we usually use the 'bar' notation. This is because only the characteristic is negative, the mantissa is always positive.

When logarithms have been used to simplify arithmetic, the answer we obtain will be expressed as a power of 10. In order to change the answer back into the form of an ordinary number, it is necessary to use **antilogarithm** tables. (**Antilogs.** for short.) In antilog. tables each number is prefaced by the decimal point; this reminds us to look up only the mantissa and not the characteristic.

Example
Use antilogarithm tables to write $10^{2.5168}$ as a four-figure number.
$$10^{2.5168} = 10^2 \times 10^{0.5168}$$
$$= 10^2 \times 3.287 \quad \text{(from antilog. tables)}$$
$$= 328.7.$$

31.4 USE OF LOGARITHMS

Logarithms are indices and therefore they obey the rules of indices. Using them makes arithmetic easier.

If a question asks for an **exact** answer, logarithms **cannot** be used since the answers will only be **approximate**.

Multiplication and division
To multiply numbers we add their logarithms and to divide numbers we subtract their logarithms. The number which is the final answer is found by using antilog. tables.

It is much easier to use logarithms if we set out numbers and logs as shown in the following examples. After doing the working a check should be made on your answer.

Example

Evaluate 32.78 × 572.1 using logarithms.

number	log
$10^1 \times 3.278$	1.5156
$10^2 \times 5.721$	+2.7575
$10^4 \times 1.875$ ←——— antilog.	4.2731	(adding logs)

Hence $32.78 \times 572.1 = 18\,750$.

Check: $32.78 \times 572.1 \approx 30 \times 600 = 18\,000$.

Example

Use logs to work out 362.1 ÷ 7.659.

number	log
$10^2 \times 3.621$	2.5588
7.659	−0.8842
$10^1 \times 4.728$ ←——— antilog.	1.6746	(subtracting logs)

Hence $362.1 \div 7.659 = 47.28$.

Check: $362.1 \div 7.659 \approx 360 \div 8 = 45$.

Powers

To raise a number to a given power using logarithms, multiply the log of the number by the power.

Example

Evaluate, using logs, $(3.65)^3$.

number	log
3.65	0.5623
	$\times 3$
$10^1 \times 4.863$ ←——— antilog.	1.6869	(multiplying log by 3, to cube)

Hence $(3.65)^3 = 48.63$.

Check: $3^3 = 27$ and $4^3 = 64$.

When the number is less than one, take care with the sign of the characteristic.

Example

Evaluate $(0.754)^2$.

number	log
$10^{-1} \times 7.54$	$\bar{1}.8774$
	$\times 2$
$10^{-1} \times 5.685$ ←——— antilog.	$\bar{1}.7548$	(since $2 \times \bar{1} = -2$ and $-2+1 = -1$)

Hence $(0.754)^2 = 0.5685$.

Check: $(0.754)^2 \approx 0.7^2 = 0.49$.

Roots

To find the *n*th root of a number, divide the log of the number by *n*.

Example

Evaluate $\sqrt[4]{673.4}$.

number	log
$10^2 \times 6.734$	$4\lfloor 2.8283$
5.094 ←——— antilog.	0.7071	(dividing log by 4 to take fourth root)

Hence $\sqrt[4]{673.4} = 5.094$.

Check: $5^4 = 625$.

When finding the *n*th root of a number less than one, we must make the characteristic exactly divisible by *n* before doing the division.

Example
Find $\sqrt[3]{0.4271}$.

number	log
$10^{-1} \times 4.271$	$\bar{1}.6305$
	$3\,\lfloor\,\overline{3} + 2.6305$ (since $\overline{3} + 2 = \overline{1}$)
$10^{-1} \times 7.530 \xleftarrow{\text{antilog.}}$	$\overline{1} + 0.8768$ (dividing each part separately by 3)

Hence $\sqrt[3]{0.4271} = 0.753$.
Check: $(0.753)^3 \approx 0.7^3 = 0.343$.

Several operations
When a combination of operations are used in a problem, it is important to set down the work clearly.

Example
Use logarithms to find $\dfrac{(5.23)^2 \times 0.3684}{\sqrt{0.754}}$.

number	log	
$(5.23)^2$	$0.7185 \times 2 =$	1.4370
$10^{-1} \times 3.684$		$+\,\overline{1}.5663$
		1.0033 (log of numerator)
$\sqrt{(10^{-1} \times 7.54)}$	$\overline{1}.8774 \div 2 =$	$-\,\overline{1}.9387$ (log of denominator)
$10^1 \times 1.161 \xleftarrow{\text{antilog.}}$		1.0646 (subtracting logs)

Answer $= 11.61$.

Check: $\dfrac{5^2 \times 0.4}{\sqrt{0.8}} \approx \dfrac{10}{0.9} \approx 11$.

---

32 Transformation of formulae

The formula $s = \dfrac{(u+v)t}{2}$ is used in Physics to obtain the displacement s of an object which travels with constant acceleration in a straight line. s can be found if u (starting velocity), v (the final velocity) and t (the time of travelling) are known. However, if we know s, u and t, how can we find v?

We can find v if we first make it the **subject** of the equation, *i.e.* write v in terms of the other three quantities. For example,

$$s = \frac{(u+v)t}{2}$$

$2s = (u+v)t$	clear fractions
$2s = ut + vt$	clear brackets
$vt = 2s - ut$	collect terms in v together
$v = \dfrac{2s - ut}{t}$	divide by t.

To **transform a formula**, that is to make one quantity the subject of an equation, the normal rules of algebra must be followed. In general, the following steps should be performed in this order:

 (*i*) remove square, or other, roots;

 (*ii*) clear fractions;

 (*iii*) clear brackets;

 (*iv*) collect together all the terms involving the required subject;

 (*v*) if necessary, factorise the terms on each side of the equation;

 (*vi*) isolate the required subject, usually by division by a factor.

The following example will illustrate this method.

Example

$$If\ P = \sqrt{\left(\frac{nQ}{na+b}\right)}, find\ n\ in\ terms\ of\ P, Q, a\ and\ b.$$

$$P^2 = \frac{nQ}{na+b}$$	square each side to remove square root
$$P^2(na+b) = nQ$$	clear fractions
$$P^2na + P^2b = nQ$$	clear brackets
$$P^2b = nQ - P^2na$$	collect terms in n together
$$P^2b = n(Q - P^2a)$$	factorise
$$\frac{P^2b}{Q - P^2a} = n$$	divide by the factor $(Q - P^2a)$.

Hence, $n = \dfrac{P^2b}{Q - P^2a}$ and n has been made the subject of the equation.

Note: Although all six steps were used in the above example, not all will be necessary for all examples. However, you should work through steps (*i*) to (*vi*) in order, omitting only those steps which are not necessary.

---

33 Variation

33.1 DIRECT VARIATION

If a car is travelling along a straight road at constant speed, the distance travelled is directly proportional to the time for which it travels. We say that the distance (d) travelled **varies directly** as the time (t) for which it travels. We write this in symbols as:

$$d \propto t.$$

This means that if the time, t, is doubled, the distance, d, will also be doubled. If t is halved, d will also be halved and so on. If a graph of d against t is drawn the result will be a straight line passing through the origin. The gradient of the graph will be constant and equal to $\dfrac{d}{t}$,

i.e. $\dfrac{d}{t} = k$ where k is a **constant of proportionality** equal to the gradient.

Any situation in which one variable varies directly as another can be described by such an equation involving a constant of proportionality.

Example

The extension (e) produced in a stretched spring varies directly as the tension (T) in the spring. If a tension of six units produces an extension of 2 cm, what will be the extension produced by a tension of 15 units?

$e \propto T \Rightarrow \dfrac{e}{T} = k$ the constant of proportionality

i.e. $e = kT.$

Given, $e = 2\ cm\ when\ T = 6$

$$2 = k \times 6$$

so $k = \dfrac{1}{3}.$

The equation connecting e and T is, therefore,

$$e = \frac{1}{3}T.$$

Hence, when $T = 15$ units,

$$e = \frac{1}{3} \times 15 \, \text{cm}$$

$$= 5 \, \text{cm}.$$

Sometimes a variable varies directly as a power of another. For example, the area of a circle (A) varies directly as the square of its radius (r). In this case the constant of proportionality will be π, since $A = \pi r^2$.

Example

If y varies directly as the cube of x and $y = 24$ when $x = 2$, find the value of y when $x = \frac{1}{2}$.

$$y \propto x^3 \Rightarrow \frac{y}{x^3} = k \qquad \text{the constant of proportionality}$$

i.e. $\qquad y = kx^3.$

Given, $y = 24$ when $x = 2$

$$24 = k \times 2^3$$

$$= k \times 8$$

so $\qquad k = 3.$

The equation connecting y and x is

$$y = 3x^3.$$

Hence, when $x = \frac{1}{2}$

$$y = 3 \times \left(\frac{1}{2}\right)^3$$

$$= \frac{3}{8}.$$

33.2 Inverse variation

If y **varies inversely** as x then $y \propto \frac{1}{x}$. In this case the equation connecting y and x is $y = \frac{k}{x}$, where k is the constant of proportionality.

Example

The illumination (I) of a bulb varies inversely as the square of the distance (d). If the illumination is five units at a distance of 3 m, what is the illumination at a distance of 2 m?

$$I \propto \frac{1}{d^2} \Rightarrow I = \frac{k}{d^2}.$$

Given $I = 5$ when $d = 3$

$$5 = \frac{k}{9}$$

so $\qquad k = 45.$

Therefore, $I = \frac{45}{d^2}.$

Hence, when $d = 2$

$$I = \frac{45}{4} \, \text{units}$$

$$= 11\frac{1}{4} \, \text{units}.$$

33.3 Joint variation

The formula for the volume (V) of a right circular cylinder with radius (r) and height (h) is:

$$V = \pi r^2 h.$$

We can see that V varies as the height h and also as the square of the radius (r). V is said to **vary jointly** as the height and the square of the radius.

Example

The electrical resistance (R) of a piece of wire with a circular cross section varies directly as the length (l) and inversely as the square of the radius (r). If the resistance of a 4.5 cm length is 2 ohms and the radius of the wire is 0.3 cm, what length of wire will have a resistance of 10 ohms?

$$R \propto \frac{l}{r^2} \Rightarrow R = k \times \frac{l}{r^2}.$$

When $r = 0.3$ and $l = 4.5$, $R = 2$.

Therefore, $2 = k \times \dfrac{4.5}{0.09}$,

so $\qquad k = \dfrac{1}{25}$.

Hence, when $R = 10$ and $r = 0.3$

$$10 = \frac{1}{25} \times \frac{l}{0.09}.$$

Therefore, $l = 25 \times 0.9$ cm

$\qquad\qquad = 22.5$ cm.

34 Angles and parallels

34.1 ANGLES

The **angle** between two lines which meet at a point is the amount of turning required to change direction from one line to the other. The amount of turning is measured in degrees (°) or radians.

A **full turn** or complete revolution is 360°.
Angles at a point add up to 360°.
For example, in Fig. 34.1,

$$a + b + c + d = 360°.$$

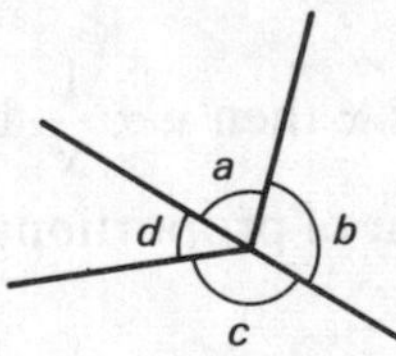

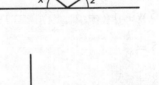

Fig. 34.1

A **half turn** is 180°.
Adjacent angles on a straight line add up to 180°.
For example, in Fig. 34.2,

$$x + y + z = 180°.$$

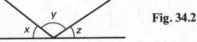

Fig. 34.2

A **quarter turn** is 90°.
This is also called a **right angle** and is usually shown as in Fig. 34.3.

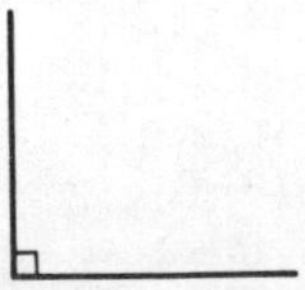

Fig. 34.3

An **acute** angle is an angle which is less than 90°.

An **obtuse** angle is an angle which is between 90° and 180°.

A **reflex** angle is an angle which is between 180° and 360°.

Figure 34.4 shows (*i*) an acute angle, (*ii*) an obtuse angle, (*iii*) a reflex angle.

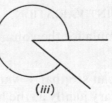

(*i*)   (*ii*)   (*iii*)

Fig. 34.4

Two angles are said to be **supplementary** if their sum is 180°.

For example, in Fig. 34.5 a and b are supplementary since $a + b = 180°$.

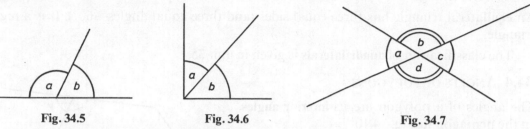

Fig. 34.5   Fig. 34.6   Fig. 34.7

Two angles are said to be **complementary** if their sum is 90°. For example, in Fig. 34.6 a and b are complementary since $a + b = 90°$.

When two straight lines intersect the **vertically opposite angles** are equal (Fig. 34.7).

a and c are vertically opposite; $a = c$.

b and d are vertically opposite; $b = d$.

This is because $a + b = 180°$ (angle on a straight line)

and $b + c = 180°$ (angle on a straight line).

Hence $a = c$.

Similarly for b and d.

34.2 PARALLELS

Two lines are said to be **parallel** if they have the same direction. Parallel lines never meet and are usually shown with an arrow ($\longrightarrow$).

A **transversal** is a line which intersects two or more parallel lines.

Alternate angles are formed when a transversal cuts parallel lines (Fig. 34.8).

These alternate angles are equal

$a_1 = a_2$, alternate angles

$b_1 = b_2$, alternate angles

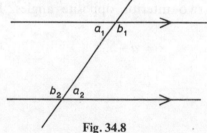

Fig. 34.8

Corresponding angles are also formed when a transversal cuts parallel lines (Fig. 34.9). These corresponding angles are equal

$p_1 = p_2$, corresponding angles

$q_1 = q_2$, corresponding angles

$r_1 = r_2$, corresponding angles

$s_1 = s_2$, corresponding angles

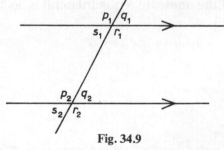

Fig. 34.9

34.3 POLYGONS

A **polygon** is a closed plane shape with a finite number of straight sides.

A polygon's name gives its number of sides (or angles). For example, **tri**angle (**3**), **quad**rilateral (**4**), **pent**agon (**5**), **hex**agon (**6**), **hept**agon (**7**), **oct**agon (**8**), **non**agon (**9**), **deca**gon (**10**).

A **regular** polygon is one in which all the sides and angles are equal.

The polygon with the least number of sides is a **triangle**. Triangles can be classified by the kind of angles or the kind of sides they have.

An **acute angled** triangle is one in which all the angles are acute, *i.e.* less than 90°.

A **right angled** triangle is one in which one angle is a right angle, *i.e.* 90°.

An **obtuse angled** triangle is one in which one angle is obtuse, *i.e.* between 90° and 180°.

A **scalene** triangle is one in which all the sides (and all the angles) are different.

An **isosceles** triangle has two equal sides (and the angles opposite these sides are equal).

An **equilateral** triangle has three equal sides (and three equal angles—60°). It is a regular triangle.

The classification of **quadrilaterals** is given in unit 35.1.

34.4 ANGLES OF POLYGONS

The angles of a polygon are its **interior angles**.
In the pentagon in Fig. 34.10
angle *x* is the **interior** angle at *P*,
angle *y* is an **exterior** angle at *P*.

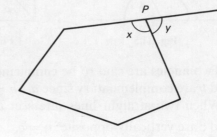

Fig. 34.10

Triangle
The sum of the angles in a triangle is 180°. In Fig. 34.11

$$a+b+c = 180°.$$

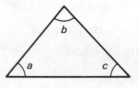

Fig. 34.11

The exterior angle of a triangle is equal to the sum of the two interior opposite angles. In Fig. 34.12

$$x = a+b.$$

Fig. 34.12

Quadrilateral
The sum of the angles in a quadrilateral is 360°. In Fig. 34.13

$$a+b+c+d = 360°.$$

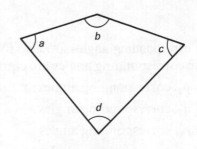

Fig. 34.13

Any polygon
An *n*-sided polygon can be divided into $(n-2)$ triangles.

Since the angle sum for each triangle is 180°, the angle sum for an *n*-sided polygon is $(n-2) \times 180°$.

If the polygon is regular, each angle $= \dfrac{(n-2)}{n} \times 180°$.

The sum of the exterior angles of a polygon $= 360°$.

If the polygon is regular, each exterior angle $= \dfrac{360°}{n}$.

35 Quadrilaterals

A **quadrilateral** is a four sided polygon, *i.e.* a plane figure with exactly four straight sides. The sum of the interior angles of a quadrilateral is 360°.

35.1 CLASSIFICATION

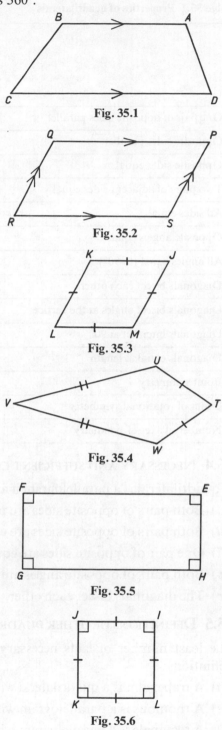

(*i*) A **trapezium** is a quadrilateral which has a pair of parallel sides.
In Fig. 35.1, *ABCD* is a trapezium.

Fig. 35.1

(*ii*) A **parallelogram** is a quadrilateral which has two pairs of parallel sides.
In Fig. 35.2, *PQRS* is a parallelogram.

Fig. 35.2

(*iii*) A **rhombus** is a quadrilateral which has four sides of equal length.
In Fig. 35.3, *JKLM* is a rhombus.
Since a rhombus has two pairs of parallel sides it is also a parallelogram and a trapezium.

Fig. 35.3

(*iv*) A **kite** is a quadrilateral having two pairs of adjacent sides equal in length.
In Fig. 35.4, *TUVW* is a kite.
If all four sides are of equal length, the kite is a rhombus.

Fig. 35.4

(*v*) A **rectangle** is a quadrilateral with each interior angle equal to 90°.
In Fig. 35.5, *EFGH* is a rectangle.
Since a rectangle has four equal angles it has two pairs of parallel sides.
Therefore, a rectangle is also a parallelogram and a trapezium.

Fig. 35.5

(*vi*) A **square** is a quadrilateral with four equal angles and four sides of equal length.
In Fig. 35.6, *IJKL* is a square.
A square is also a rectangle with four equal sides.
A square is also a rhombus with four equal angles.

Fig. 35.6

35.2 QUADRILATERAL FAMILY TREE

This is an easy way to remember the relationships between special quadrilaterals:

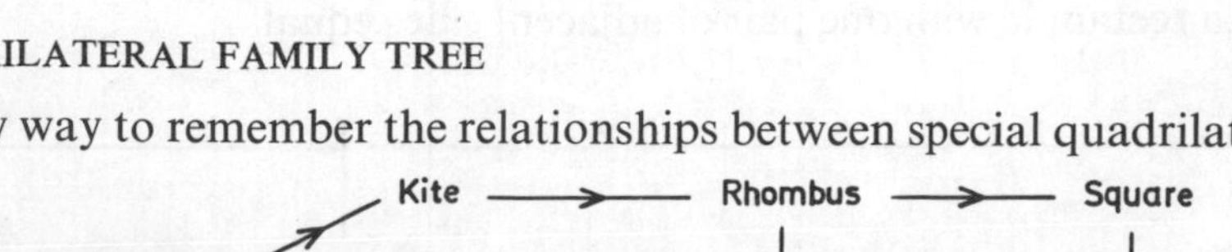

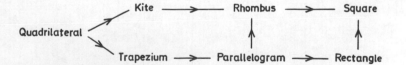

Following the arrows you can see that:
e.g. Rhombus is a special kite.
Square is a special rhombus and kite.
It is also a special rectangle, parallelogram, trapezium, etc.

35.3 PROPERTIES

Some important properties of these quadrilaterals are listed in Table 35.1.

Table 35.1 Properties of quadrilaterals

	Trapezium	Parallelogram	Rhombus	Kite	Rectangle	Square
One pair of opposite sides parallel	✓	✓	✓	✕	✓	✓
Opposite sides parallel	✕	✓	✓	✕	✓	✓
Opposite sides equal	✕	✓	✓	✕	✓	✓
Two pairs of adjacent sides equal	✕	✕	✓	✓	✕	✓
All sides equal	✕	✕	✓	✕	✕	✓
Opposite angles equal	✕	✓	✓	✕	✓	✓
All angles equal (to 90°)	✕	✕	✕	✕	✓	✓
Diagonals bisect each other	✕	✓	✓	✕	✓	✓
Diagonals bisect angles at the vertices	✕	✕	✓	✕	✕	✓
Diagonals intersect at 90°	✕	✕	✓	✓	✕	✓
Diagonals equal in length	✕	✕	✕	✕	✓	✓
Point symmetry	✕	✓	✓	✕	✓	✓
Order of rotational symmetry	1	2	2	1	2	4
Number of axes of symmetry	0	0	2	1	2	4

35.4 NECESSARY AND SUFFICIENT CONDITIONS FOR A PARALLELOGRAM

A quadrilateral is a parallelogram if any one of the following is true:

(*i*) Both pairs of opposite sides are parallel.

(*ii*) Both pairs of opposite sides are equal.

(*iii*) One pair of opposite sides are equal and parallel.

(*iv*) Both pairs of opposite angles are equal.

(*v*) The diagonals bisect each other.

35.5 DEFINITIONS OF OTHER QUADRILATERALS

The least number of facts necessary to describe each figure are given in the following definitions:

(*i*) A trapezium is a quadrilateral with one pair of sides parallel.

(*ii*) A rhombus is a parallelogram with one pair of adjacent sides equal.

(*iii*) A rectangle is a parallelogram with one right angle.

(*iv*) A square is a rectangle with one pair of adjacent sides equal.

36 Similarity and congruence

36.1 SIMILARITY

Two objects, plane or solid, are said to be **similar** if they are the same shape, *i.e.* one is an **enlargement** (or reduction) of the other. For example,

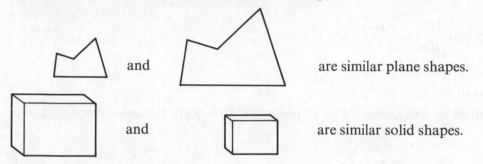

and   are similar plane shapes.

and   are similar solid shapes.

Areas of similar plane shapes

If two plane shapes are similar, then the ratio of their areas is the **square** of the **scale factor** of the enlargement.

For example, if the ratio of the corresponding sides of two similar polygons is k, then the ratio of the areas of the polygons is k^2. In other words, if the scale factor of an enlargement is k, then the **area factor** of the enlargement is k^2.

Volumes of similar solids

If two solids are similar, then the ratio of their volumes is the **cube** of the **scale factor** of the enlargement.

For example, if the ratio of the corresponding sides of two similar solids is k, then the ratio of the volumes of the solids is k^3. In other words, if the scale factor of an enlargement is k, then the **volume factor** of the enlargement is k^3.

Example

If two solids are similar and lengths in one are five times the corresponding lengths in the other, state the ratio of (i) *corresponding areas, and* (ii) *their volumes.*

Since the scale factor (ratio of corresponding sides) is 5:

(*i*) areas in the larger shape are $5^2 = 25$ times the corresponding areas in the smaller shape (*i.e.* the ratio of corresponding areas is $1:25$), and

(*ii*) the volume of the larger shape is $5^3 = 125$ times the volume of the smaller shape (*i.e.* the ratio of their volumes is $1:125$).

The ideas contained in this example are very important and should be fully understood and remembered (see unit 13.3 for another example).

36.2 SIMILAR TRIANGLES

Similar triangles are a special case.

Two triangles are similar if one of the following conditions is satisfied:

(*i*) the angles of one triangle are equal to the angles of the other triangle;

$\triangle ABC$ is similar to $\triangle XZY$, because $\angle A = \angle X$, $\angle B = \angle Z$, $\angle C = \angle Y$.

(*ii*) the ratios of corresponding sides are equal;

$\triangle PQR$ is similar to $\triangle DEF$, if

$$\frac{PQ}{DE} = \frac{QR}{EF} = \frac{RP}{FD}.$$

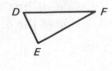

(*iii*) the ratios of two corresponding sides
are equal and the included angles are
equal.

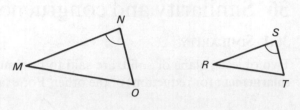

$\triangle MNO$ is similar to $\triangle RST$, if,
for example,

$$\angle N = \angle S \text{ and } \frac{MN}{RS} = \frac{NO}{ST}.$$

36.3 CONGRUENCE

Two objects, plane or solid, are said to be **congruent** if they are the same shape and size.
For example,

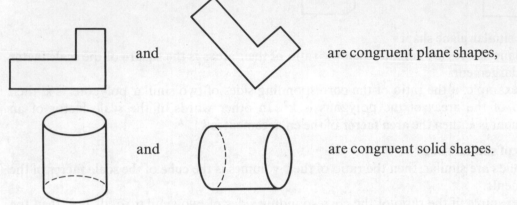

and   are congruent plane shapes,

and   are congruent solid shapes.

36.4 CONGRUENT TRIANGLES

Congruent triangles are a special case.
    Two triangles are congruent if one of the following conditions is satisfied:

(*i*) three sides of one triangle are equal to the
three sides of the other triangle (SSS);

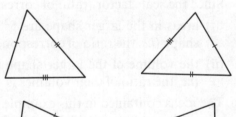

(*ii*) two sides and the included angle of one
triangle are equal to two sides and the
included angle of the other triangle (SAS);

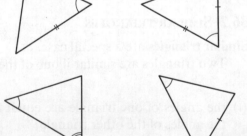

(*iii*) two angles and the corresponding side of
each triangle are equal (AAS);

(*iv*) they are both right angled triangles and
their hypotenuses are equal and one other
side of one triangle is equal to one other
side of the other triangle (RHS).

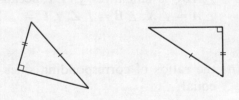

37 Bearings and scale drawing

37.1 COMPASS DIRECTIONS AND BEARINGS

The eight main **compass points** are shown in
Fig. 37.1.
North (N), East (E), South (S) and West (W)
are called the **cardinal points**.

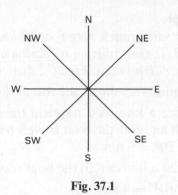

Fig. 37.1

A **compass direction** is measured as an acute angle from N or S to E or W.

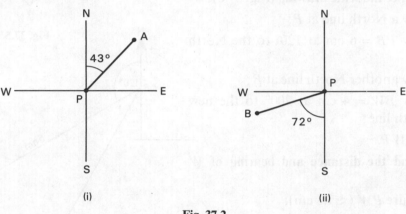

Fig. 37.2

For example, in Fig. 37.2, the compass direction of (*i*) *A* from *P* is N 43° E,
                                                    (*ii*) *B* from *P* is S 72° W.

A **bearing** is measured as a clockwise angle from North (N) and given as a three-digit
number.

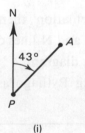

Fig. 37.3

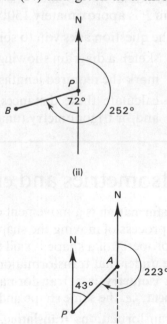

For example, in Fig. 37.3 the bearing of

(*i*) *A* from *P* is 043°,
(*ii*) *B* from *P* is 252°.

Note: To find the bearing of *P* from *A*, draw
a North line through *A* as shown in Fig. 37.4.
The bearing of *P* from *A* is 223°.

Fig. 37.4

37.2 SCALE DRAWING

A **scale drawing** is one in which all lengths are drawn to the
same scale. When making a scale drawing it is advisable to use
the following method:

  (*i*) draw a rough sketch;
 (*ii*) choose a suitable scale to use as much paper as is sensible;
(*iii*) state the chosen scale at the top of the drawing, *e.g.* scale 1 cm represents 2 km;
 (*iv*) draw clear North lines in drawings which use bearings;
  (*v*) give the answers to questions in actual distances, not scale distances.

Example

A boat sails from a port P at 12 knots on a bearing of 120° for half an hour until it reaches a buoy B. It then sails on a bearing of 200° at the same speed until it reaches a wreck W after a further 20 minutes. Find the distance and bearing of W from P by scale drawing.

Figure 37.5 shows the rough sketch.

Since a knot is 1 nautical mile per hour, in half an hour the boat travels 6 nm.
So $PB = 6$ nm.

In 20 minutes ($\frac{1}{3}$h) the boat travels 4 nm.
So $BW = 4$ nm.

The chosen scale is 1 cm represents 1 nm.

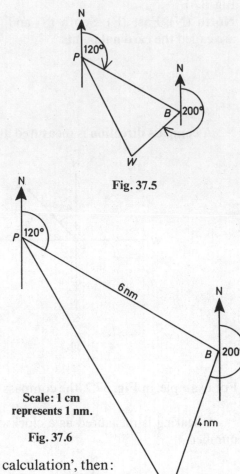

Fig. 37.5

To make the scale drawing (Fig. 37.6):

 (i) draw a North line at P;

 (ii) draw $PB = 6$ cm at 120° to the North line;

 (iii) draw another North line at B;

 (iv) draw $BW = 4$ cm at 200° to the new North line;

 (v) join WP.

To find the distance and bearing of W from P:

 (a) measure PW (≈ 7.8 cm);

 (b) measure the angle made by PW with the North line at P ($\approx 150\frac{1}{2}°$).

Hence, the distance of W from P is approximately 7.8 nm; the bearing of W from P is approximately $150\frac{1}{2}°$.

Scale: 1 cm represents 1 nm.

Fig. 37.6

If the question asks you to solve the problem 'by calculation', then:

 (a) sketch a diagram showing the given information and N-lines clearly,

 (b) mark the required lengths and/or angles on your diagram,

 (c) calculate these distances and/or bearings using Pythagoras' Theorem (unit 40) and/or trigonometry (units 41 and 42).

---

38 Isometries and enlargement

A **transformation** is a movement of a plane shape from one position to another in its plane. In the process of moving the shape may be turned over or enlarged.

A property of a shape is said to be **invariant** under a given transformation if it does not change under that transformation.

An **isometry** is a transformation in which the original and transformed shapes are **congruent**, *i.e.* the same shape and size.

The transformations **translation**, **rotation** and **reflection** are all isometries. Enlargement, shear and stretch are not isometries.

Two plane shapes are **directly congruent** if one can be fitted exactly on top of the other.

Two plane shapes are **oppositely congruent** if one can be fitted exactly on top of the other after being turned over.

38.1 TRANSLATION

In a **translation**, every point in the plane is displaced by the same amount and in the same direction.

In Fig. 38.1, the triangle *ABC* (the **object**) has been translated to a new position $A_1B_1C_1$ (the **image**).

The line segments AA_1, BB_1, CC_1 are all parallel and equal in length.

Hence a translation is exactly determined by a displacement vector (see unit 49.1). In this case the vector $\overrightarrow{AA_1}$ describes the translation. (Since $\overrightarrow{AA_1} = \overrightarrow{BB_1} = \overrightarrow{CC_1}$, any one of these three describes the translation.)

Under a translation, an object and its image are directly congruent.

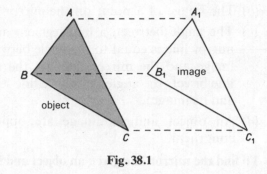

Fig. 38.1

38.2 ROTATION

In a **rotation** every point on the object turns through the same angle about the centre of rotation. A rotation is described by (*i*) the centre of rotation, (*ii*) the angle of rotation (in degrees), (*iii*) the direction of rotation (clockwise or anti-clockwise). Anti-clockwise rotations are positive. Clockwise rotations are negative.

In Fig. 38.2 the triangle *ABC* (the object) has been rotated to a new position $A_1B_1C_1$ (the image).

(*i*) The centre of rotation is *O*.

(*ii*) The angle of rotation is $\theta°$.

(*iii*) The direction of rotation is anti-clockwise, so it is positive.

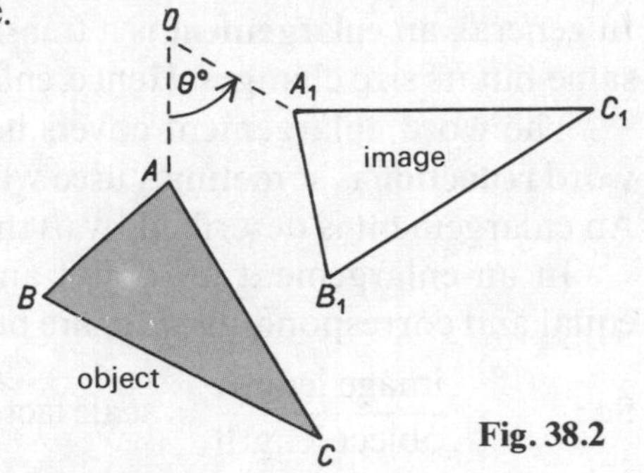

The properties of rotation are:

(*a*) The centre of rotation is the only **invariant point** (*i.e.* the only fixed point).

(*b*) The centre of rotation can lie anywhere in the plane.

(*c*) Every line segment turns through the same angle, the angle of rotation.

(*d*) An object and its image are directly congruent.

Fig. 38.2

To find the centre of rotation given an object and its image:

(*i*) join two corresponding points on the object and its image;

(*ii*) draw the perpendicular bisector of this line segment;

(*iii*) repeat for two other corresponding points.

The point of intersection of the two perpendicular bisectors is the centre of rotation (Fig. 38.3).

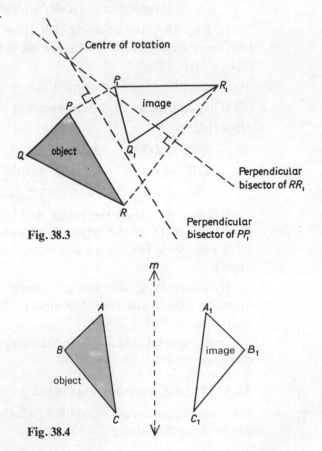

Fig. 38.3

38.3 REFLECTION

A **reflection** is determined if the position of the mirror line is known.

In Fig. 38.4 the triangle *ABC* (the object) has been reflected to a new position $A_1B_1C_1$ (the image).

The mirror line *m* is of infinite length and is double sided.

The properties of reflection are:

(*a*) A point and its image are equidistant from the mirror line.

Fig. 38.4

(*b*) The image of a point on the mirror line is the point itself.

(*c*) The angle between a line segment and the mirror line is equal to the angle between its image and the mirror line (*i.e.* the mirror line bisects the angle between a line segment and its image).

(*d*) An object and its image are oppositely congruent.

To find the mirror line given an object and its image:

(*i*) join two corresponding points on the object and its image;

(*ii*) draw the perpendicular bisector of this line segment.

The perpendicular bisector is the mirror line (Fig. 38.5).

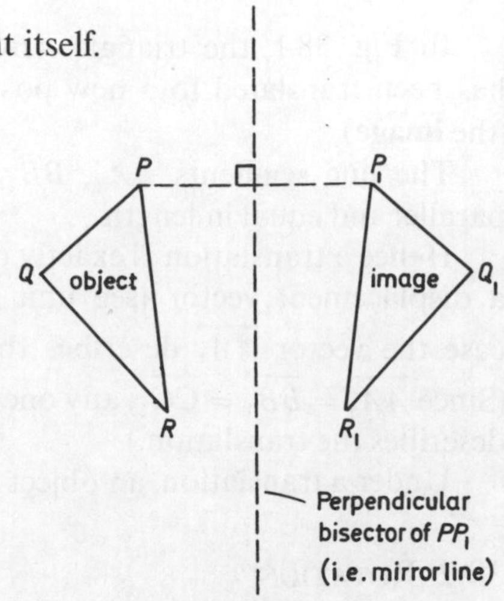

Perpendicular bisector of PP_1 (*i.e.* mirror line)

Fig. 38.5

38.4 ENLARGEMENT

In general, an **enlargement** is a transformation in which the shape of the object remains the same but its size changes. Hence, enlargement is not an isometry.

The word enlargement covers both an increase and decrease in size of an object. The word **reduction** is sometimes used when the size of the object decreases.

An enlargement is described by (*i*) the centre (an invariant point), (*ii*) the scale factor.

In an enlargement an object and its image are **similar**, *i.e.* corresponding angles are equal and corresponding sides are proportional.

So: $\dfrac{\text{image length}}{\text{object length}} = \text{scale factor}$

i.e.   image length = scale factor × object length.

Also: $\dfrac{\text{image area}}{\text{object area}} = (\text{scale factor})^2$

i.e.   image area = (scale factor)^2 × object area.

In Fig. 38.6, the triangle *ABC* (the object) has been enlarged to become a new triangle $A_1B_1C_1$ (the image).

(*i*) The centre of enlargement is *O*.

(*ii*) The scale factor of the enlargement is $k(>1)$.

Note that:

$$OA_1 = kOA \qquad \text{Also, } AB \parallel A_1B_1$$
$$OB_1 = kOB \qquad \qquad BC \parallel B_1C_1$$
$$OC_1 = kOC \qquad \qquad CA \parallel C_1A_1$$

If $0 < k < 1$, then the image will be on the same side of *O* as the object but nearer to *O* as in Fig. 38.7. The image is a reduction of the object.

If $k < 0$, then the image appears on the opposite side of the centre of enlargement and is inverted as in Fig. 38.8.

In the special case $k = -1$, the object and its image are oppositely congruent.

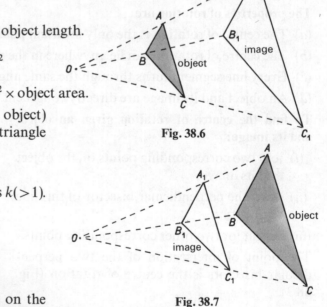

Fig. 38.6

Fig. 38.7

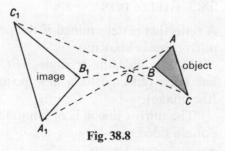

Fig. 38.8

38.5 MATRIX TRANSFORMATIONS

With the exception of translation (which is described by a vector) all these transformations can be described using 2×2 matrices.

In Fig. 38.9 the point $P(x, y)$ has position vector $\overrightarrow{OP} = \begin{pmatrix} x \\ y \end{pmatrix}$.

Premultiplying $\begin{pmatrix} x \\ y \end{pmatrix}$ by some 2×2 matrix M produces

$\begin{pmatrix} x' \\ y' \end{pmatrix}$ the position vector of the image point $P'(x', y')$,

i.e. $M \begin{pmatrix} x \\ y \end{pmatrix} = \begin{pmatrix} x' \\ y' \end{pmatrix}$.

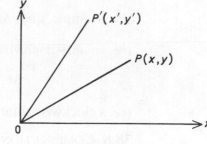

Fig. 38.9

Different matrices M produce different transformations in the plane. The following are the most useful matrices:

(i) Reflection

(a) Reflection in the x-axis (matrix M_x) (Fig. 38.10).

$$M_x = \begin{pmatrix} 1 & 0 \\ 0 & -1 \end{pmatrix} \text{ since } \begin{pmatrix} 1 & 0 \\ 0 & -1 \end{pmatrix} \begin{pmatrix} x \\ y \end{pmatrix} = \begin{pmatrix} x \\ -y \end{pmatrix}, \text{ i.e. } P(x, y) \rightarrow P_1(x, -y)$$

(b) Reflection in the y-axis (matrix M_y)

$$M_y = \begin{pmatrix} -1 & 0 \\ 0 & 1 \end{pmatrix} \text{ since } \begin{pmatrix} -1 & 0 \\ 0 & 1 \end{pmatrix} \begin{pmatrix} x \\ y \end{pmatrix} = \begin{pmatrix} -x \\ y \end{pmatrix}, \text{ i.e. } P(x, y) \rightarrow P_2(-x, y).$$

(c) Reflection in the line $y = x$ (matrix M_{xy})

$$M_{xy} = \begin{pmatrix} 0 & 1 \\ 1 & 0 \end{pmatrix} \text{ since } \begin{pmatrix} 0 & 1 \\ 1 & 0 \end{pmatrix} \begin{pmatrix} x \\ y \end{pmatrix} = \begin{pmatrix} y \\ x \end{pmatrix}, \text{ i.e. } P(x, y) \rightarrow P_3(y, x).$$

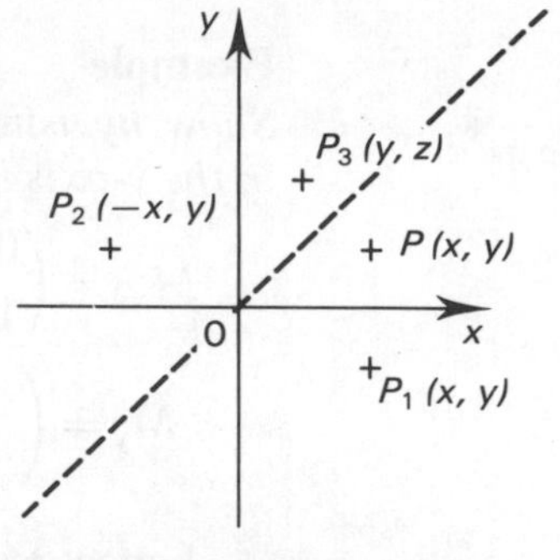

Fig. 38.10

(ii) Rotation

(a) Anti-clockwise rotations of $90°$ (matrix M_1), $180°$ (matrix M_2), and $270°$ (matrix M_3), i.e. rotations of $+90°$, $+180°$ and $+270°$.

$$M_1 = \begin{pmatrix} 0 & -1 \\ 1 & 0 \end{pmatrix}, \qquad M_2 = \begin{pmatrix} -1 & 0 \\ 0 & -1 \end{pmatrix}, \qquad M_3 = \begin{pmatrix} 0 & 1 \\ -1 & 0 \end{pmatrix}.$$

These three can be checked by using the methods in (i).

(b) Clockwise rotations of $90°$, $180°$ and $270°$, i.e. rotations of $-90°$, $-180°$ and $-270°$, are produced by M_3, M_2 and M_1 respectively.

(iii) Enlargement

Enlargement, scale factor k (matrix M_E)

$$M_E = \begin{pmatrix} k & 0 \\ 0 & k \end{pmatrix} \text{ since } \begin{pmatrix} k & 0 \\ 0 & k \end{pmatrix} \begin{pmatrix} x \\ y \end{pmatrix} = \begin{pmatrix} kx \\ ky \end{pmatrix}, \text{ i.e. } P(x, y) \rightarrow P_1(kx, ky).$$

Notice that $|M_E| = k^2$, the area factor of the enlargement.

38.6 TRANSFORMATION MATRICES

Transformation matrices can be worked out by finding the images of $(1, 0)$ and $(0, 1)$ under the given transformation and using the following method:

If $P(1, 0) \rightarrow P_1(a, b)$

and $Q(0, 1) \rightarrow Q_1(c, d)$ under a transformation,

then $M = \begin{pmatrix} a & c \\ b & d \end{pmatrix}$ is the matrix which describes the transformation.

For example, for reflection in $y = -x$ (Fig. 38.11)

$P(1, 0) \rightarrow P_1(0, -1)$

$Q(0, 1) \rightarrow Q_1(-1, 0)$

then $M = \begin{pmatrix} 0 & -1 \\ -1 & 0 \end{pmatrix}$ is the matrix describing this transformation.

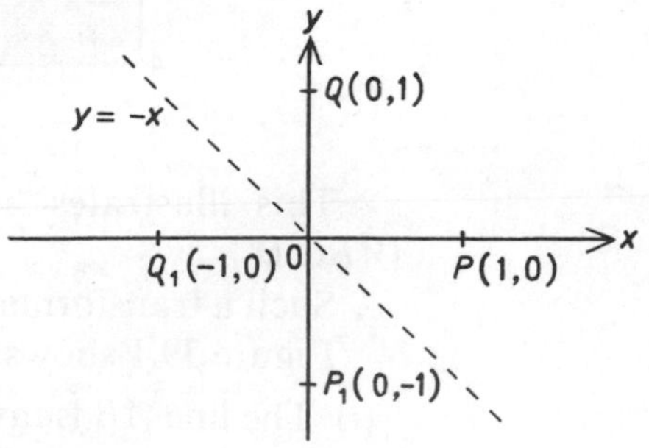

Fig. 38.11

Notice that, for the transformations reflection, rotation and enlargement, the origin is an invariant point.

38.7 INVERSE TRANSFORMATIONS

If M is the matrix of a transformation and $|M| \neq 0$, then M^{-1} is the matrix of the **inverse transformation**.

For example, since $M_1 = \begin{pmatrix} 0 & -1 \\ 1 & 0 \end{pmatrix}$ represents a rotation through $+90°$

(*i.e.* an anti-clockwise rotation through $90°$),

$$M_1^{-1} = \begin{pmatrix} 0 & 1 \\ -1 & 0 \end{pmatrix}$$ represents a rotation through $-90°$

(*i.e.* a clockwise rotation through $90°$) and M_1^{-1} is the inverse of M_1.

38.8 COMBINATION OF TRANSFORMATIONS

If M and N are two matrices representing two transformations for which the origin is an invariant point, then NM is a matrix which represents the result of M followed by N.

Example

Show, by using matrix multiplication, that a reflection in the line $y = x$ followed by a reflection in the y-axis is equivalent to an anti-clockwise rotation through $90°$.

$M_{xy} = \begin{pmatrix} 0 & 1 \\ 1 & 0 \end{pmatrix}$ is the matrix which represents a reflection in $y = x$.

$M_y = \begin{pmatrix} -1 & 0 \\ 0 & 1 \end{pmatrix}$ is the matrix which represents a reflection in the y-axis

hence, $M_y M_{xy} = \begin{pmatrix} -1 & 0 \\ 0 & 1 \end{pmatrix} \begin{pmatrix} 0 & 1 \\ 1 & 0 \end{pmatrix}$

$$= \begin{pmatrix} 0 & -1 \\ 1 & 0 \end{pmatrix}$$ which represents a rotation through $+90°$.

---

39 Shear and stretch

39.1 SHEAR

Figure 39.1(*i*) shows a pack of playing cards ($ABCD$) on a card table. A horizontal force applied to the top card moves all but the bottom card. Figure 39.1(*ii*) shows the final shape of the pack.

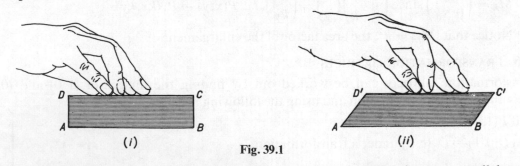

(*i*)

Fig. 39.1

(*ii*)

This illustrates how we can transform a rectangle ($ABCD$) into a parallelogram ($ABC'D'$).

Such a transformation is called a **shear**.

Figure 39.1 shows that this shear has the following properties:

 (*i*) The line AB is invariant
      (the bottom card does not move).

 (*ii*) The distance of a point from the invariant line remains the same
      (each card remains the same distance from the table).

(*iii*) The area of the rectangle $ABCD$ is the same as the area of the parallelogram
      $ABC'D'$
      (the length and thickness of each card remains the same).

A **shear** is fully described if we know (*i*) the invariant line, (*ii*) the image of a point not on the invariant line.

In Fig. 39.2 the rectangle $OABC$ (the object) has undergone a shear to become a parallelogram OAB_1C_1 (the image).

For this shear,

(*i*) the invariant line is the *x*-axis;

(*ii*) the image of $B(2, 3)$ is $B_1(5, 3)$.

We can see that the *x*-axis is the invariant line since O and A are fixed points. For this reason the shear is said to be parallel to the *x*-axis.

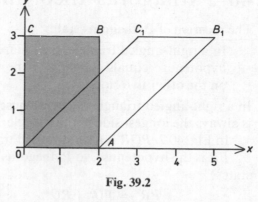

Fig. 39.2

The properties of a shear are:

(*a*) Every point on the invariant line remains fixed.

(*b*) All points equidistant from the invariant line move the same amount.

(*c*) The area of a plane figure remains invariant.

39.2 STRETCH

A plane shape is **stretched** if it is enlarged in one direction only. A stretch is fully described if we know (*i*) the direction of stretch, (*ii*) the ratio of corresponding lengths in the direction of the stretch.

Area of stretched figure = area of original figure × scale factor.

In Fig. 39.3 the rectangle $OABC$ (the object) has undergone a stretch to become another rectangle OA_1B_1C (the image). This stretch is:

(*i*) in a positive direction, parallel to the *x*-axis;

(*ii*) in the ratio $3 : 5$, *i.e.* $1 : \frac{5}{3}$.

Area OA_1B_1C = area $OABC \times \frac{5}{3}$.

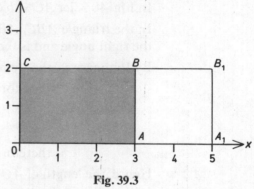

Fig. 39.3

39.3 MATRIX TRANSFORMATIONS

(*a*) Shear

(*i*) Shear parallel to the *x*-axis (the invariant line), (matrix M_{sx})

$$M_{sx} = \begin{pmatrix} 1 & k \\ 0 & 1 \end{pmatrix} \text{ since } \begin{pmatrix} 1 & k \\ 0 & 1 \end{pmatrix}\begin{pmatrix} x \\ y \end{pmatrix} = \begin{pmatrix} x+ky \\ y \end{pmatrix} \text{ i.e. } P(x,y) \rightarrow P_1(x+ky, y)$$

so, points equidistant from the *x*-axis move by equal amounts, ky.

(*ii*) Shear parallel to the *y*-axis (the invariant line), (matrix M_{sy})

$$M_{sy} = \begin{pmatrix} 1 & 0 \\ k & 1 \end{pmatrix} \text{ since } \begin{pmatrix} 1 & 0 \\ k & 1 \end{pmatrix}\begin{pmatrix} x \\ y \end{pmatrix} = \begin{pmatrix} x \\ y+kx \end{pmatrix} \text{ i.e. } P(x,y) \rightarrow P_1(x, y+kx)$$

so, points equidistant from the *y*-axis move by equal amounts, kx.

(*b*) Stretch

(*i*) Stretch parallel to the *x*-axis, (matrix M_{tx})

$$M_{tx} = \begin{pmatrix} k & 0 \\ 0 & 1 \end{pmatrix} \text{ since } \begin{pmatrix} k & 0 \\ 0 & 1 \end{pmatrix}\begin{pmatrix} x \\ y \end{pmatrix} = \begin{pmatrix} kx \\ y \end{pmatrix} \text{ i.e. } P(x,y) \rightarrow P_1(kx, y)$$

so, the ratio of the stretch is $1 : k$.

(*ii*) Stretch parallel to the *y*-axis, (matrix M_{ty})

$$M_{ty} = \begin{pmatrix} 1 & 0 \\ 0 & k \end{pmatrix} \text{ since } \begin{pmatrix} 1 & 0 \\ 0 & k \end{pmatrix}\begin{pmatrix} x \\ y \end{pmatrix} = \begin{pmatrix} x \\ ky \end{pmatrix} \text{ i.e. } P(x,y) \rightarrow P_1(x, ky)$$

so, ratio of the stretch is $1 : k$.

Notice, $|M_{sx}| = |M_{sy}| = 1$, *i.e.* area remains invariant under a shear but,

$|M_{tx}| = |M_{ty}| = k - 0 = k$, *i.e.* ratio object area : image area $= 1 : k$ for stretches.

Notice also that for shear and stretch, the origin is an invariant point.

40 Pythagoras' theorem

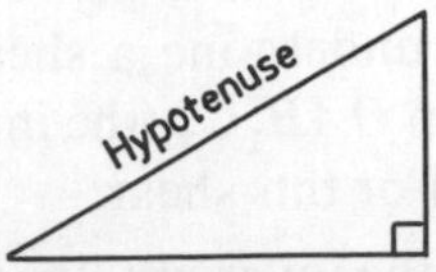

The **theorem of Pythagoras** states:

> 'In a right-angled triangle, the square on the hypotenuse equals the sum of the squares on the other two sides.'

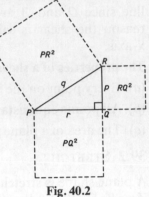

Fig. 40.1

In a right-angled triangle the **hypotenuse** is the side opposite the right angle (Fig. 40.1) and is always the longest side in the triangle.

In Fig. 40.2, PQR is a right-angled triangle with $\angle Q = 90°$.

PR is the hypotenuse, so Pythagoras' theorem states:

$$PR^2 = PQ^2 + RQ^2.$$

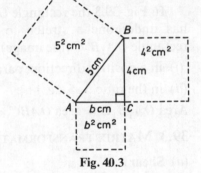

If p is the side opposite P, etc., Pythagoras' theorem can be written in the form:

$$q^2 = r^2 + p^2.$$

Fig. 40.2

Example

In a triangle ABC, $AB = 5$ cm, $BC = 4$ cm and $\angle C = 90°$. Find the length of AC.

In Fig. 40.3, let $AC = b$ cm.

In the triangle ABC, AB is the side opposite the right angle and is the hypotenuse.

By Pythagoras' theorem, $AB^2 = BC^2 + AC^2$

$$\text{therefore} \quad 5^2 = 4^2 + b^2$$
$$b^2 = 5^2 - 4^2$$
$$= 9$$
$$\text{therefore} \quad b = 3.$$

Hence, the length of AC is 3 cm.

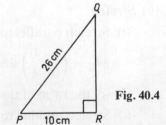

Fig. 40.3

This is a special triangle called a $(3, 4, 5)$ triangle because of the length of its sides. Any right-angled triangle whose sides are in the same ratios, $3:4:5$, is also called a $(3, 4, 5)$ triangle. For example, if the lengths of the sides of a right-angled triangle are 12 cm, 16 cm and 20 cm, then the triangle is a $(3, 4, 5)$ triangle.

$(3, 4, 5)$ is called a **Pythagorean triple**. There are many other Pythagorean triples and another simple one is $(5, 12, 13)$. These two should be remembered: they occur frequently in questions.

Example

In the triangle PQR, $PQ = 26$ cm, $PR = 10$ cm and $\angle R = 90°$. What is the length of QR?

In Fig. 40.4

$PR = 10$ cm $= 2 \times 5$ cm,

$PQ = 26$ cm $= 2 \times 13$ cm.

Hence, $QR = 2 \times 12$ cm $= 24$ cm

since triangle PQR is a $(5, 12, 13)$ triangle.

Fig. 40.4

The **converse** of Pythagoras' theorem is also true, *i.e.* if the square on the longest side of a triangle equals the sum of the squares on the other two sides, then the triangle is right angled. The angle opposite the longest side is the right angle.

An extension of this is useful if we want to know if the largest angle of a triangle is obtuse or acute. We know if it is 90° by the converse theorem.

If $a^2 > b^2 + c^2$, then the angle is obtuse ($>90°$),

if $a^2 < b^2 + c^2$, then the angle is acute ($<90°$),

where a is the length of the longest side.

Example

In a triangle XYZ, XZ = 3 cm, XY = 6 cm and YZ = 7 cm. What type of angle is ∠X?

In Fig. 40.5

$XZ^2 = 3^2 = 9$, $XY^2 = 6^2 = 36$ and

$YZ^2 = 7^2 = 49$.

If $\angle X = 90°$, $ZY^2 = XZ^2 + XY^2$.

But $ZY^2 = 49$ and $XZ^2 + XY^2 = 9 + 36 = 45$.

Therefore $ZY^2 > XZ^2 + XY^2$ (since 49 > 45).

Hence $\angle X > 90°$, *i.e.* $\angle X$ is obtuse.

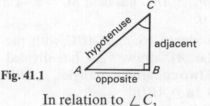

Fig. 40.5

Pythagoras' theorem is often used in conjunction with Trigonometry (see unit 41) in order to solve problems involving unknown sides and angles in triangles.

41 Trigonometry

41.1 Trigonometrical ratios

Let *ABC* be a right-angled triangle with $\angle B = 90°$ (Fig. 41.1). *AC* is the hypotenuse, *i.e.* the side opposite the right angle.

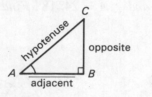

Fig. 41.1

In relation to ∠A,
CB is the opposite side, and
AB is the adjacent side.

In relation to ∠C,
AB is the opposite side, and
CB is the adjacent side.

The **trigonometrical ratios**, **sine (sin)**, **cosine (cos)** and **tangent (tan)** for ∠A are:

$$\sin A = \frac{\text{opposite}}{\text{hypotenuse}} = \frac{CB}{AC} \qquad \text{so,} \quad \text{opposite} = \text{hypotenuse} \times \sin A$$

$$\cos A = \frac{\text{adjacent}}{\text{hypotenuse}} = \frac{AB}{AC} \qquad \text{so,} \quad \text{adjacent} = \text{hypotenuse} \times \cos A$$

$$\tan A = \frac{\text{opposite}}{\text{adjacent}} = \frac{CB}{AB} \qquad \text{so,} \quad \text{opposite} = \text{adjacent} \times \tan A$$

Remember: if you have to solve a right-angled triangle,

 (*i*) to find an angle, given two sides, use one of the equations on the left;

(*ii*) to find a side, given an angle and another side, use one of the equations on the right.

In each case, the equation you choose must involve the side or angle you wish to find and the other information you are given.

Note: If you are given two sides and have to find the third side in a right-angled triangle, use the theorem of Pythagoras.

Example

In the triangle PQR (Fig. 41.2), ∠R = 90°, PQ = 7 cm and QR = 4.6 cm. Find ∠P and ∠Q.

First find ∠P.

In relation to ∠P, *QR* is the opposite side.

We also know the length of *PQ*, the hypotenuse. So, to find ∠P use,

$$\sin P = \frac{\text{opposite}}{\text{hypotenuse}}$$

$$= \frac{QR}{PQ} = \frac{4.6}{7} = 0.6571.$$

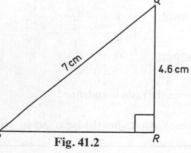

Fig. 41.2

Hence, $\angle P = 41° 05' (04')$ (from natural sines tables).

Further, since $\triangle PQR$ is right angled,

$\angle Q = 90° - \angle P = 48° 55'$.

The next example uses a different ratio.

Example

In triangle XYZ (Fig. 41.3), $\angle X = 90°$,
$\angle Z = 37° 45'$ and $YZ = 13.4$ cm.
Find XZ to 3 significant figures.

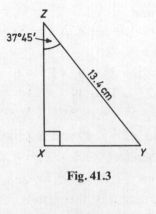

Fig. 41.3

To find XZ use

adjacent = hypotenuse × cosine.

$$XZ = YZ \cos Z$$
$$= 13.4 \times \cos 37° 45' \text{ cm}$$
$$= 13.4 \times 0.7907 \text{ cm}$$
$$= 10.6 \text{ cm (3 sf)}.$$

To solve an isosceles triangle,
draw a perpendicular to the base like this:

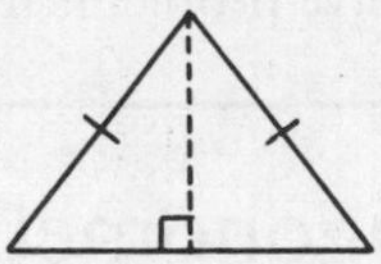

Fig. 41.4

Example

An isosceles triangle ABC has base BC = 3.4 cm and $\angle A = 24° 18'$. Find the lengths of the
equal sides to 2 sf.

Figure 41.5 shows triangle ABC with the
perpendicular AD drawn. AD has divided
$\triangle ABC$ into two congruent triangles, $\triangle ABD$
and $\triangle ACD$. In $\triangle ABD$,

opposite = hypotenuse × sine

$$BD = AB \times \sin 12° 09'$$
$$1.7 \text{ cm} = AB \times 0.2105 \text{ cm}.$$

So, $AB = \dfrac{1.7}{0.2105} \text{ cm}$

$$= 8.1 \text{ cm (2 sf)}.$$

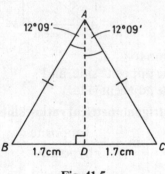

Fig. 41.5

41.2 TRIGONOMETRICAL RATIOS OF STANDARD ANGLES

Figure 41.6(*i*) shows an equilateral triangle of side 2 units and Fig. 37.6(*ii*) shows a
right-angled isosceles triangle with equal sides of 1 unit.

With the aid of Fig. 41.6 and listing
the values of the three ratios for the
standard angles of 0° and 90° we have:

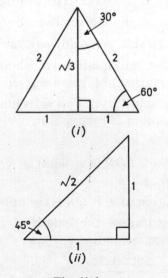

	0°	30°	45°	60°	90°
sine	0	$\dfrac{1}{2}$	$\dfrac{1}{\sqrt{2}}$	$\dfrac{\sqrt{3}}{2}$	1
cosine	1	$\dfrac{\sqrt{3}}{2}$	$\dfrac{1}{\sqrt{2}}$	$\dfrac{1}{2}$	0
tangent	0	$\dfrac{1}{\sqrt{3}}$	1	$\sqrt{3}$	*

*means the ratio is undefined

Fig. 41.6

These ratios should be used in questions involving these angles.

42 The sine and cosine rules

These rules are used to solve triangles in which there are no right angles. If a triangle is right angled, use the methods in unit 41.1.

42.1 THE SINE RULE

In any triangle ABC, the **sine rule** can be written as:

(i) $\dfrac{a}{\sin A} = \dfrac{b}{\sin B} = \dfrac{c}{\sin C}$

or

(ii) $\dfrac{\sin A}{a} = \dfrac{\sin B}{b} = \dfrac{\sin C}{c}$

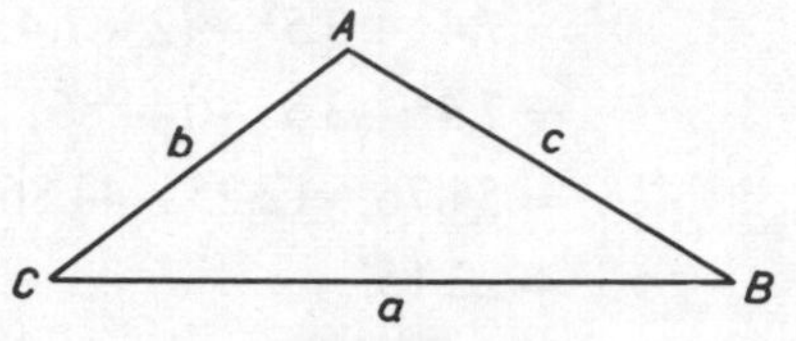

Fig. 42.1

where a, b and c are the sides opposite the angles A, B and C.

If a triangle has no right angle we use (i) to find the length of a side if one other side and two angles are known, or (ii) to find another angle if two sides and one angle are known.

Remember: if two angles are known we can find the third since the angle sum of a triangle is 180°.

Example

In a triangle PQR, $\angle P = 56° 25'$, PQ = 6.4 cm and RQ = 7.6 cm. Solve the triangle (i.e. find all sides and angles).

Let r be the side opposite R, etc.

(a) We first find R using the sine rule ((ii) above).

$$\frac{\sin R}{r} = \frac{\sin P}{p} \quad \text{(we do not need to enter } Q \text{ or } q \text{ since neither are known)}$$

$$\frac{\sin R}{6.4} = \frac{\sin 56° 25'}{7.6}$$

therefore, $\sin R = 6.4 \times \dfrac{0.8331}{7.6} = 0.7017$.

Hence $\angle R = 44° 34'$.

So $\angle Q = 180° - (56° 25' + 44° 34') = 79° 01'$.

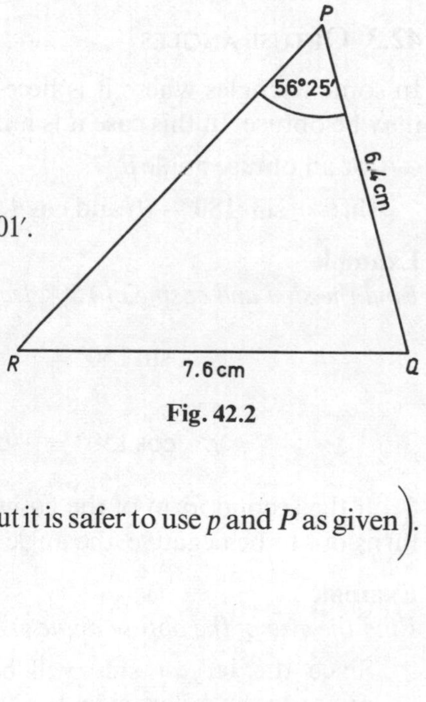

(b) We next find PR using the sine rule ((i) above).

$$\frac{q}{\sin Q} = \frac{p}{\sin P} \left(\text{we could put } \frac{q}{\sin Q} = \frac{r}{\sin R}, \text{ but it is safer to use } p \text{ and } P \text{ as given} \right).$$

$$\frac{q}{\sin 79° 01'} = \frac{7.6}{\sin 56° 25'}$$

therefore, $q = 0.9817 \times \dfrac{7.6}{0.8331} = 8.956$ cm.

So $q = PR = 9.0$ cm (1 dp).

42.2 THE COSINE RULE

In any triangle ABC, the **cosine rule** can be written as:

$$a^2 = b^2 + c^2 - (2bc \cos A)$$

where a, b, and c are the sides opposite angles A, B, and C.

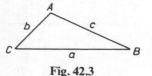

Fig. 42.3

If a triangle has no right angle we use the cosine rule to find the length of the third side if two sides and the included angle are known.

Example

In Fig. 42.4, $XY = 3.5$ cm, $YZ = 7.4$ cm and $\angle Y = 30°$. Find XZ correct to 1 dp.

Let x be the side opposite $\angle X$, *etc.*

Using the cosine rule

$$y^2 = x^2 + z^2 - (2xz \cos y)$$
$$y^2 = 7.4^2 + 3.5^2 - (2 \times 7.4 \times 3.5 \times \cos 30°)$$
$$= 7.4^2 + 3.5^2 - (44.86)$$
$$= 54.76 + 12.25 - 44.86$$
$$= 22.15.$$

So $y = \sqrt{22.15} = 4.706$.

Hence, $XZ = 4.7$ cm (1 dp).

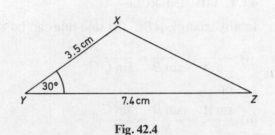

Fig. 42.4

Note: If we had been asked to solve the triangle completely, we would have proceeded to find another angle next using the sine rule.

The cosine rule, $a^2 = b^2 + c^2 - (2bc \cos A)$, can be rewritten as:

$$\cos A = \frac{b^2 + c^2 - a^2}{2bc}$$

and used to find an angle if all three sides of a triangle are known.

For example, if $a = 3$ cm, $b = 4$ cm and $c = 6$ cm (Fig. 42.5),

$$\cos A = \frac{4^2 + 6^2 - 3^2}{2 \times 4 \times 6} = \frac{43}{48} = 0.8960.$$

Hence, $\angle A = 26° 22'$.

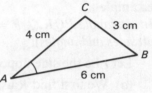

Fig. 42.5

42.3 Obtuse angles

In some triangles where it is necessary to use the sine and/or cosine rules one of the angles may be obtuse. In this case it is necessary to remember the following:

for an obtuse angle θ,

$$\sin \theta = \sin (180° - \theta) \text{ and } \cos \theta = -\cos (180° - \theta). \text{ (See unit 43.)}$$

Example

Find the sine and cosine of 150°, leaving your answer in surd form.

$$\sin 150° = \sin (180° - 150°) = \sin 30° = \frac{1}{2}$$

$$\cos 150° = -\cos (180° - 150°) = -\cos 30° = -\frac{\sqrt{3}}{2}.$$

If the second form of the cosine rule is used to find an angle in a triangle and the cosine turns out to be negative, the angle will be obtuse.

Example

Find the size of the obtuse angle in a triangle with sides 2.4 cm, 3.6 cm and 4.7 cm.

Since the largest side will be opposite the largest angle, the obtuse angle will be opposite the 4.7 cm side. Let its value be θ.

$$\cos \theta = \frac{2.4^2 + 3.6^2 - 4.7^2}{2 \times 2.4 \times 3.6} = \frac{-3.37}{17.28} = -0.1950.$$

Hence $\theta = 180° - 78° 45' = 101° 15'$ (since $\cos 78° 45' = 0.1950$).

43 Further trigonometry

43.1 THE GENERAL ANGLE

Figure 43.1 shows a circle, centre O, radius 1 unit.

Ox, Oy are Cartesian axes.

The radius OP initially lies along OA.

As OP rotates in a positive (anticlockwise) sense, it describes an angle θ.

PN is the perpendicular from P to the x-axis.

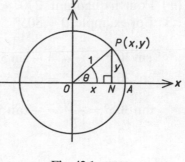

Fig. 43.1

For any angle θ, the three trigonometrical ratios, **sine**, **cosine**, **tangent** are defined as:

$$(i) \quad \sin \theta = \text{the } y \text{ co-ordinate of } P;$$
$$(ii) \quad \cos \theta = \text{the } x \text{ co-ordinate of } P;$$
$$(iii) \quad \tan \theta = \frac{\text{the } y \text{ co-ordinate of } P}{\text{the } x \text{ co-ordinate of } P}.$$

As P moves round the circle, its co-ordinates will be positive or negative depending upon the quadrant in which P appears. (A quadrant is a quarter circle.)

43.2 THE TRIGONOMETRICAL RATIOS

The following four diagrams illustrate the method of finding the trigonometrical ratios of any angle θ.

The ratios in the examples are all related to those for the angle 55°.

(i) First quadrant: $0° < \theta < 90°$.
For example, $\theta = 55°$.

$$\sin 55° = q$$
$$\cos 55° = p$$
$$\tan 55° = \frac{q}{p}.$$

Fig. 43.2

(ii) Second quadrant: $90° < \theta < 180°$.
For example, $\theta = 125°$.

$$\sin 125° = q \quad = \sin 55°$$
$$\cos 125° = -p = -\cos 55°$$
$$\tan 125° = \frac{q}{-p} = -\tan 55°.$$

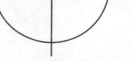

Fig. 43.3

(iii) Third quadrant: $180° < \theta < 270°$.
For example, $\theta = 235°$.

$$\sin 235° = -q = -\sin 55°$$
$$\cos 235° = -p = -\cos 55°$$
$$\tan 235° = \frac{-q}{-p} = \tan 55°.$$

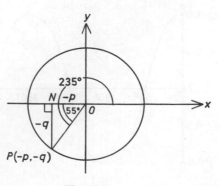

Fig. 43.4

(*iv*) Fourth quadrant: $270° < \theta < 360°$.
For example, $\theta = 305°$.

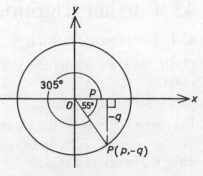

$$\sin 305° = -q = -\sin 55°$$
$$\cos 305° = p \quad = \cos 55°$$

$$\tan 305° = \frac{-q}{p} = -\tan 55°.$$

Fig. 43.5

The signs ($+$ or $-$) of the trigonometric ratios are summarized in Fig. 43.6. This shows that the following ratios are positive:

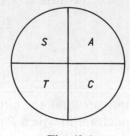

(*i*) in the **first** quadrant, **all** (A);
(*ii*) in the **second** quadrant, the **sines** (S);
(*iii*) in the **third** quadrant, the **tangents** (T);
(*iv*) in the **fourth** quadrant, the **cosines** (C).

Fig. 43.6

43.3 THE RATIOS OF $0°$, $90°$, $180°$, $270°$, $360°$

The ratios of these special angles are shown in the table below:

	$0°$	$90°$	$180°$	$270°$	$360°$
sin	0	1	0	-1	0
cos	1	0	-1	0	1
tan	0	*	0	*	0

* means the tangent is undefined for these angles.

43.4 GRAPHS OF TRIGONOMETRICAL FUNCTIONS

As θ increases beyond $360°$, the graphs for the sines, cosines and tangents of the angle repeat. Figures 43.7, 43.8, 43.9 show the graphs of these functions for positive angles.

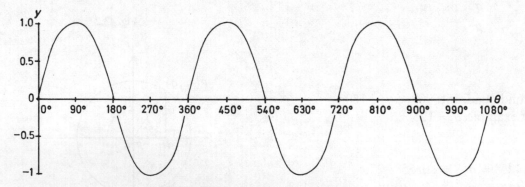

Fig. 43.7 The graph of $y = \sin\theta$

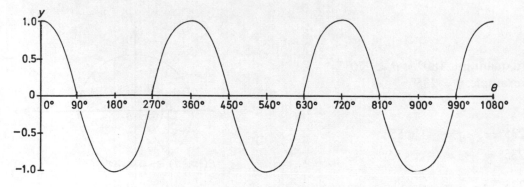

Fig. 43.8 The graph of $y = \cos\theta$

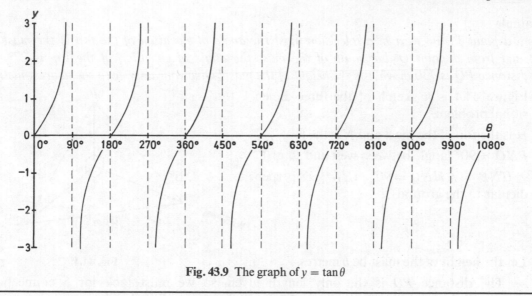

Fig. 43.9 The graph of $y = \tan\theta$

44 Three-dimensional trigonometry

44.1 THE ANGLE BETWEEN A LINE AND A PLANE

In Fig. 44.1, the line L and the plane P intersect at A.

To find the angle between L and P, drop a perpendicular from any point B on the line to intersect the plane at N. Join AN.

The angle θ between AB and AN is the angle between the line and the plane.

44.2 THE ANGLE BETWEEN TWO PLANES

If two planes are not parallel they intersect in a straight line.

In Fig. 44.2, LM is the line of intersection of two planes P and P_1.

From N, any point on LM, a line NA is drawn in P perpendicular to LM. Similarly, NB is drawn in P_1 perpendicular to LM.

Angle $ANB = \theta$ is the angle between the two planes.

If P_1 is horizontal, AN is the **line of greatest slope** in P.

Fig. 44.1

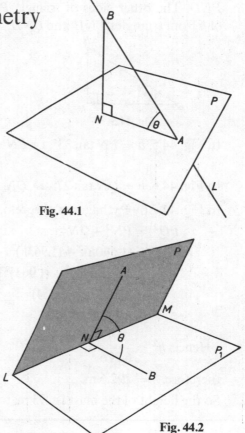

Fig. 44.2

44.3 TRIGONOMETRY

Three-dimensional problems in trigonometry are most easily solved if:

(*i*) a sketch of the three-dimensional problem is drawn first and angles between lines and planes or two planes clearly marked;

(*ii*) the plane shapes needed for each section of the working are drawn separately as required.

Questions sometimes refer to angles of elevation or depression. An **angle of elevation** (or **depression**) is always measured upwards (or downwards) from the horizontal line of sight (Fig. 44.3).

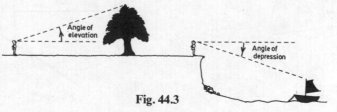

Fig. 44.3

Example

From a point P due west of a television mast the angle of elevation of the top of the mast is 33° and from a point Q due south of the mast the angle of elevation of the top is 27°. If the distance PQ is 730 m what is the height of the mast? Give your answer to the nearest metre.

Figure 44.4 is a sketch of the three-dimensional problem.

H is the top of the mast and *N* is the foot.

$PNQ = 90°$ (angle between west and south).

$\angle HNP = \angle HNQ = 90°$ (*HN* is perpendicular to the ground).

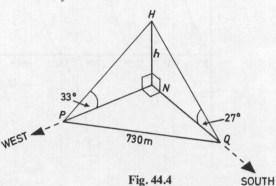

Fig. 44.4

Let the height of the mast be *h* metres.

The distance *PQ* is the only length given, so we must look for a connection between *PQ* and *h* in the diagram. *PQ* is the hypotenuse of the right-angled triangle *PNQ*. The other sides of triangle *PNQ* are *PN* and *NQ*. These can be found in terms of *h* from triangles *PNH* and *QNH*.

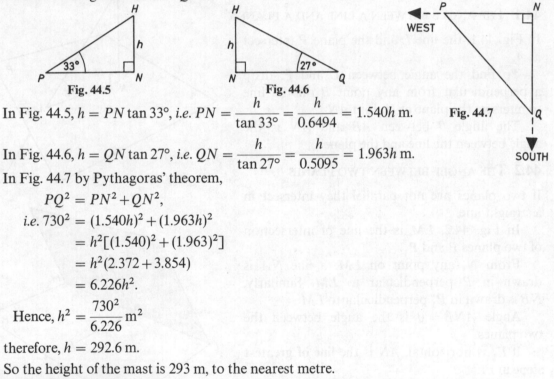

Fig. 44.5   **Fig. 44.6**   **Fig. 44.7**

In Fig. 44.5, $h = PN \tan 33°$, i.e. $PN = \dfrac{h}{\tan 33°} = \dfrac{h}{0.6494} = 1.540h$ m.

In Fig. 44.6, $h = QN \tan 27°$, i.e. $QN = \dfrac{h}{\tan 27°} = \dfrac{h}{0.5095} = 1.963h$ m.

In Fig. 44.7 by Pythagoras' theorem,

$$PQ^2 = PN^2 + QN^2,$$
$$\text{i.e. } 730^2 = (1.540h)^2 + (1.963h)^2$$
$$= h^2[(1.540)^2 + (1.963)^2]$$
$$= h^2(2.372 + 3.854)$$
$$= 6.226h^2.$$

Hence, $h^2 = \dfrac{730^2}{6.226} \text{ m}^2$

therefore, $h = 292.6$ m.

So the height of the mast is 293 m, to the nearest metre.

45 The circle

45.1 Definitions

A circle is the set of points which are all the same distance from a fixed point. The fixed point is called the centre of the circle and the distance from the centre to any point on the circle is called the radius (plural radii) (Fig. 45.1).

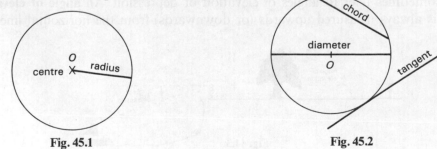

Fig. 45.1   **Fig. 45.2**

A chord is a straight line joining any two points on a circle (Fig. 45.2).

A diameter is any chord passing through the centre of a circle.

A tangent is a straight line which touches a circle at one point only.

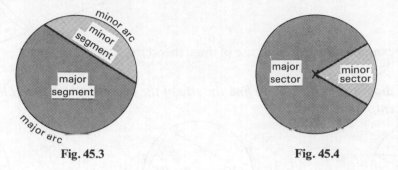

Fig. 45.3   Fig. 45.4

An arc is part of a circle.

A segment is an area enclosed by an arc and a chord.

A sector is an area enclosed by two radii and an arc (Fig. 45.4).

A cyclic quadrilateral is a quadrilateral with all its vertices lying on a circle.

Concentric circles are circles having the same centre.

45.2 'ANGLES IN A CIRCLE' THEOREMS

The following theorems about angles in circles are important and should be known. Their converses are also true and are useful when proving that given points are concyclic, *i.e.* lie on the same circle.

1 The angle subtended by an arc at the centre of a circle is twice that which it subtends at any point on the remaining part of the circumference (Fig. 45.5).

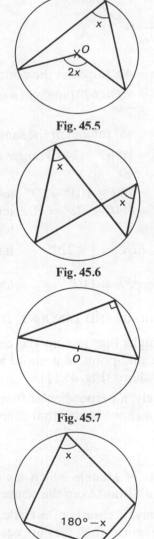

Fig. 45.5

2 Angles in the same segment, subtended by the same arc, are equal (Fig. 45.6).

Conversely, if the line joining two points subtends equal angles at two other points on the same side of it, the four points lie on the same circle.

Fig. 45.6

3 The angle in a semicircle is a right angle (Fig. 45.7).

Conversely, if a circle passes through the vertices of a right-angled triangle, then the hypotenuse of the triangle is a diameter of the circle.

Fig. 45.7

4 The opposite angles of a cyclic quadrilateral are supplementary (*i.e.* they add up to 180°) (Fig. 45.8).

Conversely, a quadrilateral in which two opposite angles are supplementary is cyclic.

Fig. 45.8

5 The exterior angle of a cyclic quadrilateral is equal to the interior opposite angle (Fig. 45.9).

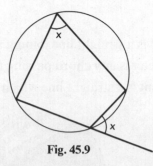

Fig. 45.9

The following example illustrates the use of these theorems.

Example

In each of the diagrams in Fig. 45.10 find the size of the angle marked with a letter. In each case, O is the centre of the circle.

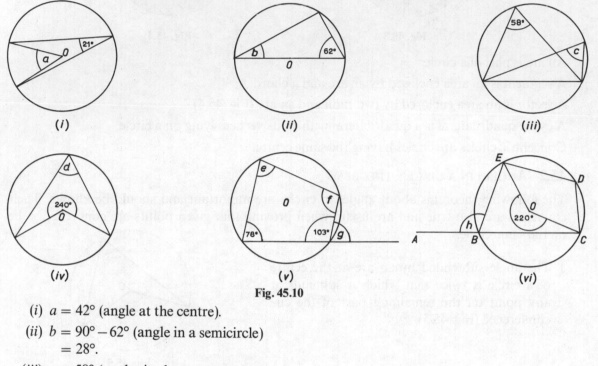

(*i*)　　　　　　(*ii*)　　　　　　(*iii*)

(*iv*)　　　　　　(*v*)　　　　　　(*vi*)

Fig. 45.10

(*i*)　$a = 42°$ (angle at the centre).

(*ii*)　$b = 90° - 62°$ (angle in a semicircle)
　　　$= 28°$.

(*iii*)　$c = 58°$ (angles in the same segment).

(*iv*)　$d = \frac{1}{2}(360° - 240°)$ (angle at the centre and angle in a circle is 360°)
　　　　$= 60°$.

(*v*)　$e = 180° - 103° = 77°$　(cyclic quadrilateral supplementary angles);
　　　$f = 180° - 78° = 102°$　(cyclic quadrilateral supplementary angles);
　　　$g = 77°$　　　　　　　　(cyclic quadrilateral exterior angle).

(*vi*)　$\angle EDC = \frac{1}{2} \times 220°$　　(angle at the centre)
　　　　　　　$= 110°$,
　　　hence $h = 110°$　　　　(cyclic quadrilateral exterior angle).

45.3 'CHORD AND TANGENT' THEOREMS

1 A straight line joining the centre of a circle to the mid-point of a chord is perpendicular to the chord (Fig. 45.11).

Conversely, a perpendicular from the centre of a circle to a chord bisects that chord.

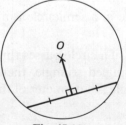

Fig. 45.11

2 Chords of a circle which are equal in length are equidistant from the centre (Fig. 45.12).

Conversely, if chords of a circle are equidistant from the centre, then they are equal in length.

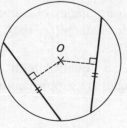

Fig. 45.12

3 The tangent at any point of a circle is perpendicular to the radius through the point of contact (Fig. 45.13).

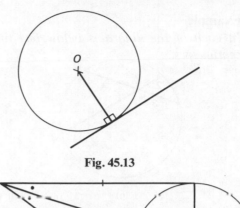

Fig. 45.13

4 If two tangents are drawn to a circle from a point outside the circle, then:

   (*i*) the tangents are equal in length;

   (*ll*) the line joining the centre to the point outside the circle bisects the angle between the tangents;

   (*iii*) this line also bisects the angle between the radii drawn to the points of contact.

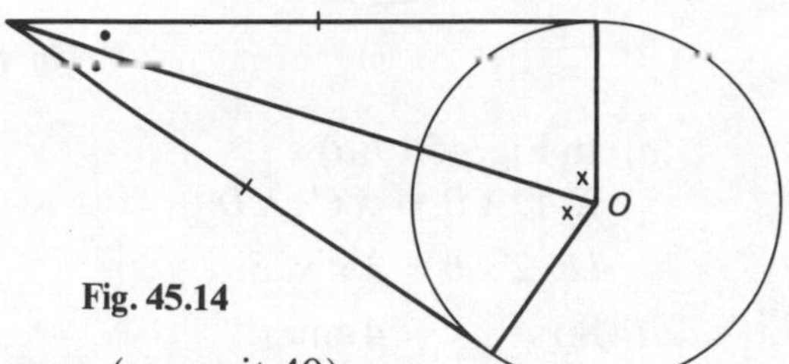

Fig. 45.14

These theorems are often used with Pythagoras' theorem (see unit 40).

Example

In a circle of radius 13 cm, calculate the distance from the centre of a chord which is 24 cm long.

In Fig. 45.15, *AB* is a chord of the circle with centre *O*. $OM \perp AB$, so *M* is the mid-point of *AB*.

So $OA = 13$ cm   (radius)

and $AM = \frac{1}{2} \times 24$ cm $= 12$ cm.

By Pythagoras' theorem in $\triangle AOM$,

$$OA^2 = OM^2 + AM^2$$
$$13^2 = OM^2 + 12^2.$$

So $OM^2 = 13^2 - 12^2$

$\therefore$ $OM = \sqrt{25} = 5$ cm.

Fig. 45.15

5 If two circles touch, then the point of contact lies on the straight line through the centres.

Note: In Fig. 45.16(*i*) the distance between the centres is $R + r$ where *R* and *r* are the radii of the two circles and in Fig. 45.16(*ii*) the distance between the centres is $R - r$ (where $R > r$).

(i) touching 'outside'   *(ii)* touching 'inside'

Fig. 45.16

6 If two chords of a circle intersect either inside or outside a circle, then the rectangle contained by the parts of the one is equal to the rectangle contained by the parts of the other.

The converse is also true.

   In Fig. 45.17, $AP . AQ = AR . AS$.

(i) intersecting inside   *(ii)* intersecting outside

Fig. 45.17

In Fig. 45.18, one of the chords has become a tangent. In this case,

$$AP . AQ = AT^2.$$

Note: The distances are always taken from the point of intersection of the chords.

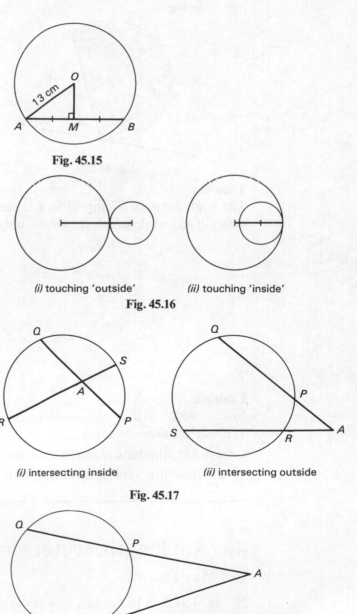

Fig. 45.18

Example

In each of the diagrams below find the lengths marked by letters. The lengths are all in centimetres.

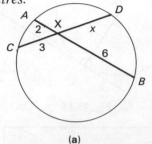

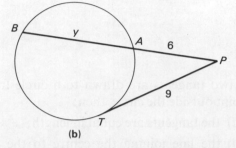

(a)   **Fig. 45.19**   (b)

(a) In Fig. 45.19(a)
$$XA . XB = XC . XD$$
i.e. $2 \times 6 = 3 \times x.$
So $\quad x = 4$ cm.

(b) In Fig. 45.19(b)
$$PA . PB = PT^2$$
$$6 \times (6+y) = 9^2$$
$$y = 7.5 \text{ cm.}$$

45.4 'ALTERNATE SEGMENT' THEOREM

Figures 45.20 and 45.21 illustrate an 'alternate segment'.

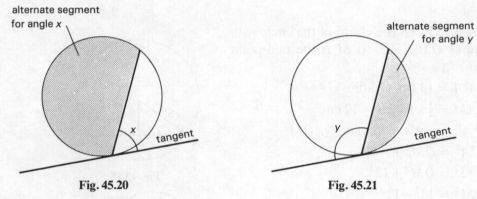

alternate segment for angle x

alternate segment for angle y

Fig. 45.20   **Fig. 45.21**

Theorem

The angle between a tangent to a circle and a chord drawn through the point of contact is equal to any angle which the chord subtends in the alternate segment (Fig. 45.21).

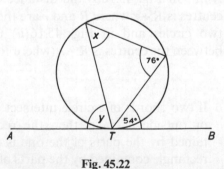

Example

In Fig. 45.22, AB is a tangent to the circle at T. Find the values of x and y.

Fig. 45.22

$x = 54°$ (alternate segment theorem),

$y = 76°$ (alternate segment theorem).

---

46 Arc length, sectors and segments

46.1 ARC LENGTH

In Fig. 46.1, r is the radius of a circle centre O.
The circumference of the circle is $2\pi r$.

If the minor arc AB subtends an angle $\theta°$ at O,

then **arc length** $AB = \dfrac{\theta}{360} \times$ circumference,

i.e. arc length $AB = \dfrac{\theta}{360} \times 2\pi r$.

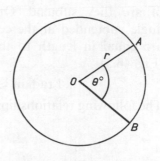

46.2 SECTOR AREA

In Fig. 46.1, the area of the circle is πr^2.

The area of the **sector** $AOB = \dfrac{\theta}{360} \times$ area of the circle,

i.e. sector area $AOB = \dfrac{\theta}{360} \times \pi r^2$.

Fig. 46.1

Example

In Fig. 46.2, the radius of the circle, centre O, is 5 cm and the angle of the sector AOB is 30°. Find the arc length AB and the area of the sector AOB. Give both answers correct to 3 sf. (Take $\pi = 3.142$.)

The circumference of the circle $= 2 \times \pi \times 5$ cm.

$$\text{Arc length } AB = \frac{30}{360} \times 2 \times \pi \times 5 \text{ cm}$$

$$= \frac{\pi \times 5}{6} \text{ cm}$$

$$= \frac{3.142 \times 5}{6} \text{ cm} = 2.62 \text{ cm (3 sf)}.$$

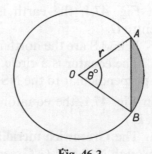

The area of the circle $= \pi \times 5^2$ cm^2.

Fig. 46.2

$$\text{Sector area } AOB = \frac{30}{360} \times \pi \times 5^2 \text{ cm}^2$$

$$= \frac{3.142 \times 25}{12} \text{ cm}^2 = 6.55 \text{ cm}^2 \text{ (3 sf)}.$$

46.3 SEGMENT AREA

In Fig. 46.3, r is the radius of a circle centre O.
The area of the **segment** AB (shaded) is given by:
segment area AB = sector area AOB − area of triangle AOB.

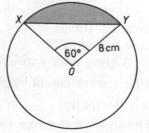

Fig. 46.3

In problems requiring segment areas it is usually best to use the formula: area of a triangle $= \frac{1}{2}ab \sin C$ (see unit 10.3). In these problems a and b are both equal to r (the radius) and $\angle C = \theta°$ (the sector angle).

Hence segment area $AB = \dfrac{\theta}{360} \times \pi r^2 - \frac{1}{2}r^2 \sin \theta°$.

Example

In Fig. 46.4, O is the centre of a circle radius 8 cm. Find the area of the shaded segment XY to 2 sf. (Take $\pi = 3.142$.)

$$\text{Area of sector } XOY = \frac{60}{360} \times \pi \times 8^2 \text{ cm}^2$$

$$= 33.52 \text{ cm}^2.$$

$$\text{Area of triangle } XOY = \frac{1}{2} \times 8 \times 8 \times \sin 60° \text{ cm}^2$$

$$= 27.712 \text{ cm}^2.$$

Hence, segment area $XY = 33.52 - 27.712$ cm^2

$$= 5.8 \text{ cm}^2 \text{ (2 sf)}.$$

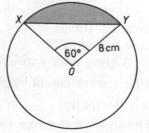

Fig. 46.4

46.4 RADIAN MEASURE

Radians measure angles in terms of the lengths of arc they subtend. One radian (1^c) is the angle subtended at the centre of a circle by an arc equal in length to the radius of the circle (Fig. 46.5).

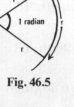

Fig. 46.5

$$1 \text{ radian} \approx 57.3°.$$

The following relationships between radians and degrees are useful to know.

$$2\pi \text{ radians} = 360°$$

$$\pi \text{ radians} = 180°$$

$$\frac{\pi}{2} \text{ radians} = 90°.$$

If the arc AB subtends an angle θ radians at O (Fig. 46.6), then:

(*i*) the arc length $AB = r\theta$;

(*ii*) the sector area $AOB = \frac{1}{2}r^2\theta$;

(*iii*) the segment area AB

$$= \text{sector area } AOB - \text{area of triangle } AOB$$
$$= \frac{1}{2}r^2\theta - \frac{1}{2}r^2\sin\theta$$
$$= \frac{1}{2}r^2(\theta - \sin\theta).$$

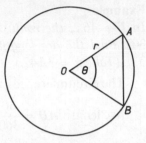

Fig. 46.6

Remember: these results are only true if θ is measured in radians.

---

47 Latitude and longitude

In Fig. 47.1, the earth is shown as a sphere, centre O.

N and S are the north and south **poles**.

The **equator** is a circle, centre O, whose plane is perpendicular to the NS axis.

(In Fig. 47.1, the equator passes through W, B, A, E.)

The **Greenwich meridian** is the circle passing through N, S and G, Greenwich (England).

Any point on the surface of the earth can be described by two co-ordinates, both angles:

(*i*) the **latitude**—measured in degrees north or south of the equator,

(*ii*) the **longitude**—measured in degrees east or west of the Greenwich meridian.

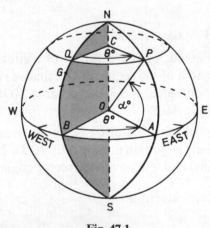

Fig. 47.1

For example, in Fig. 47.1, P is the point ($\alpha°$N, $\theta°$E).

Any point on the equator has latitude $0°$, *e.g.* $A(0°$N, $\theta°$E).

Any point on the Greenwich meridian has longitude $0°$, *e.g.* $Q(\alpha°$N, $0°$E). The point $B(0°$N, $0°$E) lies on both the equator and the Greenwich meridian.

The circle passing through P and Q whose plane is parallel to the equator is called the **circle of latitude** $\alpha°$N or the **parallel of latitude** $\alpha°$N. This is because all points on the circle have latitude $\alpha°$N.

A **great circle** is any circle with centre O. The most important ones are:

(*a*) the **meridians of longitude**,

(*b*) the equator.

The shortest distance between any two points on the surface of the earth is along a great circle.

A **nautical mile (nm)** is the length of an arc of a great circle which subtends an angle of 1 minute (1′) at O. A **knot** is a speed of 1 nautical mile per hour.

47.1 MERIDIANS OF LONGITUDE

All meridians of longitude have the same radius, the radius of the earth, and pass through the N and S poles.

Two points lie on the same meridian of longitude if:

 (*i*) their angles of longitude are the same, or,

 (*ii*) their angles of longitude are $x°E$ and $y°W$ and $x° + y° = 180°$.

For example,

 (*i*) P (53°S, 48°W) and Q (12°N, 48°W) lie on the same meridian since the angle of longitude (48°W) is the same for both P and Q;

 (*ii*) R (17°N, 34°E) and S (81°N, 146°W) lie on the same meridian since $34° + 146° = 180°$ (Fig. 47.2).

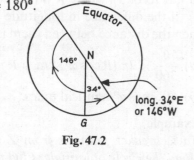

Fig. 47.2

The distance along a meridian of longitude

The distance between two points on a meridian of longitude is the length of an arc of a circle, radius R, where R is the radius of the earth.

If the difference in latitude between two places on the same circle of longitude is $θ°$, then the distance between them is:

(*a*) $\dfrac{θ}{360} \times 2πR$ km, if R is the radius of the earth in km,

(*b*) $60 \times θ$ nautical miles.

Example

Find the distance between A (20°N, 15°E) and B (56°N, 15°E), in (a) km, if the radius of the earth is 6370 km, (b) nautical miles. (Take π = 3.142.)

Since the angle of longitude (15°E) is the same for A and B, the distance is measured along the circle of longitude 15°E (Fig. 47.3).

$∠AOB = 56° − 20° = 36.$

(*a*) Arc length $AB = \dfrac{36}{360} \times 2πR$ (R, radius of earth)

$$= \dfrac{π \times 6370}{5} \text{ km}$$

$$= 4002 \text{ km}.$$

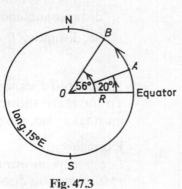

Fig. 47.3

(*b*) 1 nm is the distance subtended by an angle of 1′ on a great circle.
The angular distance $AB = 36°$

$$= 60 \times 36 \text{ minutes}$$

$$= 2160′.$$

So, distance $AB = 2160$ nautical miles.

47.2 CIRCLES OF LATITUDE

All circles of latitude are parallel to the equator.

Circles of latitude can have different radii.

Two points lie on the same circle of latitude if their angles of latitude are the same.

　For example, L (29°N, 53°W) and M (29°N, 76°W) lie on the same circle of latitude since the angle of latitude (29°N) is the same for both L and M.

　It is possible to find the radius of a circle of latitude if the angle of latitude is known.

In Fig. 47.4, the radius of a circle of latitude, $\alpha°N$ (or $\alpha°S$) is $CP = R\cos\alpha°$, where R is the radius of the earth.

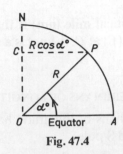

Fig. 47.4

The distance along a circle of latitude

The distance between two points on a circle of latitude is the length of an arc of a circle, radius $R\cos\alpha°$, where R is the radius of the earth and $\alpha°$ is the angle of latitude.

If the difference in longitude between two places on the same circle of latitude $\alpha°N$ is $\theta°$, then the distance between them is:

(*a*) $\dfrac{\theta}{360} \times 2\pi (R\cos\alpha°)$ km, if R is the radius of the earth in km,

(*b*) $60 \times \cos\alpha°$ nautical miles.

Example

An icebreaker journeys from Z (80°N, 20°E) to P (80°N, 160°W) by travelling eastwards along the circle of latitude. Find the distance travelled by the icebreaker in (a) km, if the radius of the earth is 6370 km, (b) in nautical miles. (Take $\pi = 3.142$.)

Since the angle of latitude (80°N) is the same for Z and P, the distance is measured along the circle of latitude 80°N (Fig. 47.5).

In Fig. 47.5, N is the north pole and M is a point on the Greenwich meridian.

$\angle ZNP = 20° + 160° = 180°$.

(*a*) Arc length $ZP = \dfrac{180}{360} \times 2\pi(R\cos 80°)$

$= 3473$ km.

(*b*) Angular distance $ZP = 180°$

$= 60 \times 180$ minutes

$= 10\,800'$.

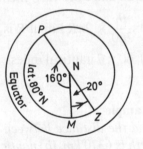

Fig. 47.5

Since 1 nm is the distance subtended by an angle of $1'$ on a great circle, the distance subtended by an angle of $1'$ in a circle of latitude 80°N is $1\cos 80°$ nm.

So, distance $ZP = 10\,800 \times \cos 80°$ nautical miles

$= 1875$ nautical miles.

The shortest distance between two points

To travel the shortest distance between two points on the surface of the earth, the journey must take place along a great circle.

Example

In the previous example, if a submarine goes from Z to P along the great circle via the north pole, what is the distance in nautical miles?

The circle of latitude 160°W is the same as the circle of longitude 20°E (Fig. 47.6). (Since $160° + 20° = 180°$).

The angular distance $ZP = 20°$

$= 20 \times 60$ minutes

$= 1200'$.

Since the submarine travels from Z to P along a meridian, the distance $ZP = 1200$ nautical miles.

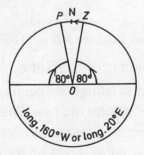

Fig. 47.6

48 Constructions and loci

48.1 CONSTRUCTIONS

Unless otherwise stated, only **pencil**, **ruler** and **compasses** are used for constructions.
The notation used in this section to illustrate constructions is that shown in Fig. 48.1.

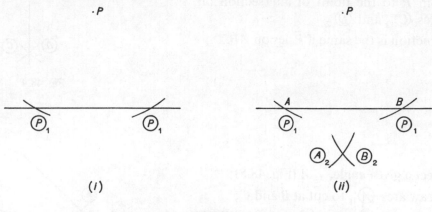

(*i*)   (*ii*)

Fig. 48.1

In Fig. 48.1(*i*), both arcs are marked P_1. The P means that they are both drawn with P as centre; the suffix 1 means that they each have the same radius.

In Fig. 48.1(*ii*), the points A and B are the points where the arcs P_1 cut the straight line. The arc A_2 has centre A. The arc B_2 has centre B. The suffix 2 means that they both have the same radius and were drawn after the arcs with suffix 1, *i.e.* after the arcs P_1.

Arcs marked with a different suffix mean that they could have a different radius.

For example, in Fig. 48.1(*ii*), the arcs P_1 have radius 3 cm. Each of the arcs A_2 and B_2 has radius 2 cm.

(*a*) To construct a triangle ABC with sides of given lengths (Fig. 48.2):

(*i*) draw a base line, any length;

(*ii*) mark a point A on the line;

(*iii*) mark off the length AB with compasses;

(*iv*) draw arc A_1 with given radius AC;

(*v*) draw arc B_2 with given radius BC;

(*vi*) join AC and BC.

Notice that the construction lines do not start and finish at the vertices A, B and C but pass through these points.

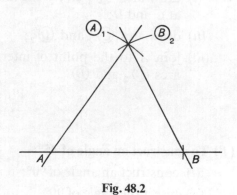

Fig. 48.2

(*b*) To construct the perpendicular bisector of a given line segment AB (Fig. 48.3):

(*i*) draw arcs A_1;

(*ii*) draw arcs B_1;

(*iii*) draw the perpendicular bisector through the intersecting arcs.

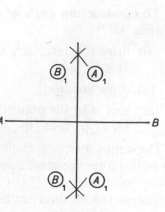

Fig. 48.3

(c) **To construct a perpendicular to a given line segment *AB*, from a given point *P*** (Fig. 48.4):

    (i) draw arcs $\textcircled{P}_1$ to cut *AB* at *C* and *D*;

    (ii) draw arcs $\textcircled{C}_2$ and $\textcircled{D}_2$;

    (iii) join *P* to the point of intersection of arcs $\textcircled{C}_2$ and $\textcircled{D}_2$.

The construction is the same if *P* lies on *AB*.

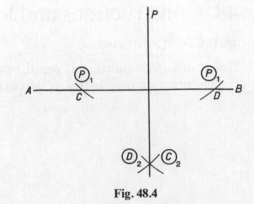

Fig. 48.4

(d) **To bisect a given angle, $\angle A$** (Fig. 48.5):

    (i) draw arcs $\textcircled{A}_1$ to cut at *B* and *C*;

    (ii) draw arcs $\textcircled{B}_2$ and $\textcircled{C}_2$;

    (iii) join *A* to the point of intersection of $\textcircled{B}_2$ and $\textcircled{C}_2$.

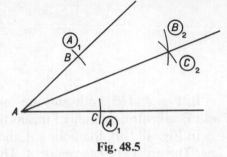

Fig. 48.5

(e) **To construct an angle of 90° at *A* on a line** (Fig. 48.6):

    (i) draw arcs $\textcircled{A}_1$ to cut the line segment at *C* and *D*;

    (ii) draw arcs $\textcircled{C}_2$ and $\textcircled{D}_2$;

    (iii) join *A* to the point of intersection of arcs $\textcircled{C}_2$ and $\textcircled{D}_2$.

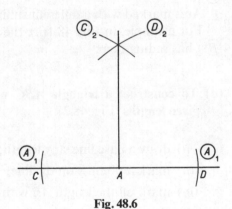

Fig. 48.6

(f) **To construct an angle of 45°:**

    (i) construct an angle of 90°;

    (ii) bisect the angle of 90°.

(g) **To construct an angle of 60° at *A* on a line** (Fig. 48.7):

    (i) draw the 'large' arc $\textcircled{A}_1$ to cut the line at *B*;

    (ii) draw arc $\textcircled{B}_1$;

    (iii) join *A* to the point *C* of intersection of arcs $\textcircled{A}_1$ and $\textcircled{B}_1$.

The supplementary angle, 120°, is obtained as a bonus from the same construction. Further, if *B* is joined to *C*, $\triangle ABC$ is an equilateral triangle, so this method can be used to construct an equilateral triangle.

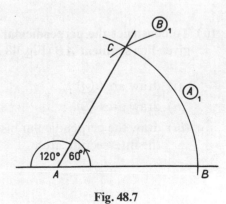

Fig. 48.7

(*h*) **To construct an angle of 30°:**

    (*i*) construct an angle of 60°;

    (*ii*) bisect the angle of 60°.

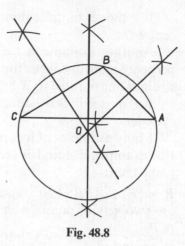

(*i*) **To construct the circumcircle of a given triangle *ABC*** (Fig. 48.8):

    (*i*) construct the perpendicular bisector of each side;

    (*ii*) the point of intersection is the centre, *O*, of the circumcircle.

Fig. 48.8

(*j*) **To construct the incircle of a given triangle *ABC*** (Fig. 48.9):

    (*i*) construct the bisectors of the three interior angles;

    (*ii*) the point of intersection is the centre, *O*, of the incircle;

    (*iii*) construct a perpendicular from *O* to any side of the triangle to find the radius of the incircle.

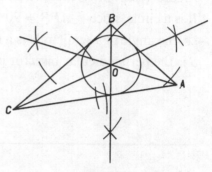

Fig. 48.9

(*k*) **To divide a line segment *AB* into *n* equal parts** (Fig. 48.10):

    (*i*) draw *AC* any length, at any acute angle to *AB*;

    (*ii*) using compasses, step off *n* equal lengths along *AC* ($P_1, P_2, \ldots P_n$) are the *n* points equally spaced;

    (*iii*) join $P_n B$;

    (*iv*) using a set square, draw a further $n-1$ lines parallel to $P_n B$ and passing through $P_1, P_2 \ldots P_{n-1}$;

    (*v*) *AB* has now been divided into *n* equal lengths.

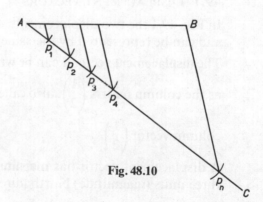

Fig. 48.10

(*l*) **To divide a line segment *AB* in the ratio *n* : *m*, divide it into *n* + *m* equal parts as described in (*l*).**

For example, to divide a line segment *AB* in the ratio 2 : 3, divide it into 5 equal parts first (Fig. 48.11).

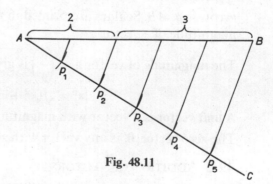

Fig. 48.11

48.2 Loci

The **locus** of a point is the path it traces as it moves according to some conditions. The plural of locus is **loci**.

For example, if *O* is a fixed point in the plane and *P* is a moving point in the plane, then the locus of *P* which moves such that the distance *OP* is constant, is a circle centre *O*.

The locus of *P* can be written, $\{P : OP = \text{constant}\}$ where *O* is a fixed point and *P* a moving point in the plane.

If P moves in three dimensions and O is a fixed point, $\{P : OP = \text{constant}\}$ is a sphere, centre O.

Another example is the locus of a point P which moves in the plane such that its perpendicular distance from a fixed line XY in the plane is constant. The locus of P is a straight line parallel to XY.

If P moves in three dimensions and XY is any fixed line, then the locus of P is a circular cylinder.

Many examples of loci rely on the chord and angle properties of the circle (see unit 45). For example, if A and B are fixed points in the plane and P is a moving point in the same plane then:

$R = \{P : \angle APB = 90°\}$ and $S = \{P : AP = PB\}$
are two sets of points which represent the loci
of P.

Figure 48.12 shows these two loci.

R is a circle, since $\angle APB = 90°$,

i.e. the angle in a semicircle is a right angle.

S is the perpendicular bisector of AB.

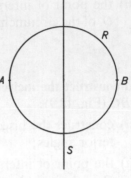

Fig. 48.12

---

49 Vectors

49.1 DISPLACEMENT VECTORS

In Fig. 49.1 the two displacements $\overrightarrow{AB}$ and $\overrightarrow{CD}$ are **equivalent** and can be represented by the same vector **a**.

The **displacement vector a** can be written

as the column matrix $\begin{pmatrix} 1 \\ 2 \end{pmatrix}$, also called the

column vector $\begin{pmatrix} 1 \\ 2 \end{pmatrix}$.

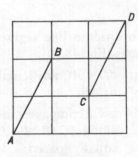

Fig. 49.1

A displacement vector has **magnitude** (size) and **direction**. For example, a displacement of three units (magnitude) North (direction) is a displacement vector.

A **scalar** has only magnitude. For example, a distance of three units (magnitude) is a scalar.

In print, a vector is denoted by a heavy type, *e.g.* **a**, or by two capital letters and an arrow, *e.g.* $\overrightarrow{AB}$. Scalars are printed in normal type, *e.g.* a. Either $|\mathbf{a}|$ or a is used to mean the magnitude of a vector **a**.

The **magnitude** of vector $\mathbf{a} = \begin{pmatrix} x \\ y \end{pmatrix}$ is given by:

$$|\mathbf{a}| = \sqrt{(x^2 + y^2)}.$$

A **unit vector** is a vector with magnitude 1.

The **zero vector**, **0**, is any vector with zero magnitude.

49.2 ADDITION OF VECTORS

Vectors are added using the **parallelogram law of addition** (Fig. 49.2)

$$\overrightarrow{PQ} + \overrightarrow{QR} = \overrightarrow{PR} \qquad \overrightarrow{PS} + \overrightarrow{SR} = \overrightarrow{PR}$$

or

i.e. $\mathbf{a} + \mathbf{b} = \mathbf{c}$ *i.e.* $\mathbf{b} + \mathbf{a} = \mathbf{c}$.

Hence, the addition of vectors is commutative.

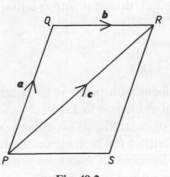

Fig. 49.2

Vector addition is also associative, *i.e.* $(\mathbf{a}+\mathbf{b})+\mathbf{c} = \mathbf{a}+(\mathbf{b}+\mathbf{c})$.
The set of all vectors form a group under addition.
(See unit 18.2.)

To **subtract** a vector, add its inverse.
In Fig. 45.3,

$$\mathbf{a}-\mathbf{b} = \mathbf{a}+{}^{-}\mathbf{b}.$$

If $\mathbf{b} = \mathbf{a}$, $\mathbf{a}+({}^{-}\mathbf{a}) = \mathbf{0}$, the zero vector.

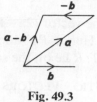

Fig. 49.3

49.3 MULTIPLICATION BY A SCALAR

If **a** is any vector,

then 2**a** is a vector parallel to and in the same direction as **a** but with twice the magnitude,
and $-2\mathbf{a}$ is a vector parallel to but in the opposite direction as **a** and twice the magnitude
(Fig. 49.4).

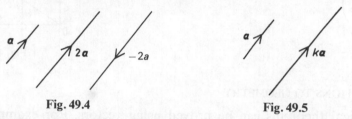

Fig. 49.4   **Fig. 49.5**

If k is a scalar, then k**a** is a vector parallel to **a** but with k times the magnitude (Fig.
49.5). If $k > 0$, then k**a** is in the same direction as **a**. If $k < 0$, then k**a** is in the opposite
direction to **a**.

Multiplication by a scalar is distributive over vector addition,
i.e. $k(\mathbf{p}+\mathbf{q}) = k\mathbf{p}+k\mathbf{q}$, where k is a scalar and **p**, **q** are vectors.

The following example will help to illustrate the use of vectors.

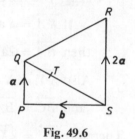

Example
In Fig. 49.6, $ST = 2TQ$, $\overrightarrow{PQ} = \mathbf{a}$, $\overrightarrow{SR} = 2\mathbf{a}$ and $\overrightarrow{SP} = \mathbf{b}$.

(*a*) *Find, in terms of **a** and **b**,*

(i) $\overrightarrow{SQ}$,   (ii) $\overrightarrow{TQ}$,   (iii) $\overrightarrow{RQ}$,   (iv) $\overrightarrow{PT}$,   (v) $\overrightarrow{TR}$.

Fig. 49.6

(*b*) *What do your answers to (iv) and (v) in part (a) tell you about the points P, T, R?*

(*a*)   (i) $\overrightarrow{SQ} = \overrightarrow{SP}+\overrightarrow{PQ} = \mathbf{b}+\mathbf{a}$ (or $\mathbf{a}+\mathbf{b}$ by commutativity)

(ii) $\overrightarrow{TQ} = \dfrac{1}{3}\overrightarrow{SQ} = \dfrac{1}{3}(\mathbf{a}+\mathbf{b})$

(iii) $\overrightarrow{RQ} = \overrightarrow{RS}+\overrightarrow{SQ} = -2\mathbf{a}+(\mathbf{a}+\mathbf{b})$

$$= \mathbf{b}-\mathbf{a}$$

(iv) $\overrightarrow{PT} = \overrightarrow{PS}+\overrightarrow{ST}$

$$= {}^{-}\mathbf{b}+\frac{2}{3}\overrightarrow{SQ} \qquad \left(\text{since } \overrightarrow{ST} = \frac{2}{3}\overrightarrow{SQ}, \text{ i.e. } \overrightarrow{ST} = 2\overrightarrow{TQ}\right)$$

$$= {}^{-}\mathbf{b}+\frac{2}{3}(\mathbf{a}+\mathbf{b}) = \frac{2}{3}\mathbf{a}-\frac{1}{3}\mathbf{b}$$

$$= \frac{1}{3}(2\mathbf{a}-\mathbf{b})$$

(v) $\overrightarrow{TR} = \overrightarrow{TS}+\overrightarrow{SR}$

$$= -\frac{2}{3}(\mathbf{a}+\mathbf{b})+2\mathbf{a}$$

$$= \frac{4}{3}\mathbf{a}-\frac{2}{3}\mathbf{b} = \frac{2}{3}(2\mathbf{a}-\mathbf{b}).$$

(b) Since $\overrightarrow{PT} = \frac{1}{3}(2\mathbf{a} - \mathbf{b})$ and $\overrightarrow{TR} = \frac{2}{3}(2\mathbf{a} - \mathbf{b})$, $\overrightarrow{PT}$ and $\overrightarrow{TR}$ are both multiples of the same vector $(2\mathbf{a} - \mathbf{b})$.

Hence PT and TR are parallel and T is common to both line segments, so P, T, R lie on the same line, *i.e.* they are co-linear.

49.4 POSITION VECTORS

The displacement vector from the origin O to a point P in the plane is called the **position vector** of P, written $\overrightarrow{OP}$.

In Fig. 49.7,
$\overrightarrow{OP} = \mathbf{r}$ is the position vector of $P(3, 2)$,

$$i.e.\ \mathbf{r} = \begin{pmatrix} 3 \\ 2 \end{pmatrix}.$$

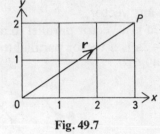

Fig. 49.7

49.5 APPLICATIONS TO GEOMETRY

Many geometrical theorems can be proved using vectors. For example, the mid-point theorem can be proved this way.

The mid-point theorem states that the line joining the mid points·of two sides of a triangle is parallel to the third side and half its length.

In Fig. 49.8 ABC is a triangle and X, Y are the mid points of AB and AC respectively.

If $\overrightarrow{XA} = \mathbf{a}$ and $\overrightarrow{AY} = \mathbf{b}$

then $\overrightarrow{BA} = 2\mathbf{a}$ and $\overrightarrow{AC} = 2\mathbf{b}$.

Also $\overrightarrow{XY} = \overrightarrow{XA} + \overrightarrow{AY} = \mathbf{a} + \mathbf{b}$

and $\overrightarrow{BC} = \overrightarrow{BA} + \overrightarrow{AC} = 2\mathbf{a} + 2\mathbf{b} = 2(\mathbf{a} + \mathbf{b})$.

Therefore $\overrightarrow{BC} = 2\overrightarrow{XY}$.

Hence XY is parallel to BC and half the length of BC.

The converse of the theorem is also true.

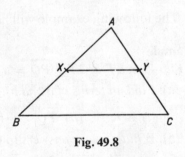

Fig. 49.8

50 Graphical representation of data

When information has been gathered from a survey it can be represented in different ways. One way would be to list it in tables of figures. However, it is often useful to present the **data** (information gathered) in the form of a picture or **diagram**. Such diagrams are often easier to read than tables of figures. Some of the most common ways of representing data are illustrated below. Each one should be given an appropriate title.

50.1 BAR CHART

A **bar chart** is a graph having two axes. Normally, the **frequency** (number of items) is plotted on the vertical axis and the items in the survey are listed along the horizontal axis. The following points should always be observed when drawing a bar chart:

(i) Label each axis carefully.

(ii) Make the width of each bar the same.

(iii) Make the length of the bar correspond to the frequency.

(iv) Make the width of the whole chart as large as possible on the paper you are given.

Example

A bag is found to contain beads of the following colours:

Colour	Red	Blue	Green	Yellow	Black	White
No. of beads	25	16	28	20	8	11

Draw a bar chart for this information.

Figure 50.1 shows this information on a bar chart.

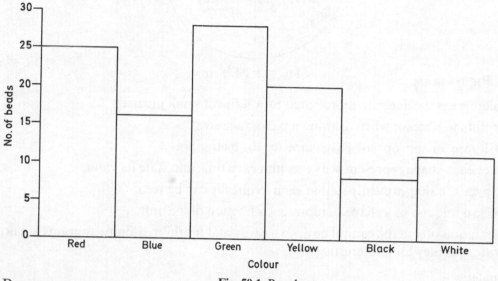

Fig. 50.1 Bar chart

50.2 PIE CHART

A **pie chart** is a circular diagram which looks like a pie which has been cut into portions ready for eating. The portions are sectors of the circle; each sector being proportional in area to the frequency of the item.

The following points should always be observed when drawing a pie chart:

 (*i*) the angle of each sector must be calculated first

 (*ii*) the angle of each sector must be drawn with a protractor

(*iii*) label each sector carefully

(*iv*) make the radius of the circle as large as possible.

Example

In a survey 400 people were asked which Sunday newspaper they preferred to read. The number of people naming each paper was:

The Sunday Times	75	The Observer	50
News of the World	150	The Sunday Telegraph	25
The Sunday Mirror	100		

Draw a pie chart for this data.

In the pie chart the full circle (360°) represents 400 people, so,

$$\frac{75}{400} \times 360° = 67\tfrac{1}{2}° \text{ represents The Sunday Times readers}$$

$$\frac{150}{400} \times 360° = 135° \text{ represents News of the World readers}$$

$$\frac{100}{400} \times 360° = 90° \text{ represents The Sunday Mirror readers}$$

$$\frac{50}{400} \times 360° = 45° \text{ represents The Observer readers}$$

$$\frac{25}{400} \times 360° = 22\tfrac{1}{2}° \text{ represents The Sunday Telegraph readers}$$

$$\text{Total} = \overline{360°}.$$

Figure 50.2 shows the pie chart for the data.

Fig. 50.2 Pie chart

50.3 PICTOGRAM

In a **pictogram** the data are represented by a series of small pictures.

The points to observe when drawing a pictogram are:

  (*i*) Choose an appropriate easy shape for the pictogram.
 (*ii*) Let each shape represent the same unit each time and state its value.
(*iii*) Space the shapes evenly so that each frequency can be seen.
(*iv*) Use a fraction of a shape to represent a fraction of the unit.

A fraction of a shape cannot be drawn easily and for this reason pictograms are not very accurate, but they look interesting.

Example

In a factory there are 615 employees. Of these 150 are men, 350 are women, 75 are boys under 18 and 40 are girls under 18. Show this information as a pictogram.

Let each pin-man 👤 represent 50 employees.

Figure 50.3 shows the resulting pictogram.

Men

Women

Boys under 18

Girls under 18

Fig. 50.3 Pictogram showing types of employee in a factory

50.4 HISTOGRAM

A **histogram** is similar to a bar chart. In a bar chart the height of a bar represents the frequency. In a histogram the **area** of a bar represents the frequency.

Histograms are useful when we want to represent data which are grouped into class intervals. In this case the width of a bar is proportional to the size of the class interval. If the class intervals are equal then the bars in the histogram will be of equal width.

Example

The following is a list of marks (out of 100) gained by 36 boys in a test. Arrange them into class intervals of 10 marks (i.e. 0–9 etc.) and draw a histogram illustrating these data.

68	25	49	76	12	51	34	22	74
56	81	50	45	92	58	85	34	69
67	55	52	73	31	48	41	56	98
84	66	56	44	39	45	51	68	70

What is the modal class? Find the mode. (See unit 16.2.)

Grouping the data into class intervals of 10 marks gives:

Marks	No. of boys	Marks	No. of boys
0–9	0	50–59	9
10–19	1	60–69	5
20–29	2	70–79	4
30–39	4	80–89	3
40–49	6	90–99	2

The histogram for these data is shown in Fig. 50.4.

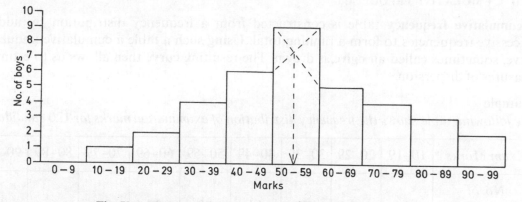

Fig. 50.4 Histogram showing marks gained by 36 boys in a test

The modal class is 50–59 since the frequency for this class is the greatest.

The mode is calculated as follows:

The frequency of the modal class (50–59) is nine.

The frequency of the preceding class (40–49) is six and the frequency of the following class (60–69) is five.

This means that the frequency of the modal class is three more than the preceding class and four more than the following class.

The mode, therefore, is the mark which divides the modal class in the ratio 3 : 4.

The modal class is an interval of 10 marks and must be divided in the ratio of 3 : 4, *i.e.* in the ratio $\frac{3}{7}$ to $\frac{4}{7}$.

Hence, the mode $= 49\frac{1}{2} + \frac{3}{7} \times 10$

$\approx 53.8 = 54$ (to the nearest full mark).

The dotted lines on the diagram illustrate a quick method of dividing the modal class and hence finding an approximate value for the mode.

50.5 MEASURES OF DISPERSION

The **range** of a set of data is the difference between the greatest and least values.

The **dispersion** of a set of data is the clustering or spread of the data. Although the range can be used to measure dispersion it is not a good measure since it can be affected by extreme values.

The **interquartile range** is a better measure of dispersion since it is unaffected by extreme values.

If a set of data is arranged in order of size, the **median** is the middle value.

Q_L, the **lower quartile**, is the value below which approximately a quarter of the data lies.

Q_U, the **upper quartile**, is the value above which approximately a quarter of the data lies.

The interquartile range is $Q_U - Q_L$.

The **semi-interquartile range**, $\frac{1}{2}(Q_U - Q_L)$ is another measure of dispersion.

Figure 50.5, illustrates these for a set of data arranged in order.

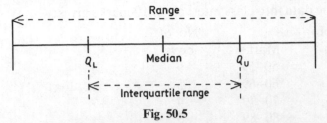

Fig. 50.5

Note: **Quartiles** divide the data into quarters. **Sextiles** divide data into six equal parts and **percentiles** divide them into one hundred equal parts.

50.6 CUMULATIVE FREQUENCY

A **cumulative frequency** table is constructed from a frequency distribution by adding successive frequencies to form a running total. Using such a table a cumulative frequency curve, sometimes called an **ogive**, is drawn. The resulting curve then allows us to estimate measures of dispersion.

Example

The following table shows the frequency distribution of examination marks for 120 candidates.

Exam Marks	10–19	20–29	30–39	40–49	50–59	60–69	70–79	80–89	90–99
No. of candidates	2	6	7	14	20	35	29	6	1

Construct a cumulative frequency table and use it to draw a cumulative frequency curve for the above distribution. From the curve estimate:

(i) the median mark, ((i) the interquartile range. If the pass mark is 45, what percentage pass the paper? If 75 % of the candidates are to pass, what should the pass mark be?

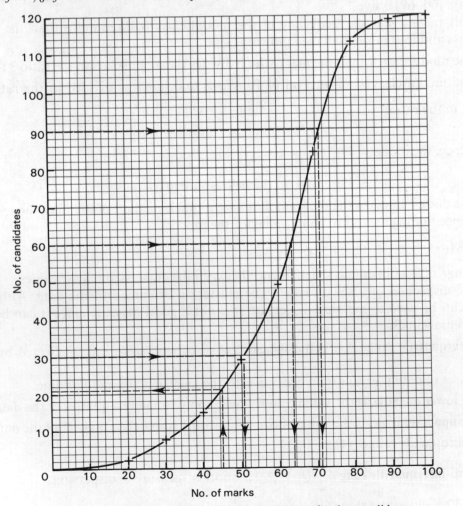

Fig. 50.6 The cumulative frequency curve for 120 examination candidates

The cumulative frequency (cf) table is:

Marks	cf	Marks	cf
Less than 20	2	Less than 60	49
„ „ 30	8	„ „ 70	84
„ „ 40	15	„ „ 80	113
„ „ 50	29	„ „ 90	119
		„ „ 100	120

The ordered pairs $(20, 2)$, $(30, 8)$ etc. are plotted to give the ogive (Fig. 50.6).

(*i*) The median mark is the mark corresponding to a cf of 60 (since there are 120 candidates). The median mark is, therefore, 64.

(*ii*) The lower quartile (Q_L) is 50.5 and the upper quartile (Q_U) is 71.5. Hence, the interquartile range $= 71.5 - 50.5 = 21$.

The ogive shows that 21 candidates score less than 45 marks. Hence $120 - 21 = 99$ candidates pass.

If 75 % of the candidates pass, then 25 % fail, *i.e.* 30 candidates fail. The ogive shows that 30 candidates have less than 51 marks, and so 51 is the required pass mark.

51 Probability

A statement such as, 'the chance of my winning a big prize with a Premium Bond must be 1 in 50 000', is concerned with assessing the likelihood of a particular event taking place.

The number we assign to the likelihood of an event taking place is called its **probability**. A probability is always written as a fraction, the value of which lies between 0 and 1.

In the above example, the probability of winning a prize is $\dfrac{1}{50\,000}$.

There are two exceptions:

(*i*) the probability of a certainty is 1 (*e.g.* the sun will rise again);

(*ii*) the probability of an impossibility is 0 (*e.g.* the moon is made of green cheese).

51.1 TYPES OF PROBABILITY

When an experiment is performed there will be a result. The result is called an **outcome**. If the experiment is repeated a large number of times and the different outcomes are recorded, we can say:

experimental probability of a particular outcome occurring

$$= \frac{\text{number of times the particular outcome occurred}}{\text{number of times the experiment was performed}}.$$

When the circumstances of an experiment are always the same we can arrive at a value for the probability of an outcome by mathematical reasoning without actually having to perform the experiments. This type of probability is called theoretical probability.

The **theoretical probability** of a particular event A occurring is usually referred to as $p(A)$ where:

$$p(A) = \frac{\text{number of different outcomes in which } A \text{ occurs}}{\text{total number of outcomes}}$$

provided the total number of outcomes is finite and all the outcomes are equally likely.

Note: The probability $q(A)$ of an event *not* occurring is $p(A') = 1 - p(A)$.

Example

What is the probability of throwing a four with an unbiased die?

When an unbiased die is thrown, the possible outcomes are 1, 2, 3, 4, 5 and 6, all being equally likely. Throwing a four is an event which occurs in only one of these six possible outcomes. Hence the probability of throwing a four is $\dfrac{1}{6}$.

Using set notation can be helpful in probability questions.

Example

In an experiment one person tosses a coin and another person throws a dice. What is the probability that the outcome will be a head and a five? What is the probability that the outcome will be a tail and an even number?

If X is the set of outcomes in which the event (head, five), written $(h, 5)$, occurs, then $X = \{(h, 5)\}$. (Since no other outcome includes this event.)

If E (called the **sample space**) is the set of all possible outcomes, then $E = \{(h, 1), (h, 2), (h, 3), (h, 4), (h, 5), (h, 6), (t, 1), (t, 2), (t, 3), (t, 4), (t, 5), (t, 6)\}$.

Hence, $p(\text{head}, 5) = \dfrac{n(X)}{n(E)} = \dfrac{1}{12}$.

Further, if Y is the set of outcomes in which the event (tail, even number) occurs, then

$$Y = \{(t, 2), (t, 4), (t, 6)\}.$$

Hence, $p(\text{tail, even number}) = \dfrac{n(Y)}{n(E)} = \dfrac{3}{12} = \dfrac{1}{4}$.

51.2 MUTUALLY EXCLUSIVE EVENTS

Two events A and B are said to be **mutually exclusive** if each event takes place to the exclusion of the other. Further if two events A and B are mutually exclusive, then:

$$p(A \text{ or } B) = p(A) + p(B).$$

Example

A card is picked at random from a well shuffled pack of 52 playing cards (no jokers). What is the probability that it is an Ace or the King of Spades?

For the two events, $p(\text{Ace}) = \dfrac{4}{52}, \quad p(\text{King of Spades}) = \dfrac{1}{52}$.

Hence, $p(\text{Ace or King of Spades}) = \dfrac{4}{52} + \dfrac{1}{52} = \dfrac{5}{52}$.

51.3 INDEPENDENT EVENTS

Two events A and B are said to be **independent** if the probability that one occurs does not depend on whether or not the other has occurred. Further, if two events A and B are independent, then:

$$p(A \text{ and } B) = p(A) \times p(B).$$

Example

A man throws a die and selects a card. What is the probability that he throws a six on the die and selects the Ace of Hearts?

Clearly these are two independent events.

For the two events, $p(6) = \dfrac{1}{6}$ and $p(\text{Ace of Hearts}) = \dfrac{1}{52}$.

Hence, $p(6 \text{ and Ace of Hearts}) = \dfrac{1}{6} \times \dfrac{1}{52} = \dfrac{1}{312}$.

51.4 TREE DIAGRAMS

Sometimes questions contain a mixture of independent events and mutually exclusive events. These are often best done with the aid of **tree diagrams**.

Example

A bag contains five balls of which three are red and two are white. A ball is drawn at random from the bag, its colour noted and then replaced. A second ball is drawn from the bag. What is the probability that the two balls are (a) both white, (b) both red, (c) one of each colour?

In the diagram below w is a white ball and r is a red ball. The probabilities of each event are written on the 'branches of the tree'.

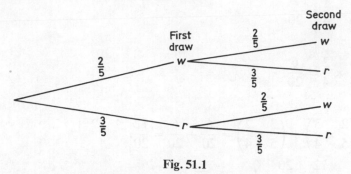

Fig. 51.1

To use a tree diagram (Fig. 51.1) start at the left and move along the branches noting the different probabilities for each outcome.

(*a*)

The probability of both balls being white, $p(w \text{ and } w) = \dfrac{2}{5} \times \dfrac{2}{5} = \dfrac{4}{25}$.

(*b*)

The probability of both balls being red, $p(r \text{ and } r) = \dfrac{3}{5} \times \dfrac{3}{5} = \dfrac{9}{25}$.

(*c*)

If the two balls drawn are of different colours there are two possibilities to consider:

(*i*) the first ball is white and the second red so,

$$p(w \text{ and } r) = \frac{2}{5} \times \frac{3}{5} = \frac{6}{25}$$

(*ii*) the first ball is red and the second white so,

$$p(r \text{ and } w) = \frac{3}{5} \times \frac{2}{5} = \frac{6}{25}.$$

(*i*) and (*ii*) are mutually exclusive, therefore the probability that the balls are of different colours $= \dfrac{6}{25} + \dfrac{6}{25} = \dfrac{12}{25}$.

Note: (*a*), (*b*) and (*c*) are the only three possible outcomes if two balls are drawn as described, hence:

$\dfrac{4}{25} + \dfrac{9}{25} + \dfrac{12}{25} = \dfrac{25}{25} = 1$ serves as a useful check. (This is true because the probability of a certainty is 1.)

51.5 CONDITIONAL PROBABILITY

Sometimes the probability of one event occurring is dependent upon a previous event having taken place, in which case the probability is said to be **conditional**.

Example

In the previous example, if the ball drawn was not replaced in the bag what would be the probability this time for (a), (b) and (c)?

This time the tree diagram would be as in Fig. 51.2.

Notice (Fig. 51.2) that this time for the second draw only four balls are in the bag.

At each stage, the probabilities for the second draw are dependent upon the results of the first draw, *i.e.* the probabilities are conditional.

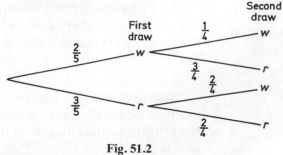

Fig. 51.2

(a)
$$p(w \text{ and } w) = \frac{2}{5} \times \frac{1}{4} = \frac{2}{20}.$$

(b)
$$p(r \text{ and } r) = \frac{3}{5} \times \frac{2}{4} = \frac{6}{20}.$$

(c)
$$p(r \text{ and } w) = \left(\frac{2}{5} \times \frac{3}{4}\right) + \left(\frac{3}{5} \times \frac{2}{4}\right) = \frac{6}{20} + \frac{6}{20} = \frac{12}{20}.$$

$$Check: \frac{2}{20} + \frac{6}{20} + \frac{12}{20} = \frac{20}{20} = 1.$$

52 Calculus

52.1 GRADIENT OF A CURVE

The **gradient of a curve** at any point is the gradient of the tangent to the curve at that point.
Remember: for a straight line,

$$\text{gradient} = \frac{\text{vertical displacement}}{\text{horizontal displacement}} \text{ (see unit 23.2)}.$$

For example, in Fig. 52.1,

$$\text{gradient of } PQ = \frac{RQ}{PR} = \frac{3}{4}.$$

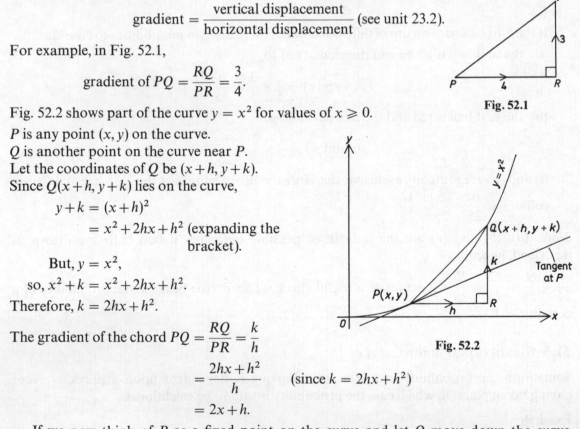

Fig. 52.1

Fig. 52.2 shows part of the curve $y = x^2$ for values of $x \geqslant 0$.

P is any point (x, y) on the curve.
Q is another point on the curve near P.
Let the coordinates of Q be $(x+h, y+k)$.
Since $Q(x+h, y+k)$ lies on the curve,

$$y+k = (x+h)^2$$
$$= x^2 + 2hx + h^2 \text{ (expanding the bracket).}$$

But, $y = x^2$,
so, $x^2 + k = x^2 + 2hx + h^2$.
Therefore, $k = 2hx + h^2$.

The gradient of the chord $PQ = \dfrac{RQ}{PR} = \dfrac{k}{h}$

$$= \frac{2hx + h^2}{h} \text{ (since } k = 2hx + h^2)$$
$$= 2x + h.$$

Fig. 52.2

If we now think of P as a fixed point on the curve and let Q move down the curve towards P, h and k get smaller. So the gradient of the chord $PQ(= 2x + h)$ changes.

As h gets smaller and smaller (*i.e.* as Q moves closer to P) the gradient of the chord PQ approaches the value $2x$ (since h is almost 0).
We write this in mathematics as:

$$\lim_{h \to 0} (2x + h) = 2x.$$

This says that as h approaches 0, the limiting value of $2x + h$ is $2x$.
This means that as Q gets nearer to P, the gradient of PQ gets closer to the gradient of the tangent to the curve at P. Indeed, in this case, the gradient of the tangent to the curve at P is $2x$.

Rather than writing limit $(2x+h) = 2x$, we simply write,
$$\frac{dy}{dx} = 2x.$$

The symbol $\dfrac{dy}{dx}$ is called the **derivative of y with respect to x**.

Other names for $\dfrac{dy}{dx}$ are the **derived function** and the **differential coefficient**.

Differentiation is the process of finding the derived function.
We can say therefore:
if the equation of a curve is given by $y = f(x)$, then the gradient of the curve at any point
is the value of $\dfrac{dy}{dx}$ at that point.

Example
Find the gradient of $y = x^2$ at the point $P(3,9)$.

At any point $P(x,y)$ on the curve $y = x^2$,

$\dfrac{dy}{dx} = 2x$ is the gradient of the curve.

At the point $P(3,9)$,

$\dfrac{dy}{dx} = 2 \times 3 = 6$,

hence the gradient of $y = x^2$ at $P(3,9)$ is 6.

52.2 DIFFERENTIATION

If $y = ax^n$ (a constant, n any real number)

then $\dfrac{dy}{dx} = anx^{n-1}$.

For example, if $y = 4x^3$,

$$\frac{dy}{dx} = 4 \times 3x^2 = 12x^2.$$

Further, if $y = \dfrac{3}{x^5} = 3x^{-5}$,   (see unit 31.1 (4))

$\dfrac{dy}{dx} = 3 \times -5 \times x^{-6}$ since $-5-1 = -6$

$\qquad = -15x^{-6}$

$\qquad = \dfrac{-15}{x^6}.$

If the index is a fraction, we still find the derivative in the same way.
For example, if $y = 5\sqrt{x} = 5x^{\frac{1}{2}}$,

$\dfrac{dy}{dx} = 5 \times \dfrac{1}{2}x^{-\frac{1}{2}}$ since $\frac{1}{2}-1 = -\frac{1}{2}$

$\qquad = \dfrac{5}{2}x^{-\frac{1}{2}}$

$\qquad = \dfrac{5}{2\sqrt{x}}$ since $x^{-\frac{1}{2}} = \dfrac{1}{\sqrt{x}}.$

A special case of $y = ax^n$ is the one where $n = 0$.
In this case $y = a$ (a constant), since $x^0 = 1$.

Therefore, $\dfrac{dy}{dx} = 0.$

Figure 52.3 shows part of the graph of $y = a$
$(a > 0)$. Since the graph is a straight line parallel
to the x axis its gradient is zero,

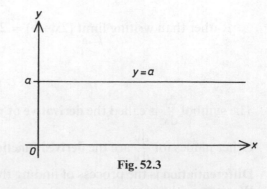

$$i.e. \frac{dy}{dx} = 0.$$

Fig. 52.3

52.3 DERIVATIVE OF A SUM OF TERMS

The derivative of a sum of terms, each of the form ax^n, is the sum of their derivatives.

For example, if $y = 3x^2 - 2x + \dfrac{7}{x} - \dfrac{4}{x^3} + 9,$

re-writing we have, $y = 3x^2 - 2x + 7x^{-1} - 4x^{-3} + 9,$

$$\text{and } \frac{dy}{dx} = 3.2x - 2 + 7 \times (-1)x^{-2} - 4 \times (-3)x^{-4}$$

$$= 6x - 2 - \frac{7}{x^2} + \frac{12}{x^4}.$$

52.4 EQUATION OF A TANGENT

To find the equation ($y = mx + c$) of a tangent to a curve:

 (i) find the gradient of the tangent (m),

(ii) find the value of c, the intercept (see unit 20.3).

Example
Find the equation of the tangent to the curve $y = (2x^2 - 1)(x + 3)$, at the point $(1, 4)$.

$$y = (2x^2 - 1)(x + 3)$$
$$= 2x^3 + 6x^2 - x - 3.$$

Now, $\dfrac{dy}{dx} = 6x^2 + 12x - 1$ is the gradient of the curve at any point.

At the point $(1, 4)$ the gradient of the curve is given by the value of $\dfrac{dy}{dx}$ when $x = 1$,

i.e. when $x = 1, \dfrac{dy}{dx} = 6.1^2 + 12.1 - 1$

$$= 17.$$

Hence, $y = 17x + c$ is the equation of the tangent with gradient 17.

Since the tangent passes through $(1, 4)$,

we have, $4 = 17 \times 1 + c,$

   i.e. $c = -13.$

The equation of the required tangent is, therefore,

$$y = 17x - 13.$$

52.5 HIGHER DERIVATIVES

If $y = 4x^5 - 3x^2 + 2x - 5$

then $\dfrac{dy}{dx} = 20x^4 - 6x + 2$ is the derived function.

If we now differentiate the derived function with respect to x $\left(\text{written } \dfrac{d^2y}{dx^2}\right)$ we get:

$$\frac{d^2y}{dx^2} = 80x^3 - 6.$$

Further, $\dfrac{d^3y}{dx^3} = 240x^2$ is the derivative of the derivative of the derived function!

$\dfrac{d^2y}{dx^2}$ is called the **second derivative**, $\dfrac{d^3y}{dx^3}$ the **third derivative** and so on.

These are all referred to as **higher derivatives**.

$\dfrac{d^2y}{dx^2}$ is sometimes written as y'', $\dfrac{d^3y}{dx^3}$ as y''' and so on.

52.6 STATIONARY POINTS

Figure 52.4 shows the Cartesian graph of a function $y = f(x)$.

From C to A, the gradient of the curve is positive.

From A to B, the gradient of the curve is negative.

From B to D, the gradient of the curve is positive.

At the points A and B the gradient of the curve is zero, *i.e.* $\dfrac{dy}{dx} = 0$ at A and B. Since the curve appears to 'turn' at A and B, these are called **turning points**.

The point A is called a point of **local maximum** since the curve has a maximum value in the neighbourhood of A.

The point B is called a point of **local minimum** since the curve has a minimum value in the neighbourhood of B.

A and B are also called **stationary points**.

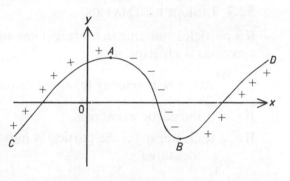

Fig. 52.4

To find stationary points:

(*i*) put $\dfrac{dy}{dx} = 0$ and solve the resulting equation to find the x-co-ordinate of the point(s);

(*ii*) find $\dfrac{d^2y}{dx^2}$ at the turning point(s);

(*iii*) (*a*) if $\dfrac{d^2y}{dx^2} < 0$, the stationary point is a maximum point;

(*b*) if $\dfrac{d^2y}{dx^2} > 0$, the stationary point is a minimum point.

Note: If $\dfrac{d^2y}{dx^2} = 0$ the type of stationary point must be determined by finding the sign of the gradient on each side of the point. Going from left to right: for a local maximum, the gradient goes $+, 0, -$; for a local minimum, the gradient goes $-, 0, +$.

Example

Find the co-ordinates of the points on the curve $y = x^3 - 3x^2 + 1$ at which y has a maximum or minimum value and distinguish clearly between these points.

$$y = x^3 - 3x^2 + 1.$$

Differentiating, $\quad \dfrac{dy}{dx} = 3x^2 - 6x.$

At stationary points $\dfrac{dy}{dx} = 0,$

$$\text{i.e. } 3x^2 - 6x = 0$$

$$\text{or } 3x(x - 2) = 0.$$

$$\text{So, } x = 0 \text{ or } 2.$$

To find which type of stationary points these are, we differentiate again,

$$\dfrac{d^2y}{dx^2} = 6x - 6.$$

(*i*) When $x = 0, \dfrac{d^2y}{dx^2} = -6 < 0$, therefore the point is a maximum point.

At this maximum point, $y = 0^3 - 3.0^2 + 1 = 1$,
and $(0, 1)$ is the maximum point.

(*ii*) When $x = 2, \dfrac{d^2y}{dx^2} = 6 > 0$, therefore the point is a minimum point.

At this minimum point, $y = 2^3 - 3 \times 2^2 + 1 = -3$,
and $(2, -3)$ is the minimum point.

52.7 LINEAR KINEMATICS

If a particle is moving in a straight line such that its displacement from a fixed point O after t seconds is s metres, then:

(*i*) $\dfrac{ds}{dt}$ ms^{-1} is its **velocity** (*v*) after t seconds, i.e. $v = \dfrac{ds}{dt}$.

If $v = 0$ the particle is at rest.

If $v < 0$, i.e. negative, the particle is moving in the opposite direction to that in which s is
    measured.

(*ii*) $\dfrac{d^2s}{dt^2}$ ms^{-2} is its **acceleration** (*a*) after t seconds, i.e. $a = \dfrac{d^2s}{dt^2} = \dfrac{dv}{dt}$.

If $a = 0$, the velocity of the particle is constant.

If $a > 0$, i.e. positive, the particle is accelerating (speeding up).

If $a < 0$, i.e. negative, the particle is being retarded (slowing down).

Example
A particle moves in a straight line so that its distance from a fixed point O after t seconds is
s metres where $s = \dfrac{1}{3}t^3 - \dfrac{3}{2}t^2 + 2t$. Show that the particle is at rest at two different times and
find these times. Find the acceleration of the particle at these times and interpret the results.

$s = \dfrac{1}{3}t^3 - \dfrac{3}{2}t^2 + 2t$, and

$v = \dfrac{ds}{dt} = t^2 - 3t + 2$, where v is the velocity of the particle.

The particle is at rest when $v = 0$,

i.e. when $t^2 - 3t + 2 = 0$

or $(t - 1)(t - 2) = 0$.

Therefore, $t = 1$ or 2 seconds.

Hence the particle is at rest at two different times.

Further, $a = \dfrac{dv}{dt} = \dfrac{d^2s}{dt^2} = 2t - 3$, where a is the acceleration of the particle.

When $t = 1$ second, $a = -1$ ms^{-2}, i.e. the particle is slowing down.

When $t = 2$ seconds, $a = 1$ ms^{-2}, i.e. the particle is speeding up.

52.8 INDEFINITE INTEGRATION

If $\dfrac{dy}{dx} = x^m$, where m is any number $(\neq -1)$ then $y = \dfrac{x^{m+1}}{m+1} + c$, and c is a constant.

The process by which we find y when we know $\dfrac{dy}{dx}$ is called **integration**.

Another way to write the above is $\displaystyle\int x^m\,dx = \dfrac{x^{m+1}}{m+1} + c\ (m \neq -1)$.

We call $\displaystyle\int x^m \, dx$ 'the **integral** of x^m with respect to x'.

The **constant of integration**, c, must be introduced because when we differentiate a constant the result is zero. Therefore, there is no unique answer to an integral of this type and we call it an **indefinite integral**.

Example

Integrate with respect to x: (a) $2x^2 - 3x + 1$,   (b) $\left(x - \dfrac{1}{x}\right)^2$.

(a) $\displaystyle\int (2x^2 - 3x + 1)\,dx = 2 \times \frac{x^3}{3} - 3 \times \frac{x^2}{2} + 1 \times x + c$, where c is constant.

$$= \frac{2}{3}x^3 - \frac{3}{2}x^2 + x + c.$$

(b) $\displaystyle\int \left(x - \frac{1}{x}\right)^2 dx = \int \left(x^2 - 2 + \frac{1}{x^2}\right) dx = \int (x^2 - 2 + x^{-2})\,dx$

$$= \frac{x^3}{3} - 2 \times x + \frac{x^{-1}}{-1} + c \quad \text{since } x^{-2+1} = x^{-1}.$$

$$= \frac{x^3}{3} - 2x - \frac{1}{x} + c, \quad \text{where } c \text{ is a constant.}$$

In linear kinematics (unit 52.7) it is useful to remember that:

(i) since $\dfrac{ds}{dt} = v,$ (ii) since $\dfrac{dv}{dt} = a,$

$$s = \int v\,dt + \text{constant.} \qquad\qquad\qquad v = \int a\,dt + \text{constant.}$$

If we are given more information, the constant of integration may be found.

Example

The velocity, v, of a particle moving in a straight line is given in terms of the time, t, by $v = t^2 - 7t + 5$. *If the particle passes the origin at* $t = 0$, *find an expression for the displacement at any time t.*

Let s be the displacement of the particle from the origin at time t,

then $\dfrac{ds}{dt} = v = t^2 - 7t + 5.$

Integrating gives $s = \displaystyle\int v\,dt = \int (t^2 - 7t + 5)\,dt$

$$= \frac{t^3}{3} - 7 \times \frac{t^2}{2} + 5t + c \qquad (c \text{ constant}).$$

Since the particle passes the origin at $t = 0$, *i.e.* $s = 0$ when $t = 0$,

we have $0 = \dfrac{0^3}{3} - 7 \times \dfrac{0^2}{2} + 5 \times 0 + c$, *i.e.* $c = 0$.

Hence, $s = \dfrac{t^3}{3} - \dfrac{7}{2}t^2 + 5t$ is the expression for the displacement s at time t.

52.9 DEFINITE INTEGRATION

The integral

$$\int_a^b f(x)\,dx = \left[\text{value of } \int f(x)\,dx \text{ when } x = b\right] - \left[\text{value of } \int f(x)\,dx \text{ when } x = a\right].$$

When we calculate this integral, the constant of integration is eliminated in the subtraction. Therefore this constant is omitted and the integral has a definite value. It is called a **definite integral** and a and b are called the **limits**.

Example

Evaluate the definite integral $\displaystyle\int_{-1}^{2} (2x^2 - 1)\,dx$.

$$\int_{-1}^{2} (2x^2 - 1)\,dx = \left[2 \times \frac{x^3}{3} - x\right]_{-1}^{2}$$

$$= \left[\frac{2}{3} \times 2^3 - 2\right] - \left[\frac{2}{3}(-1)^3 - (-1)\right]$$

$$= \left[\frac{2}{3} \times 8 - 2\right] - \left[-\frac{2}{3} + 1\right]$$

$$= \frac{10}{3} - \frac{1}{3} = \frac{9}{3} = 3.$$

52.10 AREA UNDER A CURVE

In Fig. 52.5, the shaded area A_1 is bounded by:

(i) the x-axis;

(ii) the lines $x = a$ and $x = b$;

(iii) the curve, $y = f(x)$.

The area, $A_1 = \displaystyle\int_a^b y\,dx$.

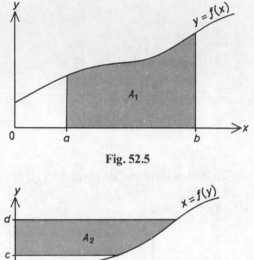

Fig. 52.5

In Fig. 52.6, the shaded area A_2 is bounded by:

(i) the y-axis;

(ii) the lines $y = c$ and $y = d$;

(iii) the curve $x = f(y)$.

The area, $A_2 = \displaystyle\int_c^d x\,dy$.

Fig. 52.6

The above two integrals for A_1 and A_2 are definite integrals.

Example

Find the area between the curve $y = 3x^2$, and:

(i) *the x-axis and the lines $x = 1$, $x = 3$;*

(ii) *the y-axis and the lines $y = 1$, $y = 9$.*

Figure 52.7 shows the two areas A_1 and A_2.

(i) $A_1 = \displaystyle\int_1^3 y\,dx$

$$= \int_1^3 3x^2\,dx = \left[3\frac{x^3}{3}\right]_1^3$$

$$= (3^3) - (1^3)$$

$$= 27 - 1 = 26 \text{ square units.}$$

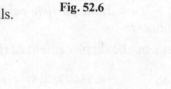

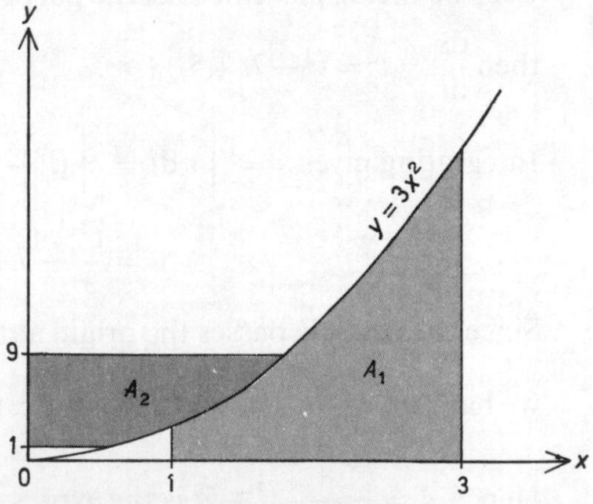

Fig. 52.7

(ii) $A_2 = \displaystyle\int_1^9 x\,dy$

$$= \int_1^9 \sqrt{\left(\frac{y}{3}\right)}\,dy \qquad \left(\text{since } y = 3x^2, x = \sqrt{\left(\frac{y}{3}\right)}\right)$$

$$= \int_1^9 \frac{1}{\sqrt{3}} y^{\frac{1}{2}}\,dy \qquad (\text{since }\sqrt{y} = y^{\frac{1}{2}})$$

$$= \frac{1}{\sqrt{3}}\left[\frac{y^{\frac{3}{2}}}{\frac{3}{2}}\right]_1^9 = \frac{1}{\sqrt{3}} \times \frac{2}{3}(9^{\frac{3}{2}} - 1^{\frac{3}{2}})$$

$$= \frac{2}{3\sqrt{3}}(27 - 1) = \frac{52}{3\sqrt{3}} \approx 10 \text{ square units.}$$

When finding the area under a curve using integration, it is safer to draw a sketch of the curve first, since areas below the x-axis are negative. Positive and negative areas must be worked out separately.

52.11 VOLUMES OF REVOLUTION

In Fig. 52.8, the area contained between the x-axis, the lines $x = a$, $x = b$ and the curve $y = f(x)$ is rotated once about the x-axis. The volume, V, of the solid formed is given by:

$$V = \int_a^b \pi y^2 \, dx,$$

and is called the **volume of revolution**.

If an area bounded by the y-axis, the lines $y = c$, $y = d$ and the curve $x = f(y)$ is rotated once about the y-axis, the volume of revolution is given by:

$$\int_c^d \pi x^2 \, dy.$$

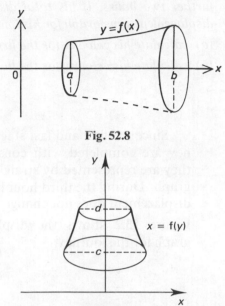

Fig. 52.8

Fig. 52.9

Example
Find the volume of the solid formed when the area between the x-axis, the lines x = 2 and x = 4, and the curve y = x² is rotated once about the x-axis. (Leave your answer as a multiple of π.)

Figure 52.10 shows the shaded area to be rotated.

$$\text{Volume of revolution} = \int_2^4 \pi y^2 \, dx$$

$$= \int_2^4 \pi (x^2)^2 \, dx$$

$$= \int_2^4 \pi x^4 \, dx = \pi \left[\frac{x^5}{5}\right]_2^4$$

$$= \frac{\pi (4^5 - 2^5)}{5}$$

$$= \frac{\pi (1024 - 32)}{5}$$

$$= \frac{\pi 992}{5} \text{ cubic units.}$$

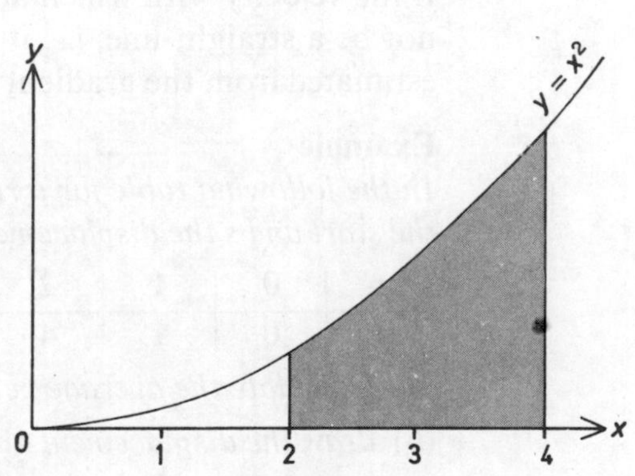

Fig. 52.10

53 Graphs in kinematics

53.1 DISPLACEMENT-TIME GRAPHS

If the **displacement** (s) of a moving point is plotted against the **time** (t) for which it travels, the resulting graph is called a **displacement-time** graph.

The displacement-time graph for an object moving with **constant velocity** is a straight line. The **velocity**, v, of the object is given by the gradient of the line (Fig. 53.1).

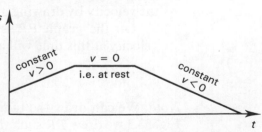

Fig. 53.1

Example

A man sets off walking with constant velocity and covers the first six km of his journey in two hours. He rests for an hour and then completes his journey, again with constant velocity, in a further two hours. If his total displacement from his starting point is eight km, draw the displacement-time graph for his journey and:

(a) *calculate his velocity for the first two hours,*

(b) *calculate his velocity for the last two hours.*

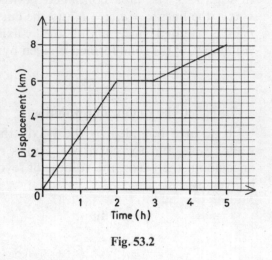

Since the first and last stages of the journey are completed with constant velocity, they are represented by straight lines on the graph. During the third hour he rests, *i.e.* his displacement does not change.

Figure 53.2 shows the displacement-time graph for the journey.

Fig. 53.2

(a)
During the first two hours the man travels six km,
therefore, his velocity during this time is $6 \text{ km} \div 2 \text{ h} = 3 \text{ km h}^{-1}$ (km/h).

(b)
During the last two hours the man travels two km,
therefore, his velocity during this time is $2 \text{ km} \div 2 \text{ h} = 1 \text{ km h}^{-1}$ (km/h).

If the velocity with which an object travels is **not constant**, its displacement-time graph will not be a straight line, *i.e.* it will be a curve. The velocity of the object at any time may be estimated from the gradient of the tangent to the curve at that time.

Example

In the following table for a racing car starting from rest, t stands for the time in seconds from the start and s the displacement in metres travelled up to that time.

t	0	1	2	3	4	5	6	7	8	9	10
s	0	1	4	9	16	24	33	42	53	67	84

(a) *Calculate the average velocity for the first 5 seconds;*

(b) *draw the displacement-time graph and estimate the actual velocity when t = 7s.*

(a)
We take the information from the table.

For the first 5s, the average velocity $= \dfrac{\text{total displacement}}{\text{total time}}$

$$= \frac{24}{5} = 4.8 \text{ ms}^{-1}.$$

(b)
Figure 53.3 shows the displacement-time graph for the racing car. Since the graph is not a straight line we cannot find the velocity when $t = 7s$. However, we can estimate the velocity by drawing a tangent to the curve at $t = 7s$ and finding its gradient.

On the graph PR is the tangent to the curve at $t = 7s$ and an estimate of the velocity at this time will be

$$\frac{QR}{PQ} = \frac{52-4}{8-3} = \frac{48}{5} = 9.6 \text{ ms}^{-1}.$$

Note: We can draw the tangent PR as long or as short as we like to find its gradient. In Fig. 53.3 we drew PR such that PQ was five units, because five is an easy number to divide by.

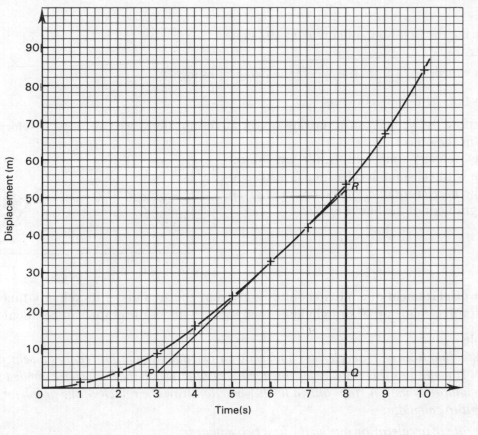

Fig. 53.3

53.2 TRAVEL GRAPHS

These are special types of displacement-time graphs, usually involving two people or vehicles travelling.

Example

The graph in Fig. 53.4 shows the journey made by two people, Les and Bill. Bill sets out from Ansgrove at mid-day to cycle to Bromsford. At the same time, Les sets off from Bromsford in his car and travels towards Ansgrove at constant speed. From the graph answer the following questions:

(*a*) *What is the distance of Ansgrove from Bromsford?*

(*b*) *How far has each man travelled by 3 pm?*

(*c*) *Calculate the overall average speed for each man.*

(*d*) *What is Bill's speed for the first hour?*

(*e*) *At what time do they meet?*

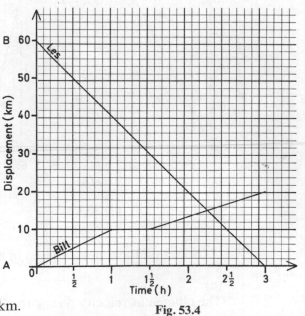

Fig. 53.4

(*a*)
The distance from Ansgrove to Bromsford is 60 km.

(*b*)
By 3 pm Les has travelled 60 km and Bill has gone 20 km.

(*c*)

For Les, average speed $= \dfrac{60 \text{ km}}{3 \text{ h}} = 20 \text{ km h}^{-1}$.

For Bill, average speed $= \dfrac{20 \text{ km}}{3 \text{ h}} = 6\frac{2}{3} \text{ km h}^{-1}$.

(*d*)

During the first hour Bill cycles at 10 km h^{-1}.

(*e*)

They meet at 2.15 pm (*i.e.* where the two graphs meet).

53.3 VELOCITY-TIME GRAPHS

If we know the velocity of a moving object at certain times we can draw a **velocity-time** graph for the object.

The velocity-time graph for an object moving with **constant acceleration** is a straight line. The **acceleration**, *a*, of the object is given by the gradient of the line (Fig. 53.5).

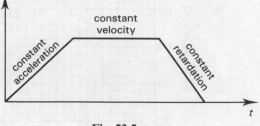

Fig. 53.5

The **displacement** of a moving object is given by the area under its velocity-time graph. If the graph is made up of straight lines, then the area under the graph can be calculated.

Example

A car, starting from rest, accelerates uniformly for two minutes until it reaches a velocity of 40 km h^{-1}. It maintains this velocity for three minutes, after which the brakes are applied slowing it down uniformly until it stops after a further minute. Draw the velocity-time graph for the car and use it to calculate:

(*a*) *the rate of acceleration during the first two minutes;*

(*b*) *the retardation during the last minute;*

(*c*) *the total displacement of the car.*

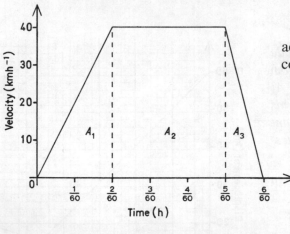

Fig. 53.6

During each stage of the journey, the acceleration is constant, hence the graph consists of three straight line segments.

Figure 53.6 shows the velocity-time graph.

$\left(\text{Notice that the times are given in hours, } e.g. \text{ two minutes} = \dfrac{2}{60} \text{ h.}\right)$

(*a*)

The change in velocity during the first two minutes is 40 km h^{-1} and the time for this change is $\dfrac{2}{60}$ h.

Hence, the acceleration during the first two minutes

$$= \text{change in velocity} \div \text{time taken}$$

$$= 40 \div \frac{2}{60} \text{ km h}^{-2}$$

$$= 1200 \text{ km h}^{-2}.$$

(b)

The retardation during the last minute

$$= \text{change in velocity} \div \text{time taken}$$

$$= 40 \div \frac{1}{60} \text{ km h}^{-2}$$

$$= 2400 \text{ km h}^{-2}.$$

(c)

The total displacement of the car is the sum of the areas A_1, A_2, A_3 under the graph.

The total displacement $= A_1 + A_2 + A_3$

$$= \left(\frac{1}{2} \times \frac{2}{60} \times 40\right) + \left(\frac{3}{60} \times 40\right) + \left(\frac{1}{2} \times \frac{1}{60} \times 40\right) \text{km}$$

$$= \frac{2}{3} + 2 + \frac{1}{3} \text{ km} = 3 \text{ km}.$$

The velocity-time graph of an object moving with **variable acceleration** is a curve and not a straight line (or series of straight lines). The **acceleration** of the moving object at any time can be estimated by finding the gradient of the tangent to the curve at that time (Fig. 53.7).

The **displacement** of the moving object may be obtained by finding an approximation to the area under the curve. This can be done by counting squares or, better still, using the **trapezium rule** (see unit 53.5).

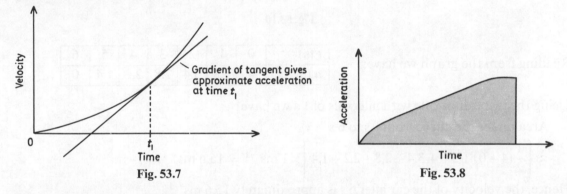

Fig. 53.7   Fig. 53.8

53.4 ACCELERATION-TIME GRAPHS

If we know the acceleration of a moving object at certain times we can draw an **acceleration-time** graph for the object.

The **velocity** of a moving object is given by the area under its acceleration-time graph (Fig. 53.8).

53.5 THE TRAPEZIUM RULE
(Sometimes called the TRAPEZOIDAL RULE)

Figure 53.9 shows the area bounded by the curve $y = f(t)$, the lines $t = a, t = b$ and t-axis.

The interval between a and b on the t-axis has been divided into five equal parts each of length h.

The lines $t = a, t = a+h, t = a+2h \ldots t = a+5h = b$ meet the curve at $A, B, C \ldots F$.

The heights of these points above the t-axis are $y_1, y_2, y_3 \ldots y_6$ respectively.

If the points $A, B, C \ldots F$ are joined by straight line segments, the required area contains six trapeziums.

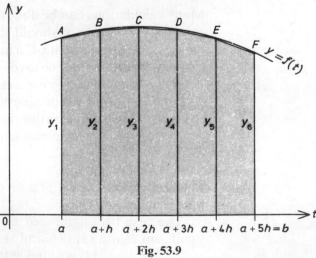

Fig. 53.9

The total area of all six trapeziums is a good approximation to the required area.

Area of trapeziums $= \frac{1}{2}(y_1 + y_2)h + \frac{1}{2}(y_2 + y_3)h + \ldots + \frac{1}{2}(y_5 + y_6)h$

$$= [\frac{1}{2}(y_1 + y_6) + y_2 + y_3 + y_4 + y_5]h.$$

This leads to the general result that:

if the interval between a and b on the t-axis is divided into n equal parts, each of length h, $\left(\text{where } h = \dfrac{b-a}{n}\right)$ then:

the area under the curve $\approx [\frac{1}{2}(y_1 + y_{n+1}) + y_2 + \ldots y_n]h$.

Example

Figure 53.10 shows the acceleration-time graph for a car during the first six seconds of its motion. Use the trapezium rule with intervals of 1 s to estimate the velocity of the car after six seconds.

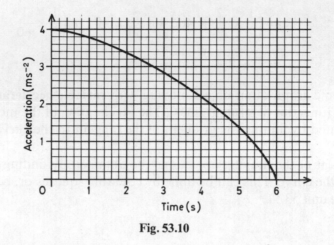

Fig. 53.10

Reading from the graph we have:

t (s)	0	1	2	3	4	5	6
a (ms^{-2})	4	3.8	3.4	2.8	2.2	1.4	0

Using the trapezium rule with intervals of 1 s we have:

Area under the curve from 0 s to 6 s

$$\approx \left[\frac{1}{2}(4+0) + 3.8 + 3.4 + 2.8 + 2.2 + 1.4\right] \times 1 \text{ ms}^{-1} = 15.6 \text{ ms}^{-1}.$$

Hence, the velocity of the car after 6 s is approximately 15.6 ms^{-1}.

---

54 Use of tables or calculator

Many calculations can be done more easily and quickly by using mathematical tables or a calculator. However, it should be remembered that the answers obtained when using these may only be approximate. If a question asks for an exact answer, then, in general, tables or a calculator should not be used.

If you are allowed to use a calculator, then make sure that you are thoroughly familiar with the operation of your particular model and practise using it efficiently. Always check that your answers are sensible by calculating approximate answers (see unit 55).

The use of some common tables is described below.

54.1 SQUARE TABLES

Figure 54.1 shows part of a set of tables of 'SQUARES' and the way to use these to find the square of 1.654.

The first two significant figures (1.6) are found in the left-hand column. The third significant figure (5) is found at the top of the main columns headed '0 to 9'. The fourth significant figure (4) is found at the top of the columns headed 'Mean Differences'.

The mean difference (13 in this example) is always added to the four-digit numeral obtained from the table (2.723 in this example) as shown in Fig. 54.1.

So, the square of 1.654 is 2.736.

SQUARES — Mean Differences

	0	1	2	3	4	5	6	7	8	9	1	2	3	4	5	6	7	8	9
10	1000	1020	1040	1061	1082	1103	1124	1145	1166	1188	2	4	6	8	10	13	15	17	19
11	1210	1232	1254	1277	1300	1323	1346	1369	1392	1416	2	5	7	9	11	14	16	18	21
12	1440	1464	1488	1513	1538	1563	1588	1613	1638	1664	2	5	7	10	12	15	17	20	22
13	1690	1716	1742	1769	1796	1823	1850	1877	1904	1932	3	5	8	11	13	16	19	22	24
14	1960	1988	2016	2045	2074	2103	2132	2161	2190	2220	3	6	9	12	14	17	20	23	26
15	2250	2280	2310	2341	2372	2403	2434	2465	2496	2528	3	6	9	12	15	19	22	25	28
16	2560	2592	2624	2657	2690	2723	2756	2789	2822	2856	3	7	10	13	16	20	23	26	30

$$\begin{array}{r} 2.723 \\ +\ \ 13 \\ \hline 2.736 \end{array}$$

Fig. 54.1 How to use tables of squares

Note: If you are using three-figure tables, ignore the reference to 'Mean Differences'.

Square root, **logarithm** and **antilogarithm tables** are all used in a similar way. However, the following differences will be noted:

(*a*) for square roots:

  (*i*) in some books two lines of figures are given for each number appearing in the left-hand column;

  (*ii*) in others, two sets of tables are given; one for numbers from 1 to 10 and the other for numbers from 10 to 100;

(*b*) in logarithm tables, no point appears between the first two significant figures;

(*c*) in antilogarithm tables, the first two significant figures are preceded by a point. This is to remind us to look up the mantissa only of a logarithm, not its characteristic.

Reciprocal tables are used in a similar way except the mean differences must be subtracted and not added, because as a number increases its reciprocal decreases.

54.2 TRIGONOMETRICAL TABLES

Trigonometrical tables are used to find **sines**, **cosines** and **tangents** of angles.

Remember: Angles are measured in either radians, or degrees (°) and minutes ('). Tables headed 'Natural sines' 'Natural cosines' and 'Natural tangents' use degrees and minutes.

Figure 54.2 shows part of a set of 'NATURAL SINES' and the way to use these to find the value of sin 47° 28'.

NATURAL SINES — Mean Differences

	0'	6'	12'	18'	24'	30'	36'	42'	48'	54'	1'	2'	3'	4'	5'
45°	·7071	7083	7096	7108	7120	7133	7145	7157	7169	7181	2	4	6	8	10
46	·7193	7206	7218	7230	7242	7254	7266	7278	7290	7302	2	4	6	8	10
47	·7314	7325	7337	7349	7361	7373	7385	7396	7408	7420	2	4	6	8	10

$$\begin{array}{r} .7361 \\ +\ \ 8 \\ \hline .7369 \end{array}$$

Fig. 54.2 How to use tables of natural sines

The number of degrees (47°) is found in the left-hand column.

The largest number of minutes less than 28', (24'), is found at the top of the main columns headed '0' to 54''. The additional minutes (4') which need to be added to 24' to make 28' are found at the top of the columns headed 'Mean Differences'.

The mean difference (8 in this example) is added to the four-digit numeral (0.7361 in this example) as shown in Fig. 54.2.

So, sin 47° 28' is 0.7369.

Natural tangent tables are used in a similar way. Natural cosine tables are also used in a similar way except that the mean differences are subtracted and not added. The reason for this is that as an angle increases from 0° to 90°:

(*a*) its sine increases from 0 to 1 so the mean difference is added;

(*b*) its cosine decreases from 1 to 0 so the mean difference is subtracted.

54.3 INVERSE TRIGONOMETRIC TABLES

Although there are antilogarithm tables, there are no 'antisine', 'anticosine' or 'antitangent' tables. If, say, we are required to find the acute angle the tangent of which is known, we must still use the **natural tangents** tables.

For example, if the tangent of an unknown acute angle is 1.3539 and we are required to find the angle:

(*i*) look up in the tables the largest number smaller than 1.3539 (1.3514 in this example) and note the corresponding angle (53° 30′);

(*ii*) next find the number in the mean differences which needs to be added to 1.3514 to make 1.3539 (25 in this example);

(*iii*) note the minutes which correspond to this number (25) at the head of the mean differences column (3′ in this case);

(*iv*) the required angle is 53° 30′ + 03′ = 53° 33′.

Natural sine tables are used in a similar way to find angles when their sines are known.

Natural cosine tables are also used in a similar way except that the corresponding minutes at the head of the mean differences columns are subtracted and not added.

Note: Sometimes when searching amongst the numbers in the mean differences the exact number required cannot be found. If this happens the nearest equivalent has to be used.

---

55 Approximations and errors

55.1 LIMITS OF ACCURACY

When a quantity is measured, the answer we get cannot be exact. There will be an **error**.

For example, if a length, measured to the nearest 0.1 cm, is found to be 8.3 cm, the true length can be anywhere between 8.25 cm and 8.35 cm, *i.e.* 8.3 ± 0.05 cm.

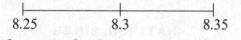

$$
\begin{array}{ccc}
8.25 & 8.3 & 8.35
\end{array}
$$

These are called the **limits of accuracy** for the measurement 8.3 cm.

Example

A rectangle has its sides given as 8 cm and 2 cm, each to the nearest centimetre. Find:

(*i*) *the largest possible value of the area;*

(*ii*) *the smallest possible length of the perimeter.*

(*i*) The largest possible value of the area is given when the sides are 8.5 cm and 2.5 cm.

Largest area = 8.5 cm × 2.5 cm

= 21.25 cm².

(*ii*) The smallest possible length of the perimeter is given when the sides are 7.5 cm and 1.5 cm.

Smallest perimeter = 2(7.5 + 1.5) cm

= 18 cm.

55.2 PERCENTAGE ERROR

The **percentage error** of a given measurement

$$
= \frac{\text{error}}{\text{true measurement}} \times 100\%.
$$

Example

The error in weighing a 2.5 kg mass is 10 g. What is the percentage error?

$$\text{Percentage error} = \frac{\text{error}}{\text{true measurement}} \times 100\%$$

$$= \frac{10 \text{ g}}{2500 \text{ g}} \times 100\%$$

$$= 0.4\%.$$

55.3 ROUNDING OFF

It is sometimes easier to compare the sizes of numbers if they are first **rounded off**.
To round off a number to the nearest unit, look at the tenths. If the figure is:

less than 5—forget it,
5 or more—add 1 to the units.

For example, (*a*) 27.3 = 27 (to the nearest unit)
        ↑———look at the tenths (3)—forget it.

(*b*) 27.9 = 28 (to the nearest unit)
        ↑———look at the tenths (9)—add 1 to the units.

(*c*) 27.5 = 28 (to the nearest unit)
        ↑———look at the tenths (5)—add 1 to the units.

Numbers can be rounded off to the nearest ten, hundred, thousand, etc., in a similar way.

To round off to the nearest ten	To round off to the nearest hundred	To round off to the nearest thousand
↓	↓	↓
2753	2753	2753
look at the units___↑	look at the tens_____↑	look at the hundreds__↑
2750	2800	3000
(to the nearest ten)	(to the nearest hundred)	(to the nearest thousand)

55.4 APPROXIMATE ANSWERS

When doing a calculation, always work out an **approximate answer**. This can be used to check whether your final answer to the calculation is sensible.

Example

Correct each number to 1 significant figure to find an approximate answer to $\dfrac{0.63 \times 7.8}{0.036}$.

$$\frac{0.63 \times 7.8}{0.036} \approx \frac{0.6 \times 8}{0.04}$$

$$= \frac{60 \times 8^2}{4^1}$$

$$= 120.$$

Section III Self-test units

This section contains a selection of questions from past examination papers. These questions can be used both to test your understanding of the topics in the book and to practise answering examination questions.

TYPES OF EXAMINATION QUESTION

There are four main types of question used in GCE, SCE and CSE Mathematics examinations:

  (*i*) multiple choice questions (not all Boards use these),
 (*ii*) multiple facet questions (not all Boards use these either),
(*iii*) short free response questions (favoured by most Boards),
(*iv*) long free response questions (used by all Boards).

The types of questions used can vary. Check with your Board and their most recent examination papers to find out which types will be used when you take the examination.

(i) Multiple choice questions

In this type you are given a question or statement followed by four or five possible answers. Of these only one will be correct. The others are wrong and are called distractors. This is because they try to distract you from the correct answer. You will have to choose one of the alternative answers and either write it or its letter down (usually in a box) or, draw a ring round the answer of your choice. Check with past papers to find out which way your Board requires you to do this. These questions may look easy, but you will normally have to do some working to find the correct answer.

Example
In this question one only of the answers (a)–(d) is correct. Write down the correct answer.

$$\frac{7}{8} - \frac{1}{6} =$$

(*a*) 3   (*b*) $\frac{17}{24}$ (*c*) $\frac{7}{48}$ (*d*) $\frac{25}{24}$

The correct answer is (*b*).

The distractors have been listed to catch out those candidates who cannot subtract fractions.

Always try to work out the answer first; most of these questions will be about basic topics which you should have revised. However, if you cannot find the correct answer to a question of this type you can make a sensible guess by eliminating obviously silly distractors.

(ii) Multiple facet questions

In this type you are given some information, followed by a series of short questions on this information. This time you will not be given any possible answers, you will be expected to find your own.

Example
Questions 1 to 3 inclusive, refer to the formula $I = \dfrac{PTR}{100}$.

  1 *Find the value of I when $P = 45$, $R = 6$, $T = 5$.*
  2 *Find the value of P when $I = 14$, $R = 4$, $T = 7$.*
  3 *Make R the subject of the formula.*

In this question each part must be worked out separately. However, each part uses the same information, *i.e.* $I = \dfrac{PTR}{100}$.

The answers to these questions are:

1 $I = \dfrac{45 \times 5 \times 6}{100} = \dfrac{1350}{100} = 13.5$

$$2 \quad 14 = \frac{P \times 7 \times 4}{100}$$

$$\text{i.e. } 14 = \frac{28P}{100}$$

$$P = \frac{\cancel{14}^{\,1} \times 100}{\cancel{28}^{\,2}} = \frac{100}{2} = 50$$

$$3 \quad I = \frac{PTR}{100}$$

$$\text{i.e. } 100I = PTR$$

$$R = \frac{100I}{PT}$$

(iii) Short free response questions
This type of question is often found on the first section of a Paper I examination paper. You will have to do the necessary working to find the answer.

Example
Express 315 *as a product of prime factors.*

Some Examination Boards will give you a box, *i.e.* [   ] or a space, *i.e.* _____ in which to put your answer. In this case you may be given full marks for the correct answer $\boxed{3^2 \times 5 \times 7}$, and no marks for a wrong answer. If there is room, you will be expected to show your working like this:

$$315 = 5 \times 63$$
$$= 5 \times 7 \times 9$$
$$= 3^2 \times 5 \times 7$$

Marks will be given for working.

(iv) Long free response questions
These questions are usually found in Section II (and/or Paper II) of GCE, SCE and CSE papers.

Hints on answering questions

Before answering a question:

- Read the whole question carefully.
- Jot down points relating to the question, *e.g.* formulae you will need, words you should know, skills you will use.
- Draw a sketch, if it helps, labelling it with the information given.
- Always draw a sketch before doing a construction or scale drawing.

When writing your answer:

- Make sure that your writing is legible.
- Write your answer neat and carefully.
- Show all your working unless the question says otherwise. Most marks are usually given for legible working, not just 'right answers'.
- State any formulae used.
- Try to explain your reasons for using a formula or stating a result.
- Do not do things you are not asked for, *e.g.* do not prove a theorem unless you are asked to do so.
- Make sure that you are answering the question the examiner has actually asked.
- Use and state the correct units, *e.g.* cm², kg, h, *etc.*
- Always do a rough estimate of any calculation to check that your answer is sensible.
- Show clearly any calculation that you have done on a calculator.
- Give your final answer to the required degree of accuracy (dp or sf).
- Leave all construction lines on the completed drawing in a construction or scale drawing.

If you get 'stuck', reread the question carefully to check that you have not missed any important information or hints given in the question itself.

When you have completed your answer, reread the question to check that you have answered all parts.

The questions

The questions given below have been divided into:

- GCE (parts I and II),

• SCE,
• CSE (parts I and II).

Part I questions are usually short and may be multi-choice, multi-facet or free response questions depending on the Board. Part II questions are usually long free response questions. Do not let the names worry you (they are for the examiner): your job is to work out the answers.

Above each question is a reference to the unit(s) in this book which are relevant to that question. If you have difficulty answering a question you can refresh your memory by working through the appropriate unit(s) again. When you have answered a question first check your answer with that given at the end of each group of questions. Then look back to the relevant unit(s) to check that your method was correct too. In most examinations marks are given for legible, correct working, not just the 'right' answers. The instructions on the examination paper will tell you if 'answers only' are required. When working through these questions assume that all working is needed. This is a good habit to acquire and may help you to spot where you have made a mistake.

Below most questions is a reference to the Board which set the question. Try to answer *all* questions on the units of the book you have studied whether they were set by your Board or not.

If you are taking a CSE examination, try answering *all* the CSE questions and the part I GCE questions. If you are taking a GCE or SCE examination, try answering *all* the questions.

GCE QUESTIONS

Part I (answers on page 172)

Unit 1

1 P and Q are subsets of the universal set $\mathscr{E}$. Given that $P \cap Q \neq \phi$, represent the following sets by shaded regions in separate Venn diagrams (i) $(P \cap Q)'$, (ii) $P' \cap Q'$.

(Joint Matriculation Board)

Unit 1

2 If $P = \{3, 6, 9, 12, 15\}$ and $Q = \{6, 12, 18\}$, list the elements of (i) $P \cap Q$, (ii) $P \cup Q$.

(Associated Examining Board)

Units 2, 16

3 (a) Find the Least Common Multiple of 63 and 147. Hence express $\dfrac{5}{147} - \dfrac{2}{63}$ as a single fraction in its lowest terms.

(b) In a trial on a racing track a car travelled 488 km in two hours 40 minutes. Calculate its average speed in kilometres per hour.

(Oxford Local Examinations)

Unit 3

4 Calculate, giving your answers in each case as a binary number,

(i) $1000_2 - 1_2$,   (ii) $11_2 \times 11_2$.

(Associated Examining Board)

Unit 3

5 Convert to base ten the largest number which can be written with three digits in base four.

(Joint Matriculation Board)

Units 4, 6

6 (a) Express in its simplest form $\dfrac{\frac{2}{3} - \frac{1}{4}}{\frac{5}{6}}$.

(b) Without using tables or slide rule, find the value of

$$\frac{(9.2 \times 10^3) \times (3.5 \times 10^{-2})}{(2.8 \times 10^4)},$$

giving your answer in the form $a \times 10^n$, where n is a whole number and a is a number between 1 and 10.

(Oxford and Cambridge Schools Examination Board)

Units 5, 6

7 Express 23.506 correct to (*i*) two decimal places, (*ii*) two significant figures.

(*Associated Examining Board*)

Unit 7

8 (Do not use logarithm tables or slide rules in this question.)

(*a*) Find the cost of a carpet measuring 6.5 m by 4.5 m if the price is £8.60 per square metre.   *£251.55*

(*b*) Express a speed of 46.5 metres per second in kilometres per hour.

(*Oxford and Cambridge Schools Examination Board*)

Unit 9   *167.4 km/h*

9 Knitting wool which was formerly sold in 1 ounce skeins is now sold in 25 g skeins for the same price per skein. Taking 16 ounces as equivalent to 453.6 g, find, in ounces, the weight of a 25 g skein, giving the result correct to three significant figures. Calculate the percentage reduction in weight of a skein of wool.

(*Oxford and Cambridge Schools Examination Board*)

Units 10, 54

10 Use your tables to calculate, correct to two significant figures,

(*i*) $(\cos 50°)^2 - (\sin 50°)^2$;   (*ii*) $\sqrt{1 + (\tan 50°)^2}$.

(*Joint Matriculation Board*)

Unit 12

11 The surface area of a sphere is given by the formula $4\pi r^2$ where r is the radius. Calculate the radius of a sphere which has surface area 89 cm^2, giving your answer correct to one decimal place.

(*Oxford Local Examinations*)

Units 12, 6

12 The edges of a rectangular block are of lengths 3 cm, 4 cm and 5 cm. Calculate its volume in **cubic metres**, giving your answer in standard form.

(*University of Cambridge Local Examinations*)

Unit 13

13 An alloy consists of three metals A, B and C, in the proportions

$A:B = 3:5$ and $B:C = 7:6$. Calculate the proportion $A:C$.

(*University of Cambridge Local Examinations*)

Unit 14

14 A man sells his car for £810 and as a result loses 10 per cent of the price he paid for it. What was the price he paid for it?   *£900*

(*Associated Examining Board*)

Unit 14

15 Calculate the sum of money that will yield a simple interest of £144 in 3 years at 8 % per annum.

(*Welsh Joint Education Committee*)

Unit 16 $\frac{4}{3}$,   *£600*

16 Give the mean, median and mode of the following set of numbers:

0, 1, 2, 3, 4, 0, 1, 2, 3, 0, 1, 2, 0, 1, 0.

(*University of London*)

Unit 17

17 The diagram shows one quarter of a figure which is symmetrical about the lines $X_1 X_2$ and $Y_1 Y_2$. Complete the figure.

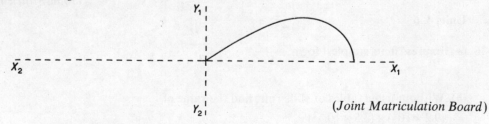

(*Joint Matriculation Board*)

Unit 18

18 Show that the set $\{-1, 0, 1\}$ is closed under multiplication. Give ONE reason why this set under multiplication does not form a group.

(*Joint Matriculation Board*)

Unit 19

19 Given that $a = 4, b = {}^-6$, write down the numerical values of

(i) $a + b$,   (ii) $2a - b$ (iii) $\dfrac{3a}{b}$,   (iv) $a^2 - b^2$,   (v) ab^2.

(Oxford Local Examinations)

Unit 19

20 Multiply out the brackets and simplify the resulting expressions as much as possible.

(i) $(x - 4)(x^2 + 4x + 16)$,   (ii) $(x - 2y)(x + 3y)$.

(Oxford Local Examinations)

Unit 20

21 Solve (i) $3x - 4 = 11$, (ii) $2(x + 6) = 18$, (iii) $\dfrac{x}{2} - 2 = 3$.

(Welsh Joint Education Committee)

Unit 20

22 Solve the equation $\dfrac{3x}{5} - \dfrac{x + 3}{20} = 18$.

(Welsh Joint Education Committee)

Unit 21

23 The function f is defined on the set $\{0, 1, 2, 3, 4, 5, 6, 7, 8, 9\}$ by $f: x \rightarrow$ the units digit in x^2. Draw the mapping diagram for f.

(Joint Matriculation Board)

Unit 23

24 Write down the equation of

(i) the straight line which has a gradient of two and which passes through the origin,

(ii) the line parallel to the line in (i) and passing through $(0, 3)$.

(Associated Examining Board)

Unit 24

25 Solve the simultaneous equations $2x + y = 10, x - 2y = 10$.

(Associated Examining Board)

Unit 25

26 Solve $3 - 2y < 11$.

(Oxford and Cambridge Schools Examination Board)

Unit 25

27 The diagram shows part of the Cartesian graphs of $x + 2y = 4$ and $3x + y = 3$.

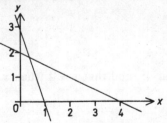

Indicate on the diagram the region for which $y \geqslant 0$ and $x + 2y \leqslant 4$ and $3x + y \geqslant 3$.

(Joint Matriculation Board)

Unit 26

28 A transformation which maps L onto L' is represented by the matrix $\begin{pmatrix} 3 & 1 \\ 5 & 2 \end{pmatrix}$. Find the inverse matrix which maps L' onto L.

(Associated Examining Board)

Unit 27

29 Factorise

(i) $x^2 - 3x$,   (ii) $x^2 - 3x - 4$.

(Oxford Local Examinations)

Unit 27

30 Factorise

(i) $4a^2 - b^2$,   (ii) $6x + 4y - 9cx - 6cy$.

(University of Cambridge Local Examinations)

Unit 28

31 Express $\dfrac{2}{x+4} - \dfrac{1}{x+2}$ as a single fraction.

(Oxford Local Examinations)

Unit 29

32 Factorise (i) $p^2 - 9$, (ii) $n^2 + 5n + 4$.

(Associated Examining Board)

Unit 29

33 Find the positive number x such that $2x^2 = x + 3$.

(Joint Matriculation Board)

Unit 30

34 Plot on the same sheet of graph paper and with the same axes the graphs of

$y = (x-2)(5-x)$ and $y = \dfrac{5}{x} - 2$ for values of x from $x = 1$ to $x = 6$.

Explain how two of the solutions of the equation $x^3 - 7x^2 + 8x + 5 = 0$ can be found from your graphs and give these solutions as accurately as you can.

(Oxford Local Examinations)

Unit 31

35 Given that the logarithm of 0.4122 is $\bar{1}.6151$, calculate the logarithm of (i) $(0.4122)^3$, (ii) $(0.4122)^{\frac{1}{5}}$.

(Associated Examining Board)

Unit 31

36 Use tables to calculate to three significant figures

(a) $\dfrac{(14.7)^2}{481.6}$,   (b) $\sqrt[5]{(0.872)}$.

(Oxford Local Examinations)

Unit 32

37 Make x the subject of the formula $p = \dfrac{k}{\sqrt{x}}$.

(Associated Examining Board)

Unit 32

38 The positive real numbers E, V and M are connected by the relation $V = \sqrt{\dfrac{2E}{M}}$. Express E in terms of V and M.

(Joint Matriculation Board)

Unit 33

39 Given that y varies inversely as x^2, and that $y = 4$ when $x = 3$, calculate the value of y when $x = 6$.

(Welsh Joint Education Committee)

Unit 34

40

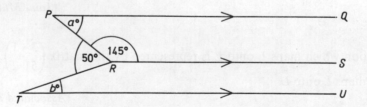

The straight lines PQ, RS, TU are parallel. Given that angle $PRS = 145°$ and angle $PRT = 50°$, find (i) a, (ii) b.

(Associated Examining Board)

Unit 35

41 The angles of a quadrilateral are $11x°$, $10x°$, $(8x+5)°$, and $(8x-15)°$. Calculate the size of the largest angle of the quadrilateral.

(Welsh Joint Education Committee)

Unit 36

42 In the diagram, *ABCD* is a trapezium with *AB* parallel to *DC*. The sides *AD* and *BC* are equal in length. The triangles *AFD*, *BFC* are congruent. Name (*i*) another pair of triangles which are congruent to one another, (*ii*) a pair of triangles which are similar but not congruent.

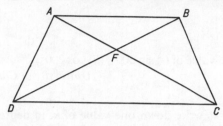

(*Joint Matriculation Board*)

Unit 37

43 The town *A* is 5 km N 32.5° W of town *B*. Calculate how many km *A* is (*i*) North of *B*, (*ii*) West of *B*. Give your answers correct to two decimal places.

(*Joint Matriculation Board*)

Unit 38

44 Under a translation the image of (2, 3) is (5, 4). Write down the co-ordinates of the image of (4, 1) under the same translation.

(*Associated Examining Board*)

Unit 38

45 (*i*) What transformation does the matrix $\begin{pmatrix} -1 & 0 \\ 0 & 1 \end{pmatrix}$ represent?

(*ii*) Write down the matrix which represents an anticlockwise rotation of 90° about the origin.

(*Associated Examining Board*)

Unit 38

46 Quadrilateral *A'B'C'D'* is an enlargement of quadrilateral *ABCD* by a scale factor of 3. Which are true and which false?

(*a*) $A'B' = \frac{1}{3} AB$.

(*b*) The area of the larger quadrilateral is six times that of the smaller.

(*c*) The perimeter of the larger quadrilateral is three times that of the smaller.

(*d*) Angle $A'B'D' = 3 \times$ Angle *ABD*.

(*Oxford and Cambridge Schools Examination Board*)

Unit 39

47 Under the transformation *V*, the image of every point $(x, 1)$ is $(x, x + 1)$. Write down:

(*i*) the co-ordinates of the point which is invariant under *V*;

(*ii*) the matrix of *V*.

(*University of Cambridge Local Examinations*)

Units 40, 11

48

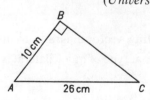

In $\triangle ABC$, the side $AB = 10$ cm, $AC = 26$ cm and $\hat{B} = 90°$. Calculate (*i*) *BC*, (*ii*) the area of $\triangle ABC$.

(*University of Cambridge Local Examinations*)

Unit 41

49 Calculate:

(*i*) tan *x*°,

(*ii*) the value of *x*,

(*iii*) the length of *BC*.

(*Associated Examining Board*)

Unit 42

50 (*a*) In a triangle, the angles are 40°, 62°, 78° and the length of the longest side is 15 cm. Use the sine rule to calculate the length of the shortest side.

(*b*) The sides of a triangle are 5 cm, 7 cm and 11 cm. Use the cosine rule to calculate the greatest angle.

(Oxford Local Examinations)

Unit 43

51 Use tables to write down the value of (*i*) sin 200°, (*ii*) cos 200°.

(University of Cambridge Local Examinations)

Unit 44

52 In each of the following cases write down one value of *x*, in degrees, such that (*i*) $\sin x = -1$, (*ii*) $\cos x = -1$, (*iii*) $\tan x = -1$.

(University of Cambridge Local Examinations)

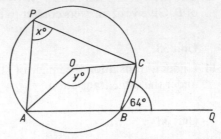

Unit 45

53 In the figure, *O* is the centre of the circle and *ABQ* is a straight line. If angle $CBQ = 64°$, find (*i*) *x*, (*ii*) *y*.

(Associated Examining Board)

Unit 46

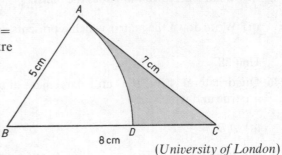

54 In the diagram, $AB = 5$ cm, $BC = 8$ cm and $CA = 7$ cm. *AD* is an arc of a circle drawn with centre *B* and radius *BA*. Show that $\cos ABC = \frac{1}{2}$.

Calculate:

(*a*) the area of $\triangle ABC$,

(*b*) the area of the shaded region *ADC*.
(Take π as 3.142.)

(University of London)

Unit 47

55 The latitude and longitude of *P* and *Q* are *P*(75°N, 115°W) and *Q*(70°N, 65°E). Write down, in nautical miles, the length of the shortest route from *P* to *Q*.

(University of Cambridge Local Examinations)

Unit 48

56 Use ruler and compasses only in this question. All construction lines should be clearly shown. Construct an isosceles triangle in which the base is 5.4 cm and the height is 6 cm. Construct, also, the circumcircle of the triangle and measure its radius.

(Oxford Local Examinations)

Unit 49

57 Given that $\overrightarrow{OA} = \mathbf{a}$ and $\overrightarrow{OB} = \mathbf{b}$, draw vector diagrams to illustrate $\mathbf{a} + \mathbf{b}$ and $\mathbf{a} - \mathbf{b}$. If *OACB* is a quadrilateral and if $\overrightarrow{OC} = \mathbf{a} + \mathbf{b}$, what type of quadrilateral is *OACB*?

(Joint Matriculation Board)

Unit 50

58 A pie-chart is used to represent the sales of three commodities *A*, *B* and *C*. The angles of the sectors representing *A*, *B* and *C* are 90°, 120° and 150° respectively. Given that the total sale is 240 tons, calculate how many tons of each commodity are sold.

(University of Cambridge Local Examinations)

Unit 51

59 I throw a pair of fair dice. Write down the probability of getting (*i*) at least one six; (*ii*) a total score of six.

$\frac{11}{36}$ $\frac{5}{36}$

(Oxford Local Examinations)

Unit 52

60 Given that $\frac{dy}{dx} = 2x + 1$ and that $y = 2$ when $x = 2$, express *y* in terms of *x*.

(Joint Matriculation Board)

Unit 52

61 Calculate the area of the region bounded by the curve $y = x^2 + 2$, the x-axis and the lines $x = 1$ and $x = 3$.

(*Joint Matriculation Board*)

Unit 53

62 The distance from X to Y is 12 km. A man leaves X at 12.00 and walks to Y at a steady speed of 6 km/h. A second man leaves Y at 12.00 and cycles to X at a constant speed, passing the first man at 12.30. On the grid provided, draw the distance-time graph for each man.

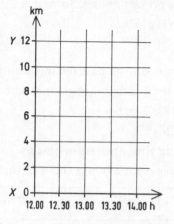

(*University of Cambridge Local Examinations*)

Part II (answers on page 173)

Unit 1

1 On Friday afternoons each member of a particular age group in a school takes part in not more than two of four possible activities, denoted by A, B, C and D. Anyone who chooses two activities must include A as one of them. Draw a Venn diagram to illustrate this, taking the entire age group as the Universal set.

Of those who opt for one activity only, the numbers taking A, B, C and D respectively are 44, 20, 16 and 10. Of those who opt for two activities, 24 choose A with B or C, and 10 choose A with C or D. Taking x as the number who choose A and C, insert appropriate numbers or expressions involving x in the seven subsets of the Venn diagram. If the number who choose B (singly or not) exceeds those who choose C (singly or not) by eight, write down and solve an equation for x, and hence determine the total number in this age group.

(*Oxford Local Examinations*)

Units 1, 2

2 (*a*) If $E = \{2, 3, 5\}$ and $F = \{3, 6, 10\}$, list the set of ordered pairs (x, y) which indicate the cartesian product $E \times F$, where $x \in E$ and $y \in F$.

Relations R and S are defined from E to F by
$R = \{(x, y) : x \text{ is a factor of } y\}$ and
$S = \{(x, y) : x \text{ and } y \text{ are both prime numbers}\}$.

With the above information

(*i*) list the sets R and S as sets of ordered pairs,

(*ii*) define the inverse relation R^{-1} of R in words and list R^{-1} as a set of ordered pairs,

(*iii*) if, in $E \times F$, R' and S' are the complements of R and S respectively, list the set $R' \cap S'$.

(*b*) N is the set of natural numbers. T is a relation defined on $N \times N$ by

$T = \{(x, y) : x \text{ is a factor of } y\}$.

Prove that if $(x, y) \in T$ and $(y, z) \in T$, then $(x, z) \in T$.

(*Associated Examining Board*)

Unit 2

3 The operations H and L are defined on the set of natural numbers by the relations

$a \, \mathrm{H} \, b = $ the highest common factor of a and b,

$a \, \mathrm{L} \, b = $ the lowest common multiple of a and b.

(*i*) Find 16 H 64,   24 L 56,
       36 H (48 H 32),   8 L (9 L 12).

(*ii*) Is each of the operations H and L commutative?

(*iii*) Give ONE example for each of the operations H and L to illustrate the fact that they are each associative operations.

(*iv*) Give an example to illustrate the fact that H is distributive over L.

(*v*) Each of the different numbers *a*, *b* and *c* is the product of the prime number *p* and one other prime number. Show that

$a \, \mathrm{H} \, b \, \mathrm{H} \, c = p$.

(Joint Matriculation Board)

Units 3, 13

4 (*a*) Change 51 from base ten into a number in base six.

(*b*) If all the numbers are given in base six, calculate

(*i*) $123 - 45$,

(*ii*) 25×53,

leaving your answers in base six.

(*c*) Drawings for a house are made on a scale of $\frac{1}{8}$. Copy and complete the following table:

	Drawing	Actual house
Length of house	1.4 m	
Width of lounge		5.6 m
Number of rooms	8	
Floor area of kitchen	0.25 m²	

(Welsh Joint Education Committee)

Units 3, 41

5 (*a*) (*i*) If both numbers are given in binary notation, calculate 1011×110, leaving your answer in binary.

(*ii*) If both numbers are given in base eight, calculate $713 - 245$, and leave your answer in base eight.

(*iii*) Convert 1 000 010 from binary to base ten.

(*iv*) Convert 245 from base eight to binary.

(*b*) The figure, which is not drawn to scale, shows a quadrilateral *ABCD* in which $BA = 7$ cm, $AE = 4$ cm, $AC = 10$ cm, $\widehat{BCD} = \widehat{CDE} = \widehat{BED} = 90°$ and $\widehat{ACD} = 54° 56'$. Calculate

(*i*) the size of $\widehat{BAE}$,

(*ii*) the length of *DE*.

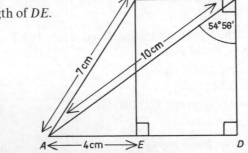

(Welsh Joint Education Committee)

Units 6, 55

6 *Neither slide rules nor logarithms may be used in this question.*

The statement that a length is correct to the nearest mm means that the true length is within ± 0.5 mm of the stated length.

A side of a rectangle is measured as 7.4 cm (correct to the nearest mm). This means that the true length is within the range 7.35 cm to 7.45 cm. State the corresponding range for the other side measured as 4.6 cm (correct to the nearest mm).

(*i*) State the dimensions of the smallest possible rectangle and calculate its area.

(*ii*) State the dimensions of the largest possible rectangle and calculate its area.

(*iii*) Calculate the maximum error that might be involved in taking the area as 7.4×4.6 cm².

State, correct to two significant figures, the areas of the rectangles used in (*i*), (*ii*) and (*iii*).

State also the number of significant figures to which these answers agree.

(Joint Matriculation Board)

Units 9, 13

7 (*a*) Given that £1 = 6.0 Deutschmark, draw a graph to show the relationship between pounds and Deutschmark for sums of money up to £1.20. From the graph read off the value of 35 pence in Deutschmark, and the value of 6.3 Deutschmark in pounds.

(*b*) The volume of a marble statue, 3 m high, is V_1; a wooden model of the statue, 20 cm high, has volume V_2 and weighs 4 kg. Calculate the ratio $V_1 : V_2$ in the form $n : 1$. Given that the wood weighs 540 kg/m^3, and the marble weighs 3000 kg/m^3, calculate the weight of the statue in tonnes (1 tonne = 1000 kg).

(*Welsh Joint Education Committee*)

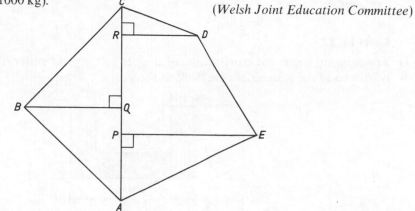

Units 1, 13.3, 40

8 The diagram shows the plan of a field *ABCDE* (not drawn to scale). *AP* = 80 m, *PQ* = 20 m, *QR* = 52 m, *RC* = 48 m, *PE* = 60 m, *RD* = 36 m, *BQ* = 40 m. Calculate:

(*i*) the perimeter of the field (correct to the nearest metre),

(*ii*) the area of the field (correct to the nearest 100 m^2).

A plan of the field is drawn to the scale 1 cm : 5 m. Calculate the area of the plan in cm^2 (correct to the nearest 10 cm^2).

(*Joint Matriculation Board*)

Units 1, 40, 46

9 The figure shows a triangular piece of hardboard *ABC* with *AB* = *AC*, *BC* = 26 cm and the angle *BAC* = 90°. A quadrant of a circle, centre *A* and radius 12 cm, is cut from the hardboard by removing the shaded portion *BCED*.

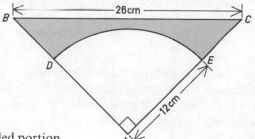

Calculate:

(*i*) the area of the shaded portion,

(*ii*) the length *AC*, and hence the perimeter of the shaded portion. (Take π to be 3.142.)

(*Associated Examining Board*)

Unit 12

10 The figure represents a vertical central cross section through a closed container consisting of a cylindrical part of internal radius 21 cm and internal height 100 cm with a hemispherical top of internal radius 21 cm.

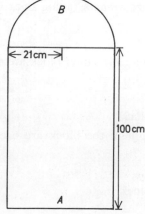

Calculate the total capacity of the container.

If the container contains liquid to a depth of 60 cm, calculate the volume of the liquid.

If the container and its contents are inverted (so A and B change places), calculate the height of the liquid in this new position.

$$\left[\text{Throughout this question take } \pi \text{ to be } \frac{22}{7}. \text{ The volume of a hemisphere of radius } r \text{ cm} = \frac{2}{3}\pi r^3 \text{ cm}^3.\right]$$

(Associated Examining Board)

Units 11, 12

11 The diagram shows the cross-section of an open rectangular gutter. The depth is a cm, the width is $2b$ cm and the material is t cm thick, as shown.

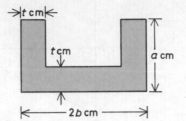

   (*i*) Find an expression in its simplest form for the perimeter of the cross-section.

  (*ii*) Prove that the volume of material required to make a piece of gutter of length c metres is $200\,tc\,(a+b-t)$ cubic centimetres.

 (*iii*) If the gutter is full of water, find an expression in cubic metres for the volume of water contained in a 10 metre length of the gutter.

(Oxford and Cambridge Schools Examination Board)

Units 13, 14

12 The total cost of building a house may be divided between materials, wages and administrative costs. In 1974 a builder found that, for a particular type of house, these costs were in the ratio of $3:6:1$. Find each of these costs for such a house whose total cost was £15 000.

By 1975, the cost of materials had risen by 15 per cent, wages by 20 per cent and administrative costs by 5 per cent. Calculate the new cost of building a similar house and the overall percentage increase in the cost.

(Oxford and Cambridge Schools Examination Board)

Units 13, 14

13 The promoter of a football pools competition takes as expenses 30 per cent of the total money staked each week. The remainder is then divided in the ratio $7:5$ to provide the first pool and the second pool respectively. The first 'dividend' is obtained by dividing the first pool by the number of first prize winners. The second dividend is obtained by dividing the second pool by the number of second prize winners. Calculate:

  (*i*) the first dividend in a week when there were 15 first prize winners and the total stake money was £90 000,

 (*ii*) the expenses taken by the promoter in another week when there were 56 second prize winners who each received a second dividend of £25.

In a third week, there were p first prize winners who each received a first dividend of £1000. Given that there were q second prize winners, obtain an expression for the second dividend.

(Joint Matriculation Board)

Units 12, 14

14 The length, breadth and height of a rectangular block are 60 cm, 30 cm and 20 cm respectively. Calculate the exact value of

  (*i*) the volume of the block,

 (*ii*) the total surface area of the block.

The length, breadth and height of the block are each increased by 35%. Calculate the resulting increase in

 (*iii*) the volume of the block,

 (*iv*) the total surface area of the block.

(Joint Matriculation Board)

Unit 16

15 The tables below show the numbers of pupils in three different groups who scored 0, 1, 2, 3 or 4 marks in a test question:

(*i*)

Marks	0	1	2	3	4
Number of pupils	1	1	3	1	x

Give the value of x if the median is 3 marks.

(*ii*)

Marks	0	1	2	3	4
Number of pupils	11	12	y	7	5

Give a possible value of y if the modal class mark is 2.

(*iii*)

Marks	0	1	2	3	4
Number of pupils	z	4	3	2	1

Calculate z if the mean is 1 mark.   (*University of Cambridge Local Examinations*)

Units 6, 19, 29

16 A man walked a distance of $2a$ kilometres at an average speed of x km/h and then a further distance of a kilometres at an average speed of $(x-4)$ km/h. Write down expressions for the times taken for each part of the journey and hence prove that the average speed for the whole journey is

$$\frac{3x(x-4)}{3x-8}\,\text{km/h}.$$

If this average speed is 6 km/h, write down an equation for x.

Hence find the average speed for the first part of the journey, noting that x must be greater than 4.   (*Oxford and Cambridge Schools Examination Board*)

Unit 18

17 The operation table for the set $N = \{1, 2, 3, 4, 5, 6\}$ under the operation $*$ is as partly shown below:

*	1	2	3	4	5	6
1	1	6	3	4	5	
2		1		3	4	
3			5	6		
4				5		
5						6
6						

Copy the table and complete it given that

(1) the set N is closed under $*$,

(2) if a, b are any two elements of N, then $a * b = b * a$ (*i.e.* the operation is commutative),

(3) the equation $a * x = b$ has one and only one solution in N (*i.e.* each element of N appears once and only once in each row, and once and only once in each column).

Explain what is meant by the statements

(*a*) 'The set N is closed under $*$',

(*b*) 'N has no identity element'.

Find a subset of three elements of N which is closed under $*$ and which does have an identity element. Name this identity element, and a pair of inverse elements.

(*University of London*)

Unit 18

18 A binary operation $\otimes$ is defined on the set $S = \{2, 4, 6, 8\}$ by $a \otimes b =$ remainder after the product ab is divided by 10. (For example, $2 \otimes 8 = 6$.)

(*i*) Copy and complete the comparison table given below for this operation:

$\otimes$	2	4	6	8
2			6	
4				
6				
8				

(*ii*) State clearly the conditions which must be satisfied for any set T under a binary operation to form a group.

(*iii*) Use your conditions in (*ii*) to prove that S under $\otimes$ forms a group.

(*iv*) If a^3 means $a \otimes a \otimes a$, with similar definitions for a^2 and a^4 show that S under $\otimes$ can be represented by $\{a, a^2, a^3, a^4\}$, where $a \in S$. Show also that there are two possible values for a and hence, find those values of $x \in S$ for which

$$a^2 \otimes x = a.$$

(*Associated Examining Board*)

Unit 21

19 Functions f and g are defined by

$$f : x \longrightarrow 2x - 1 \qquad \text{for } -2 < x < 2$$
$$g : x \longrightarrow \tfrac{1}{2}(x^2 + 1) \quad \text{for } -1 \leqslant x \leqslant 3.$$

Find expressions in terms of x for

(*i*) $f\{g(x)\}$ and

(*ii*) $g\{f(x)\}$.

(*iii*) Calculate the ranges of the functions g and $g\{f(x)\}$, and give the images of $x = \tfrac{1}{2}$ for each of these two functions.

(*iv*) Prove that there is one and only one value of x for which $x = f(x) = g(x)$.

(*Associated Examining Board*)

Units 23, 24, 38

20 (*a*) The line L_1 passes through the point $(0, 3)$ and has gradient 2. The line L_2 passes through the points $(4, 0)$ and $(0, 6)$. Write down the equations of L_1 and L_2 and calculate the co-ordinates of their common point.

(*b*) Under a rotation, the line $A'B'$ is the image of the line AB. The co-ordinates of A, B, A' and B' are $(0, 4)$, $(0, 2)$, $(1, 0)$ and $(k, 0)$ respectively, where $k > 0$. Find

(*i*) the value of k,

(*ii*) the co-ordinates of the point whose image is $(1\tfrac{1}{2}, 0)$.

(*University of Cambridge Local Examinations*)

Unit 25

21 A manufacturer has the facilities for assembling two types of cycle. The cost of components, the labour involved, and the profit on each cycle are shown in the following table:

	Cost of components £	Labour Man hours	Profit £
Type A	15	3	5
Type B	10	4	6

The total money available for materials is £180 and the total labour available is 48 man-hours. If x of type A and y of type B are made, write down all the linear constraints on x and y.

Show these on a linear programming diagram and draw a profit line. Determine the maximum profit which can be made by a suitable choice of x and y.

(*Southern Universities' Joint Board*)

Unit 25

22 A group of five boys went into a shop to buy some bars of chocolate with a total of, at most, 36 pence to spend. 'Milko' bars cost 6p each and 'Nutty' bars cost 4p each. Each boy had at least one bar of chocolate.

(*i*) If the boys buy x bars of 'Milko' and y bars of 'Nutty', write down two inequalities connecting x and y.

(*ii*) One boy insisted on having a 'Milko' although there were only four 'Milko' bars in the shop. Using a scale of 2 cm for one bar on each axis, show graphically, by shading, the members of the solution set, calling it A.

(*iii*) Find $n(A)$.

(*iv*) Which arrangement is the cheapest and what change would the boys receive?

(*v*) Which arrangements would produce the most bars of chocolate?

(*Welsh Joint Education Committee*)

Unit 26

23 (*a*) If $A = \begin{pmatrix} 2 & 1 \\ 3 & 2 \end{pmatrix}$, $B = \begin{pmatrix} -3 & -4 \\ 1 & 2 \end{pmatrix}$, determine AB, $3A - 2B$, A^{-1}, AA^{-1}. I is the unit matrix and K is a number. Find K where $A^2 + I = KA$.

(*b*) Express in matrix form, and hence solve, the simultaneous equations:
$$5x - 6y = 2$$
$$3x - 2y = -7.$$

(Southern Universities' Joint Board)

Unit 28

24 Express

(*i*) $\dfrac{3}{x-3} - \dfrac{2}{x+4}$,   (*ii*) $\dfrac{x+5}{(x-3)(x+1)} - \dfrac{x-2}{(x+4)(x+1)}$,

as single fractions, in each case giving your answer in its lowest terms. (Leave the denominators in factorised form.)

(*iii*) Use (*i*) and (*ii*) to simplify
$$\left(\frac{3}{x-3} - \frac{2}{x+4} \right) \div \left(\frac{x+5}{(x-3)(x+1)} - \frac{x-2}{(x+4)(x+1)} \right).$$

(*iv*) Solve the equation $\dfrac{x+5}{(x-3)(x+1)} - \dfrac{x-2}{(x+4)(x+1)} = \dfrac{1}{7}$.

(Oxford Local Examinations)

Units 28, 29

25 (*i*) Solve the equation $2x^2 - 8x - 3 = 0$ giving the roots to two decimal places. Hence, or otherwise, solve the equation
$$\frac{2}{y^2} - \frac{8}{y} - 3 = 0.$$

(*ii*) Simplify $\dfrac{3x}{x^2 - 4} \div \dfrac{6}{2x^2 - 4x}$.

(Southern Universities' Joint Board)

Unit 30

26 Copy and complete the given table of values of the function
$$y = \frac{x^2}{2} + \frac{18}{x} - 10$$

for the values indicated. In the table values have been corrected to one place of decimals.

x	1	1.5	2	3	4	4.5	5
$\dfrac{x^2}{2}$	0.5	1.1		4.5		10.1	
$\dfrac{18}{x}$	18	12		6		4	
-10	-10	-10		-10		-10	
y	8.5	3.1		0.5		4.1	

Draw the graph of the function for values of x from 1 to 5 using scales of 2 cm to 1 unit on both axes.

(*a*) From your graph, find the value of x giving the least value of y and this least value of y.

(*b*) By drawing a suitable straight line graph, find the positive values of x which satisfy
$$\frac{x^2}{2} + \frac{18}{x} - 10 = x.$$

(University of London)

Unit 31

27 Use logarithms to calculate to three significant figures

$$\frac{\sqrt[3]{118.5}}{6.03 \times 0.071} + \frac{1}{(3.51 - 1.4)^2}.$$

Hence evaluate

$$\frac{\sqrt[3]{118.5}}{2 \times 6.03 \times 0.071} + \frac{1}{2(3.51 - 1.4)^2}.$$

(*Southern Universities' Joint Board*)

Units 24, 27, 33

28 (*a*) Write down the factors of $x^2 - 9y^2$. Hence, or otherwise, solve the equations

$$x^2 - 9y^2 = 15,$$
$$x - 3y = 5.$$

(*b*) When a current passes through a wire, the rate at which heat is produced, W watts, is directly proportional to the square of the voltage V volts, and inversely proportional to the length of the wire l centimetres. Express W in terms of V, l and a constant of variation k. Hence calculate:

(*i*) the value of k given that $W = 800$ when $V = 200$ and $l = 40$,

(*ii*) the value of l given that $W = 800$ when $V = 240$,

(*iii*) the value of V given that $W = 800$ when $l = 48.4$.

(*Associated Examining Board*)

Unit 36

29 $ABCD$ is a rectangle. An equilateral triangle ADE is drawn outside the rectangle. The line CB is produced to F so that $\angle AFB = 30°$. Prove that triangles AEF and ADF are congruent and that the area of triangle AEF is half the area of the rectangle.

The line FD cuts AB at G, where $AG = 15$ cm, $GB = 45$ cm. Calculate the length of BF. Show that triangles AGD and BGF are similar and that $AD = \frac{1}{3}BF$.

(*Joint Matriculation Board*)

Units 37, 48 and 12, 29

30 (*a*) From a small boat P the angle of elevation of a point Q on top of a cliff is $30°$. When the boat has moved 80 m towards the base of the cliff vertically below Q, the angle of elevation of Q is $60°$. Using ruler and compasses only, construct a scaled diagram that shows the relative positions of P and Q. By construction and measurement find, and state, the height of Q above sea level.

(*b*) The parallel sides of a trapezium are y cm and $(y+1)$ cm. The distance between the parallel sides is $(y+2)$ cm and the area of the trapezium is 32 cm². Show that $2y^2 + 5y - 62 = 0$ and hence find the value of y, correct to 1 decimal place.

(*Associated Examining Board*)

Unit 38

31 The figure represents a triangle ABC, right-angled at A with an altitude AD. $AB = 3$ cm and $AC = 4$ cm.

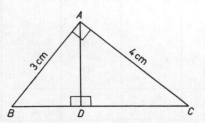

(*i*) The triangle ABD can be mapped into the triangle CAD by a rotation followed by an enlargement. Specify the centre and amount of rotation and the centre and scale factor of the enlargement.

(*ii*) The triangle ABD can be mapped into the triangle CBA by three successive transformations, the first of which is a reflection in the line BC. In the second and third transformations B remains invariant. Specify, in the correct order, the second and third transformations giving details as fully as necessary.

(*Oxford Local Examinations*)

Unit 38

32 A 2×2 matrix M represents a transformation T of the plane in which a point (x, y) is mapped onto (y, x).

  (*i*) State the matrix M and describe carefully the nature of the transformation T.

  (*ii*) Find a 2×2 matrix N which maps the point $(5, 1)$ on to $(8, 0)$ and also maps the point $(1, 5)$ on to $(0, 8)$.

  (*iii*) The matrix $L = \begin{pmatrix} 5 & 1 \\ 1 & 5 \end{pmatrix}$ maps the points $O(0, 0)$, $A(1, 0)$, $B(1, 1)$ and $C(0, 1)$ on to the points O, P, Q and R respectively. Find the area of the closed figure $OPQR$.

  (*iv*) Use your results in (*i*), (*ii*) and (*iii*) to find the factor by which the area of any plane figure is multiplied, under a transformation represented by the matrix product MNL.

(Associated Examining Board)

Unit 42

33

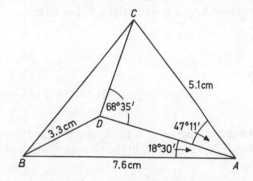

In the diagram, A, B, C and D are four points in a plane. $AB = 7.6$ cm, $AC = 5.1$ cm and $BD = 3.3$ cm. $B\widehat{A}D = 18° \, 30'$, $D\widehat{A}C = 47° \, 11'$, $A\widehat{D}C = 68° \, 35'$ and $B\widehat{D}A$ is obtuse. Calculate:

  (*i*) the area of $\triangle ABC$,

  (*ii*) CD,

  (*iii*) the obtuse angle $B\widehat{D}A$.

(University of Cambridge Local Examinations)

Units 43, 48, 54

34 (*a*) Two fixed points A and B in a plane are 6 cm apart. State the locus of a point P which moves in the plane under *each* of the following conditions and in *each* case draw a sketch labelling the locus P clearly:

  (*i*) $PA = PB$,

  (*ii*) the angle $APB = 90°$,

  (*iii*) the area of the triangle APB is $24 \, \text{cm}^2$,

  (*iv*) $PA^2 - PB^2 = 36 \, \text{cm}^2$.

(*b*) Use table to evaluate $\left(\dfrac{2 - \sin 306°}{1 + \cos 140°} \right)$.

(Associated Examining Board)

Unit 44

35 The diagram represents a solid in which the horizontal base $ABCD$ and the vertical face $ABDE$ are rectangles; $AB = 20$ cm, $BC = 10$ cm, $BF = 16$ cm. Calculate:

  (*i*) the angle which the edge CF makes with the horizontal,

  (*ii*) the length of the diagonal BD of the base,

  (*iii*) the angle which DF makes with the horizontal.

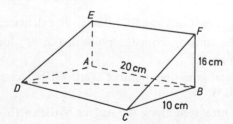

(Oxford and Cambridge Schools Examination Board)

Unit 45

36 Prove that the angles in the same segment of a circle are equal.

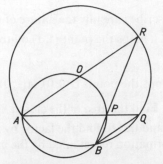

In the diagram, O is the centre of the circle $ABQR$ and lies on the circumference of the circle APB. The lines AOR, APQ and BPR are all straight. Prove that

(*i*) $A\widehat{P}B = 2A\widehat{Q}B$,

(*ii*) $\triangle BPQ$ is isosceles,

(*iii*) AR is parallel to BQ.

(University of Cambridge Local Examinations)

Unit 45

37 Prove that the angle between a tangent to a circle and a chord drawn from a point of contact is equal to the angle subtended by the chord in the alternate segment.

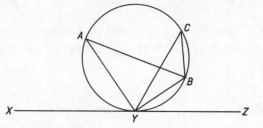

In the diagram, the line XYZ is a tangent to the circle at Y, AY bisects $\angle CYX$ and BY bisects $\angle CYZ$. Given that $\angle CYX = 2p°$ and $\angle CYZ = 2q°$ write down expressions in terms of p and q for the angles of $\triangle ABY$. Prove that:

(*a*) AB is a diameter of the circle,

(*b*) AB and CY intersect at 90°.

(University of London)

Units 46, 44

38 The portion AOB, where angle $AOB = 81°$, is removed from a circular piece of card of radius 8 cm. The radii AO and BO of the remaining portion are then brought together to produce a conical surface, the major arc AB forming the circumference of the base.

Calculate:

(*i*) the circumference of the base of the cone,

(*ii*) the base radius of the cone,

(*iii*) the height of the cone,

(*iv*) the vertical angle of the cone.

[Take π as 3.142.]

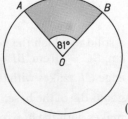

(Joint Matriculation Board)

Unit 47

39 Taking the earth to be a sphere of radius 6370 kilometres, calculate, to the nearest 10 kilometres,

(*i*) the distance along the equator from the point A (lat. 0°, long. 37° 30′E) to the point B (lat. 0°, long. 37° 30′W),

(*ii*) the distance due West from the point C (lat. 60°N, long. 37° 30′E) to the point D (lat. 60°N, long. 37° 30′W),

(*iii*) the shortest distance, measured along the surface of the earth, between the points A and C.

[Take π as 3.142.]

(Oxford and Cambridge Schools Examination Board)

Units 48, 45

40 (*a*) Draw a line $AB = 9$ cm and draw another line AC such that the angle $BAC = 55°$. *Using ruler and compasses only*, construct a circle AB as a chord such that the angle subtended by the chord AB at any point on the circumference of the major arc is equal to $55°$. Measure and state the radius of the circle.

(*b*) A triangular plot of land PQR is bounded by straight fences with $PQ = 80$ m, $PR = 100$ m and the angle $RPQ = 60°$. *Using ruler and compasses only*, construct a scaled diagram of the triangular plot and mark on it the position of a telegraph post T that is equidistant from RP and RQ, and is on the perpendicular from Q to PR. Measure and state the length QT.

(Associated Examining Board)

Unit 49

41 In the triangle OAB, X is the point on OA such that $\overline{OX} = \dfrac{2}{3}\overline{OA}$ and Y is the mid-point of $\overline{AB}$.

The point Z on OB produced is such that $\overline{OB} = \overline{BZ}$.

Given that $\overrightarrow{OA}$ is the vector **a** and $\overrightarrow{OB}$ is the vector **b**, state, in terms of **a** and **b**, the vectors (*i*) $\overrightarrow{OX}$; (*ii*) $\overrightarrow{OY}$; (*iii*) $\overrightarrow{OZ}$; (*iv*) $\overrightarrow{XY}$; (*v*) $\overrightarrow{YZ}$.

Deduce a property of the points, X, Y and Z and state the ratio of the lengths of $\overline{XY}$ and $\overline{YZ}$.

(University of Cambridge Schools Examination Board)

Unit 50

42 In a school, the number of pupils in respective age groups are shown in the following table:

Age in years	11, 12, 13, 14	15, 16	17, 18
Number of pupils	321	162	57

Illustrate this data by means of a pie-chart and give a table showing clearly the angle of each slide.

Given, in addition, the following information:

Age in years	11, 12	13, 14, 15	14, 15
Number of pupils	162	241	160

calculate how many pupils are 14 years old, making your method clear.

(University of Cambridge Local Examinations)

Unit 50

43 The weights of 50 parcels handed in at a Post Office on one day are shown in the following table:

Weight		Number of parcels
Exceeding	Not exceeding	
2 lb	6 lb	6
6 lb	10 lb	26
10 lb	14 lb	11
14 lb	18 lb	5
18 lb	22 lb	2

Use this data to illustrate the following statistical terms:

(*i*) histogram,

(*ii*) cumulative frequency diagram,

(*iii*) median,

(*iv*) semi-interquartile range.

(Joint Matriculation Board)

Unit 51

44 Two bags contain coloured marbles. The first bag contains five white and three red marbles, the second contains three white and two red marbles. A marble is taken at random out of the first bag and placed in the second bag; then a marble is taken at random out of the second bag and placed in the first bag. Find the probability that both these marbles are (*i*) white, (*ii*) red. Hence find the probability that the first bag now contains five white and three red marbles.

(Joint Matriculation Board)

Unit 52

45 An object starts from a point O and moves in a straight line. Its velocity v, at time t, is given by the formula $v = 9 + 6t - 3t^2$, where v is in metres per second and t is in seconds. Write down formulae for

(*i*) its acceleration a at time t,

(*ii*) its distance s from O at time t.

Also calculate

(*iii*) the time at which the velocity is zero,

(*iv*) the velocity at the time when the acceleration is zero,

(*v*) the distance travelled in the fourth second.

(Joint Matriculation Board)

Unit 52

46 (*a*) The total cost per hour of running a lorry is given by the expression

$$£\left(3 + \frac{v^2}{768}\right),$$

where v km/h is the average speed of the lorry. If the total cost per kilometre is $£P$, write down an expression for P in terms of v. Calculate the value of v which makes P a minimum. Find also the cost of a journey of 560 km made at this minimum average speed.

(*b*) Sketch the curve $y = x + \dfrac{1}{x^2}$ for the range of values of x where $1 \leqslant x \leqslant 4$. Find the area bounded by the curve, the x-axis and the lines $x = 2$ and $x = 3$.

(Associated Examining Board)

Unit 53

47 A and B are two points on a motorway which are 400 km apart. At 9.00 a.m. a motorist leaves A and drives towards B at a steady speed of 90 km/h. At 10.30 a.m. he stops at a service station for 30 minutes and then continues towards B at the former speed of 90 km/h.

Taking scales of 2 cm (or 1 in) to one hour on one axis and to 50 km on the other axis, draw a travel graph of the journey. Find from your graph, or otherwise, the time at which the motorist arrives at B.

A second motorist leaves B at 10.00 a.m. and drives at a steady speed of 100 km/h towards A. On the same axes, draw a travel graph of the journey of this motorist, and find from your graph, or otherwise, the time at which the two motorists pass each other and their distance from A at that time.

(Oxford and Cambridge Schools Examination Board)

SCE QUESTIONS

Unit 1

1 A universal set E is defined by

$$E = \{-4, -3, -2, -1, 0, 1, 2, 3\}.$$

A, B and C are subsets of E defined as follows:

$A = \{x : -4 < x \leqslant 2\}$

$B = \{x : x + 3 < 5\}$

$C = \{x : x^2 < 5\}$

(*a*) List the elements of the following sets:

A, B, C, B $\cap$ C, A $\cup$ B and A′, the complement of A with respect to E.

(*b*) Two numbers x and y are such that twice x is four more than y. Write down an equation in x and y which represents this relationship and then list the set of pairs of numbers (x, y) that satisfy the equation and are such that each member of the pair belongs to E.

(Scottish Examination Board)

Unit 10

2

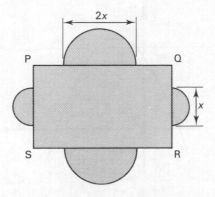

The above figure consists of a rectangle PQRS, 2 semicircles of diameter $2x$ cm and 2 semicircles of diameter x cm. PQ = 10 cm and QR = 6 cm.

(a) Show that the shaded area, A square centimetres, is given by

$$A = \frac{5}{4}(\pi x^2 + 48).$$

(b) State the maximum value of x such that no diameter extends beyond the sides of the rectangle.

(c) Calculate the value of A for this value of x, giving your answer correct to the nearest whole number. (Take $\pi = 3.14$.)

(*Scottish Examination Board*)

Unit 16

3 A man leaves his house at 10.30 and travels by car to the railway station which is 24 kilometres away. If he arrives at the station 45 minutes later, calculate the average speed of the car in kilometres per hour. How long will the man have to wait if the train, due at 11.28, is seven minutes late?

32 km/h
20 minutes

(*Scottish Examination Board*)

Unit 19

4 A motorist bought £5 worth of petrol at c pence per litre. His car uses x litres of petrol per hour. Show that, after t hours of motoring, the amount of petrol remaining, R litres, is given by

$$R = \frac{500 - cxt}{c}.$$

Express c in terms of R, t and x.

(*Scottish Examination Board*)

Unit 21

5 A function f is defined by the formula $f(x) = \sqrt{x}$, where x is a whole number.

(a) Evaluate $f(9)$.

(b) If $f(x) = 16$, find x.

(c) Without using approximations, find the value of

$$\frac{f(200)}{f(2)}.$$

(*Scottish Examination Board*)

Unit 33

6 The lift, L, produced by the wing of an aircraft varies directly as its area, A, and as the square of the airspeed, V. For a certain wing, $L = 1200$ when $A = 15$ and $V = 200$.

(a) Find an equation connecting L, A and V.

(b) If, for the same wing, the airspeed is increased by ten per cent, find the corresponding percentage increase in lift.

(*Scottish Examination Board*)

Unit 37

7

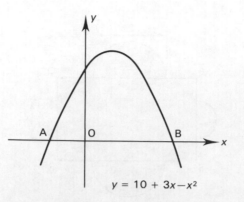

$$y = 10 + 3x - x^2$$

(a) The curve whose equation is $y = 10 + 3x - x^2$ cuts the x-axis at A$(a, 0)$ and B$(b, 0)$.

   (i) Calculate the values of a and b.

   (ii) State the equation of the axis of symmetry of the curve.

   (iii) Calculate the maximum value of the function $f(x) = 10 + 3x - x^2$.

   (iv) Find the solution set of the inequation $10 + 3x - x^2 < 0$.

(b) Solve the equation $2x^2 + 7x = 11$, giving the roots correct to 1 decimal place.

(Scottish Examination Board)

Unit 38

8

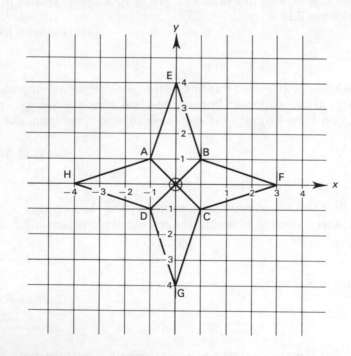

The diagram shows a star made up of four congruent kites, centred at the origin.

(a) State the exact nature of a single transformation which will map triangle EAO onto triangle GCO.

(b) If the star is given a quarter turn clockwise about O, what is the image of angle CFO?

(c) Under a certain translation HA → CF. Write down the components of this translation.

(d) What is the image of the line BE after reflection in the line AC followed by reflection in the x-axis?

(e) Under a certain dilatation with centre at the origin, K$(0, -2)$ is the image of E. Under the same dilatation, what are the co-ordinates of L, the image of A?

(Scottish Examination Board)

Unit 42

9 Calculate the size of the largest angle of the triangle ABC in which AB = 1.8 cm, BC = 2.5 cm and AC = 3.4 cm.

10

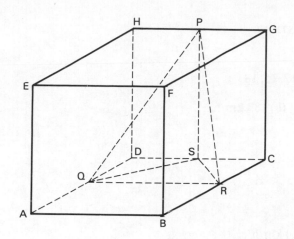

ABCDEFGH is a cube of edge 8 cm. P, Q, R and S are the mid-points of HG, AD, BC and DC respectively.

(*a*) Name the angle between PQ and the bottom face ABCD and calculate its size.

(*b*) Find the size of the angle between the planes PQS and PRS.

(*Scottish Examination Board*)

Units 45, 46

11

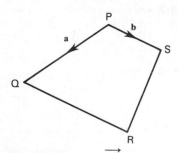

In the diagram above, O is the centre of the circle shown and A, B and C are points on the circumference such that angle AOB = 72° and BC is parallel to AO.

(*a*) Write down the size of

  (*i*) angle OBC,   (*ii*) angle ACB,   (*iii*) angle BOC,   (*iv*) angle BAC.

(*b*) State the value of the ratio

  Area of sector AOB : Area of sector BOC.

(*c*) Find an expression for the ratio

  Area of triangle AOB : Area of triangle BOC.

(*Scottish Examination Board*)

Unit 49

12

In the diagram $\overrightarrow{PQ}$ represents the vector **a** and $\overrightarrow{PS}$ the vector **b**. $\overrightarrow{QR} = 2\overrightarrow{PS}$. T is the point on QS such that QT = $\frac{2}{3}$QS.

(*a*) Give expressions in terms of **a** and/or **b** for

  (*i*) $\overrightarrow{QR}$·   (*ii*) $\overrightarrow{PR}$ (*iii*) $\overrightarrow{QS}$,   (*iv*) $\overrightarrow{QT}$,   (*v*) $\overrightarrow{PT}$.

(*b*) Using your answers to (*ii*) and (*v*) show that $\overrightarrow{PT} = k\overrightarrow{PR}$ and evaluate *k*.

(*c*) What conclusion can be made about T?

(*Scottish Examination Board*)

ANSWERS TO GCE QUESTIONS

Part I

2 (i) 6, 12; (ii) 3, 6, 9, 12, 15, 18.

3 (a) 441 (LCM), $\dfrac{1}{144}$; (b) 183 km/h.

4 (i) 111_2; (ii) 1001_2.

5 63.

6 (a) $\dfrac{1}{2}$; (b) 1.15×10^{-2}.

7 (i) 23.51; (ii) 24.

8 (a) £251.55; (b) 167.4 km/h.

9 25 g = 0.882 ounces; 11.8%.

10 (i) −0.17; (ii) 1.6.

11 2.7 cm.

12 6×10^{-5} m³.

13 $A : C = 7 : 10$.

14 £900.

15 £600.

16 Mean $\dfrac{4}{3}$, median 1, mode 0.

18

×	−1	0	1
−1	1	0	−1
0	0	0	0
1	−1	0	1

, one reason is that 0 has no inverse.

19 (i) ⁻2; (ii) 14; (iii) ⁻2; (iv) ⁻20; (v) 144.

20 (i) $x^3 - 64$; (ii) $x^2 + xy - 6y^2$.

21 (i) 5; (ii) 3; (iii) 10.

23 33.

24 (i) $y = 2x$; (ii) $y = 2x + 3$.

25 $x = 6, y = -2$.

26 $y = -4$.

28 $\begin{pmatrix} 2 & -1 \\ -5 & 3 \end{pmatrix}$.

29 (i) $x(x-3)$; (ii) $(x-4)(x+1)$.

30 (i) $(2a-b)(2a+b)$; (ii) $(3x+2y)(2-3c)$.

31 $\dfrac{x}{(x+2)(x+4)}$.

32 (i) $(p-3)(p+3)$; (ii) $(n+1)(n+4)$.

33 $\dfrac{3}{2}$.

34 Solutions approximately: 2.1 and 5.4.

35 (i) $\bar{2}.8453$; (ii) $\bar{1}.8717$.

36 (a) 0.449; (b) 0.9729.

37 $x = \left(\dfrac{k}{p}\right)^2$ or $x = \dfrac{k^2}{p^2}$.

38 $E = \dfrac{V^2 M}{2}$.

39 1.

40 (i) 35°; (b) 15°.

41 110°.

42 (*i*) △'s *ABC* and *ABD*; (*ii*) △'s *ABF* and *CDF*.

43 (*i*) 4.22 km; (*ii*) 2.69 km.

44 (7, 2).

45 (*i*) reflection in *y* axis; (*ii*) $\begin{pmatrix} 0 & -1 \\ 1 & 0 \end{pmatrix}$.

46 (*a*) F; (*b*) F; (*c*) T; (*d*) F.

47 (*i*) (0, 1); (*ii*) $\begin{pmatrix} 1 & 0 \\ 1 & 1 \end{pmatrix}$.

48 (*i*) 24 cm; (*ii*) 120 cm².

49 (*i*) $\frac{1}{2}$; (*ii*) 26° 34′; (*iii*) 11.472 cm.

50 (*a*) 9.858 cm; (*b*) 132° 10′ (11′).

51 (*i*) −0.3420; (*ii*) −0.9397.

52 (*i*) 270°; (*ii*) 180°; (*iii*) 135° (other answers possible).

53 (*i*) 64°; (*ii*) 128°.

54 (*a*) 17.32 cm²; (*b*) 4.23 cm².

55 2100 nautical miles.

56 Radius of circumcircle = 3.1 cm.

57 Parallelogram.

58 *A* = 60 tons; *B* = 80 tons; *C* = 100 tons.

59 (*i*) $\frac{11}{36}$; (*ii*) $\frac{5}{36}$.

60 *y* = *x*² + *x* − 4.

61 $12\frac{2}{3}$ square units.

Part II

1 114.

2 (*a*) *E* × *F* = {(2, 3), (2, 6), (2, 10), (3, 3), (3, 6), (3, 10), (5, 3), (5, 6), (5, 10)}; (*i*) *R* = {(2, 6), (2, 10), (3, 3), (3, 6), (5, 10)}, *S* = {(2, 3), (3, 3), (5, 3)}; (*ii*) *R* = {(*y*, *x*) : *y* is a multiple of *x*}; R^{-1} = {(6, 2), (10, 2), (3, 3), (6, 3), (10, 5)}; (*iii*) *R*′ ∩ *S*′ = {(3, 10), (5, 6)}.

3 (*i*) 16 H 64 = 16, 36 H (48 H 32) = 4, 24 L 56 = 168, 8 L (9 L 12) = 72, (*ii*) Yes.

4 (*a*) 123₆; (*b*) (*i*) 34₆, (*ii*) 2333₆;

(*c*)		Drawing	Actual house
	Length of house	1.4 m	11.2 m
	Width of lounge	0.7 m	5.6 m
	Number of rooms	8	8
	Floor area of kitchen	0.25 m²	16 m²

5 (*a*) (*i*) 1 000 010₂, (*ii*) 446₈, (*iii*) 66, (*iv*) 10 100 101₂;
(*b*) (*i*) 55° 09′, (*ii*) 4.184 cm.

6 (*i*) 7.35 cm by 4.55 cm, 33.4425 cm²; (*ii*) 7.45 cm by 4.65 cm, 34.6425 cm²; (*iii*) 0.6025 cm², 33 cm², 35 cm², 34 cm², 1 sf.

7 (*a*) 35p = 2.1 D.M., 6.3 D.M. = £1.05; (*b*) $V_1 : V_2$ = 3375 : 1, 75 tonnes.

8 (*i*) 451 m; (*ii*) 10 700 m²; 430 cm².

9 (*i*) 55.89 cm²; (*ii*) *AC* = 18.38 cm, perimeter = 57.61 cm.

10 Capacity = 158 004 cm³, volume = 83 160 cm³, height = 67 cm.

11 (*i*) 2(2*a* + 2*b* − *t*); (*iii*) $\dfrac{(a-t)(b-t)}{500}$ m³.

12 Materials = £4500, wages = £9000, administrative costs = £1500; new cost = £17 550, percentage increase = 17%.

13 (i) £2450; (ii) £1440; $\dfrac{£5000p}{7q}$.

14 (i) 36 000 cm^3; (ii) 7200 cm^2; (iii) 146.0 %; (iv) 82.25 %.

15 (i) 4; (ii) $y = 13$; (iii) 10.

16 $t_1 = \dfrac{2a}{x}, t_2 = \dfrac{a}{x-4}$; $x^2 - 10x + 16 = 0$; 8 km/h.

17

*	1	2	3	4	5	6
1	1	6	3	4	5	2
2	6	1	2	3	4	5
3	3	2	5	6	1	4
4	4	3	6	5	2	1
5	5	4	1	2	3	6
6	2	5	4	1	6	3

$\{1, 3, 5\}$; 1 is the identity element, 3 and 5.

18 (i)

⊗	2	4	6	8
2	4	8	2	6
4	8	6	4	2
6	2	4	6	8
8	6	2	8	4

(iv) $a = 2$ or 8; $x = 8$ and 2.

19 (i) x^2; (ii) $2x^2 - 2x + 1$; (iii) $\dfrac{1}{2} \leqslant g(x) \leqslant 5, \dfrac{1}{2} \leqslant g\{f(x)\} \leqslant 13, g\left(\dfrac{1}{2}\right) = \dfrac{5}{8}, g\left\{f\left(\dfrac{1}{2}\right)\right\} = \dfrac{1}{2}$.

20 (a) $L_1 : y = 2x + 3, L_2 : 3x + 2y = 12$, common point $\left(\dfrac{6}{7}, 4\dfrac{5}{7}\right)$;

    (b) (i) $k = 3$, (ii) $\left(0, 3\dfrac{1}{2}\right)$.

21 $x \geqslant 0, y \geqslant 0, 3x + 2y \leqslant 36, 3x + 4y \leqslant 48$. For maximum profit, $x = 8, y = 6$.

22 (i) $x + y \geqslant 5, 3x + 2y \leqslant 18$; (ii) $A = \{(1, 4), (1, 5), (1, 6), (1, 7), (2, 3), (2, 4), (2, 5), (2, 6), (3, 2), (3, 3),$ $(3, 4), (4, 1), (4, 2), (4, 3)\}$; (iii) $n(A) = 14$; (iv) $x = 1, y = 4$, 14p change; (v) $x = 1, y = 7$ and $x = 2, y = 6$.

23 (a) $\begin{pmatrix} -5 & -6 \\ -7 & -8 \end{pmatrix}, \begin{pmatrix} 12 & 11 \\ 7 & 2 \end{pmatrix}, \begin{pmatrix} 2 & -1 \\ -3 & 2 \end{pmatrix}, \begin{pmatrix} 1 & 0 \\ 0 & 1 \end{pmatrix}$; $K = 4$; (b) $x = -5\dfrac{3}{4}, y = -5\dfrac{1}{8}$.

24 (i) $\dfrac{x + 18}{(x - 3)(x + 4)}$; (ii) $\dfrac{14}{(x - 3)(x + 4)}$; (iii) $\dfrac{x + 18}{14}$; (iv) $x = 10$ or -11.

25 (i) $x = 4.35$ or $-0.35, y = 0.23$ or -2.9; (ii) $\dfrac{x^2}{x + 2}$.

26 (a) $x = 2.6, y = 0.3$; (b) $x = 1.75$ and 4.65.

27 11.7; 5.85.

28 (a) $(x - 3y)(x + 3y), x = 4, y = -\dfrac{1}{3}$; (b) $W = \dfrac{kV^2}{l}$; (i) $k = \dfrac{4}{5}$; (ii) $57\dfrac{3}{5}$, (iii) 220.

29 $BF = 60 \times \sqrt{3}$ cm (103.9 cm).

30 (a) 69.3 m; (b) 4.5.

31 (i) Clockwise rotation of 90° about D; enlargement: centre D, scale factor $\dfrac{4}{3}$;

    (ii) anticlockwise rotation of 53° 08′ about B followed by enlargement, centre B, scale factor $\dfrac{5}{3}$.

32 (i) $M = \begin{pmatrix} 0 & 1 \\ 1 & 0 \end{pmatrix}$, reflection in $y = x$; (ii) $N = \begin{pmatrix} \dfrac{5}{3} & -\dfrac{1}{3} \\ -\dfrac{1}{3} & \dfrac{5}{3} \end{pmatrix}$; (iii) 24 square units; (iv) 64.

33 (*i*) 17.66 cm^2; (*ii*) 4.019 cm, (*iii*) 133° 3′.

34 (*a*) (*i*) Perpendicular bisector of *AB*; (*ii*) circle, *AB* diameter; (*iii*) pair of straight lines, parallel to *AB* and each 4 cm from *AB*; (*iv*) straight line, perpendicular to *AB* passing through *B*; (*b*) 12.

35 (*i*) 58°; (*ii*) 22.36 cm; (*iii*) 35° 35′.

36 See unit 41.

37 *p*, *q*, *p* + *q* or *p*, *q*, 90°.

38 (*i*) 38.96 cm; (*ii*) 6.2 cm; (*iii*) 5.06 cm; (*iv*) 101° 37′.

39 (*i*) 8340 km; (*ii*) 4170 km; (*iii*) 6670 km.

40 (*a*) 5.5 cm; (*b*) 46.2 m.

41 (*i*) $\frac{2}{3}\mathbf{a}$; (*ii*) $\frac{1}{2}(\mathbf{a}+\mathbf{b})$; (*iii*) $2\mathbf{b}$; (*iv*) $\frac{\mathbf{b}}{2}-\frac{\mathbf{a}}{6}$; (*v*) $\frac{-\mathbf{a}}{2}+\frac{3\mathbf{b}}{2}$; ratio = 1 : 3.

42 78.

43 (*iii*) 9 lb; (*iv*) 2.516.

44 (*i*) $\frac{5}{12}$; (*ii*) $\frac{3}{16}$; (*iii*) $\frac{29}{48}$.

45 (*i*) $6(1-t)$ m/s^2; (*ii*) $(9t+3t^2-t^3)$ m; (*iii*) after 3 seconds; (*iv*) 12 m/s; (*v*) 7 m towards *O*.

46 (*a*) $P=\frac{3}{v}+\frac{v}{768}$; v = 48 km/h; £70; (*b*) $2\frac{2}{3}$ square units.

47 1.57 p.m.; 11.51 a.m.; 215 km.

ANSWERS TO SCE QUESTIONS

1 (*a*) A = $\{-3,-2,-1,0,1,2\}$, B = $\{-4,-3,-2,-1,0,1\}$, C = $\{-2,-1,0,1,2\}$, B $\cap$ C = $\{-2,-1,0,1\}$, A $\cup$ B = $\{-4,-3,-2,-1,0,1,2\}$, A′ = $\{-4,3\}$.

 (*b*) $2x=y+4$; (0, −4), (1, −2), (2, 0), (3, 2).

2 (*b*) 5 cm; (*c*) 158 cm^2.

3 32 km/h; 20 minutes.

4 $c=\dfrac{500}{R+xt}$.

5 (*a*) 3; (*b*) 256; (*c*) 10.

6 (*a*) $L=\dfrac{AV^2}{500}$; (*b*) 21 %.

7 320 km.

8 (*a*) $\frac{1}{2}$ turn about O; (*b*) $\widehat{\text{DGO}}$; (*c*) $\begin{pmatrix}5\\-1\end{pmatrix}$; (*d*) *AH*; (*e*) $(\frac{1}{2}, -\frac{1}{2})$.

9 $\widehat{\text{ABC}}$ = 103.3°.

10 (*a*) $\widehat{\text{PQS}}$ = 54.7°; (*b*) $\widehat{\text{QSR}}$ = 90°.

11 (*a*) (*i*) 72°, (*ii*) 36°, (*iii*) 36°, (*iv*) 18°; (*b*) 2 : 1; (*c*) sin 72° : sin 36°.

12 (*a*) (*i*) $2\mathbf{b}$, (*ii*) $\mathbf{a}+2\mathbf{b}$, (*iii*) $\mathbf{b}-\mathbf{a}$, (*iv*) $\frac{2}{3}(\mathbf{b}-\mathbf{a})$, (*v*) $\frac{1}{3}\mathbf{a}+\frac{2}{3}\mathbf{b}$; (*b*) $k=\frac{1}{3}$; (*c*) *P*, *T* and *R* are collinear.

Part I (answers on page 196)

Unit 1

1 There are 10 elements in the set A and 7 elements in the set B. The number of elements in the intersection $A \cap B$ is 4. Draw a Venn diagram to represent this information and find the number of elements which belong to: (a) A but not B, (b) but not A.

(Middlesex Regional Examining Board)

Unit 2

2 Write the number 2205 as the product of prime numbers.

Unit 3

3 (a) Add the base two numbers 1011 and 1101 giving your answer in base two.
(b) Convert the base two number 1110 to base ten.

(East Midland Regional Examinations Board)

Unit 4

4 (a) Show that $\dfrac{7}{9} - \dfrac{3}{4}$ is equal to $\dfrac{1}{36}$ and use this result to show that $\dfrac{7}{9}$ is greater than $\dfrac{3}{5}$.

(b) Arrange the following three numbers in order of size starting with the smallest: $\dfrac{3}{4}, \dfrac{7}{9}, \dfrac{3}{5}$.

(Middlesex Regional Examining Board)

Unit 5

5 Find the value of $16.5 \div 11$.

Unit 6

6 Write 14.48 (i) correct to two significant figures, (ii) correct to one decimal place.

(Met. Regional Examinations Board)

Unit 7

7 1 lb $\equiv$ 0.454 kg and 1 ton = 2240 lbs. How many kg are in 1 ton? (Answer to nearest kg.)

(East Midland Regional Examinations Board)

Unit 8

8 A man goes to work by train. The first stage of his journey takes 1 hr 15 min, the second stage takes 47 minutes, and he has to wait 8 minutes between stages. If the first train leaves at 0650, when does he reach his work if his office is 5 minutes walk from the station?

(Southern Regional Examinations Board)

9 A bus leaves London at 08 15 h arriving in York at 14 08 h the same day. Find the time for the journey.

(Yorkshire Regional Examinations Board)

Unit 9

10 How much Sterling is needed to pay a bill of 2400 French francs if the exchange rate is £1 $\equiv$ 9.60 French francs?

(East Midland Regional Examinations Board)

Unit 10

11 Find, as a decimal, the value of (a) $(36.2)^2$, (b) $\sqrt{41.8}$.

(East Midland Regional Examinations Board)

Unit 11

12 Calculate the area of the shaded figure.

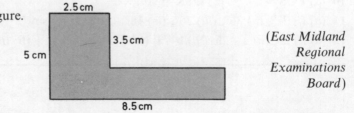

(East Midland Regional Examinations Board)

Unit 12

13 A solid right circular cylinder has a length of 14 cm and a circular cross section of 10 cm diameter. Taking $\pi = \dfrac{22}{7}$, calculate:

(i) the volume of the cylinder,

(ii) the mass of the cylinder when 1 cm^3 has a mass of 0.002 g.

(Middlesex Regional Examining Board)

Unit 13

14 A model of a boat is 30 centimetres long. The scale factor is $\frac{1}{200}$. What is the length in metres of the original boat?

(Met. Regional Examinations Board)

Unit 14

15 Calculate the simple interest on £250 at $8\frac{1}{2}\%$ per annum for four years.

(West Midlands Examinations Board)

Unit 15

16 (a) Find the total cost of postage for 3 parcels at 76p each and 12 letters at 13p each.

(b) How much change is there out of £5?

(West Midlands Examinations Board)

17 A girl buys two blouses for £8.95 each and pays for them with two £10 notes. Find:

(a) the total cost of the blouses;

(b) the amount of change she receives.

(South Western Examinations Board)

18 The rateable value of a house is £250. One year the rates payable were £200. What rate is that in pence per £?

(North West Regional Examinations Board)

19 In a particular week a man's gross wage was £92. He worked a basic 34-hour week for which he was paid £2 per hour and some overtime for which he was paid at time and a half. How many hours of overtime did he work?

(North West Regional Examinations Board)

Unit 16

20 Find the mean (average) of 4.6, 12.3, 5.6, 8.3.

(Welsh Joint Education Committee)

Unit 17

21 (a) How many axes of reflective symmetry has a regular pentagon?

(b) What is the order of rotational symmetry of a parallelogram?

Unit 18

22 The operation $*$ is given by the table:

$*$	p	q	r	s
p	q	s	p	r
q	s	r	q	p
r	p	q	r	s
s	r	p	s	q

(i) State the identity element.

(ii) State the inverse q^{-1} and s^{-1} of q and s.

Unit 19

23 (a) Simplify:

(i) $4g + 5h - 3g + 2h$;   (ii) $4g \times 5h$;   (iii) $4g \times 3g$;   (iv) $\dfrac{4g^2 h}{16gh^3}$.

(b) When $x = 2$ and $y = {}^-3$, find the value of:

(i) $2x + y$;   (ii) $2xy$.

(West Yorkshire and Lindsey Regional Examining Board)

24 Remove the brackets and simplify completely:

(i) $3(x+y) - 2(x-y)$;   (ii) $(x+2y)^2$;   (iii) $(x-2y)(x+2y)$.

(Welsh Joint Education Committee)

Unit 20

25 Solve each of the following equations:

(i) $5x - 3 = 27$,   (ii) $5x + 4 = 2x + 19$.

(Welsh Joint Education Committee)

Unit 21

26 The array given below shows all the possible ordered pairs which can be formed by relating set A to set B, i.e. the cartesian product $A \times B$, $(-2,8)$, $(-2,0)$, $(-2,-8)$, $(0,8)$, $(0,0)$, $(0,-8)$, $(2,8)$, $(2,0)$, $(2,-8)$.

(i) List the elements of set A.

(ii) Write down the ordered pairs in the above array which belong to the relations represented by (a) $x \rightarrow -4x$, (b) $x \rightarrow x^3$.

(iii) Give a function different from those of (a) and (b) in (ii) which has $\{-2, 0, 2\}$ for its domain and $\{-8, 0, 8\}$ for its range.

(Middlesex Regional Examining Board)

Unit 23

27 What is the equation of the line AB?

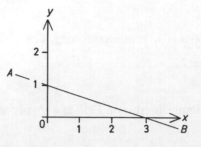

Unit 24

28 Use any appropriate method to solve the following pair of simultaneous equations:

$$3x + 2y = 17$$
$$2x - y = 9.$$

(*Yorkshire Regional Examinations Board*)

Unit 25

29 Write down the largest whole number value of x which satisfies $2x - 12 < 15 - x$.

(*Welsh Joint Education Committee*)

Unit 25

30 Write down three inequalities which describe the shaded region.

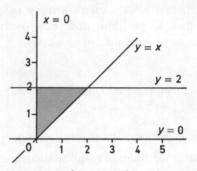

(*Associated Lanc. Schools Examining Board*)

Unit 26

31 Given that $A = \begin{pmatrix} 2 & 0 \\ 0 & 2 \end{pmatrix}$, $B = \begin{pmatrix} 3 & 1 \\ 2 & 1 \end{pmatrix}$, $C = \begin{pmatrix} 2 \\ 1 \end{pmatrix}$. Calculate:

(*a*) $A + B$,   (*b*) $2B - A$,   (*c*) AC.

Unit 27

32 Complete the following:

(*a*) $5a + 10 = 5($ $)$;   (*b*) $6x^2 + 5x - 4 = (3x + 4)($ $)$.

(*Southern Regional Examinations Board*)

33 Factorise completely $6x^2 + 2x$.

(*Yorkshire Regional Examinations Board*)

34 Factorise $2a^2 - 5a + 6ab - 15b$.

(*North West Regional Examinations Board*)

35 Factorise:

(*i*) $x^2 + 2x - 8$;   (*ii*) $x^2 - y^2$ and hence or otherwise evaluate $93^2 - 7^2$.

(*West Joint Education Committee*)

Unit 28

36 Express $\dfrac{x}{3} - \dfrac{(x-2)}{4}$ as a single fraction. Simplify your answer as far as possible.

(*East Midland Regional Examinations Board*)

Unit 29

37 Solve the equation $x^2 - 5x - 14 = 0$.

(*West Midlands Examinations Board*)

Unit 31

38 Using **logarithm tables only** evaluate the following correct to three significant figures.

$$\sqrt{\left(\frac{4.326 \times 14.82}{5.623} \right)}.$$

(*Welsh Joint Education Committee*)

Unit 31

39 Calculate $3^5 - 5^3$.

(Yorkshire Regional Examinations Board)

Unit 32

40 If $v = u + ft$, find a formula which gives t in terms of v, u and f.

(West Midlands Examinations Board)

Units 34, 35

41 Find the size of the lettered angles in each of the following:

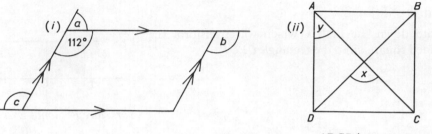

ABCD is a square

(West Yorkshire and Lindsey Regional Examining Board)

Unit 34

42 Find the size of each angle of a regular 12 sided polygon.

(West Midlands Examinations Board)

Unit 36

43 In the triangle ABC, PQ is parallel to BC.
$AP = 2$ cm and $PB = 3$ cm.
Write down the value of:

(i) $\dfrac{AP}{AB}$,   (ii) $\dfrac{\text{area } APQ}{\text{area } ABC}$

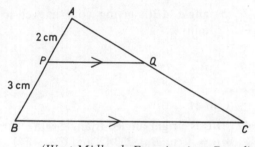

(West Midlands Examinations Board)

Unit 37

44 The sketch map shows three towns, A, B and C.

(a) What is the bearing of:

   (i) B from A,

   (ii) B and C?

(b) The triangle ABC is drawn accurately to a given
scale. Given $BC = 30$ km, find:

   (i) the scale of the map,

   (ii) the actual distance of town B from town A.

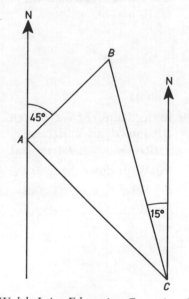

(Welsh Joint Education Committee)

Unit 38

45 Give the co-ordinates of the image of $(2, 3)$ after each of these transformations:

(a) translation by $\begin{pmatrix} -3 \\ 5 \end{pmatrix}$,

(b) rotation of $90°$ clockwise about $(0, 0)$,

(c) reflection in the line $y = -x$.

(Associated Lancs. Schools Examining Board)

Unit 38

46 Triangle *XYZ* is an enlargement of triangle *PQR*. Calculate the scale factor of the enlargement and the size of the sides labelled *r* and *y*.

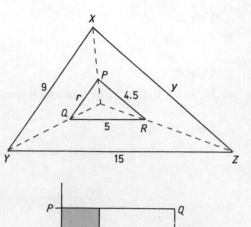

Unit 39

47 Write down the matrix which will transform the shaded square on to the rectangle *OPQR*.

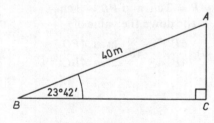

(*Yorkshire Regional Examinations Board*)

Units 40, 41

48 The diagram represents a right-angled triangle *ABC* in which angle *ACB* = 90°, *BC* = 16 cm and *AC* = 12 cm. Calculate:

(*a*) the length of *AB* in cm,

(*b*) angle *ABC*, giving your answer to the nearest minute.

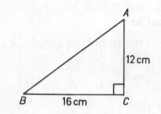

(*Yorkshire Regional Examinations Board*)

Unit 41

49 *ABC* is a right-angled triangle with *AB* = 40 m, *B* = 23° 42′ and *C* = 90°. Use tables to calculate the lengths of *AC* and *BC*.

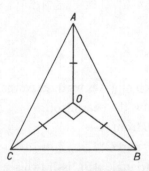

(*Welsh Joint Education Committee*)

Unit 44

50 In the figure, *OA* = *OB* = *OC*. *OB* and *OC* are horizontal. ∠*BOC* = 90°. *AO* is vertical.

(*a*) Write down the size of ∠*ABO*.

(*b*) What type of triangle is *ABC*?

(*c*) Write down the size of ∠*BAC*.

(*Yorkshire Regional Examinations Board*)

Unit 45

51 Calculate *x*.

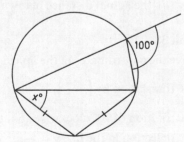

(*Met. Regional Examinations Board*)

Unit 46

52 The figure shows a circle centre Q and of radius 7 cm. A and B are points on the circumference such that the angle $AQB = 60°$.

(a) What fraction of the circle is shaded?

(b) Calculate the length of the arc AB, given $\pi = \dfrac{22}{7}$.

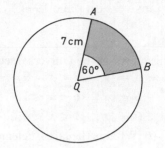

Unit 48

53 (a) Make an accurate drawing of the triangle ABC, where $AB = 6.3$ cm, $AC = 4.9$ cm, and angle $A = 30°$.

(b) What is the length of BC?

(*Associated Lancs. Schools Examining Board*)

Unit 49

54 (a) Give the vector representing the transformation which maps the point $P(3, 7)$ on to $Q(-2, 8)$.

(b) Give the vector which represents the inverse of this transformation.

(*Middlesex Regional Examining Board*)

Unit 50

55 The pie-chart illustrates the favourite colours of a group of girls.

(a) What is the angle of the sector for yellow?

(b) What fraction of the girls chose green as their favourite colour?

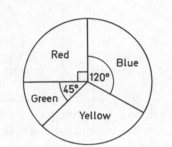

(*Yorkshire Regional Examinations Board*)

Unit 51

56 A bag contains three red discs, two yellow discs and five green discs.

(i) What is the probability that a disc chosen at random is yellow?

(ii) A second disc is chosen without returning the first. What is the probability that both discs are yellow?

(*Middlesex Regional Examining Board*)

Unit 53

57 The diagram below represents a journey taken in a car.

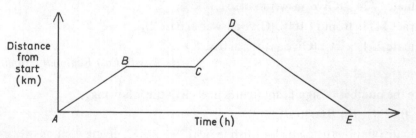

State the lines which represent:

(a) the return journey,   (b) the period when the car was stationary.

(*Yorkshire Regional Examinations Board*)

Unit 54

58 Use tables to find the following:

(i) $\sin 20° 6'$,   (ii) $\tan 35° 30'$,   (iii) $\cos 160°$.

(*Middlesex Regional Examining Board*)

Part II (answers on page 197)

Unit 1

1 In this question the Universal set $\mathscr{E}$ is all the integers from -10 to 10 inclusive. You are given the subsets $A = \{x : -9 < x < 9\}$
$$B = \{x : -6 < x \leqslant 1\}$$
$$C = \{x : -1 \leqslant x < 4\}.$$

(a)   (i) What is the largest element in B?

    (ii) What is the smallest element in A?

    (iii) How many elements are there in C?

(b) List the elements of:

   (i) $B \cap C$

  (ii) A'

 (iii) $B' \cap C$

 (iv) $A \cap (B \cup C)'$.

(East Anglian Examinations Board)

Unit 1

2 A Sports Club offers to its members football, tennis or cricket and the number of people taking part in the various sports is shown in the Venn diagram below:

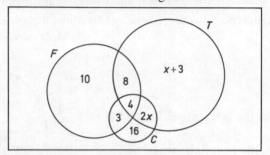

Given that set F represents those playing football, set T those playing tennis, set C those playing cricket and $\mathscr{E} = \{$members of Sports Club$\}$

(a)   (i) How many people play cricket only?

    (ii) How many people play football?

(b) How many people play football and also cricket?

(c) If 30 people play tennis, find the value of x.

(d) Calculate the percentage of football players in the club who also play tennis but do not play cricket.

Unit 3

3 (a) Write 144_{10} as a number in base (i) 6, (ii) 12.

(b) Write 144_5 as a number in base 10.

(c) Calculate $144_5 + 242_5$. (Give answer in base 5.)

(d) Calculate $\sqrt{24_6}$. (Give answer in base 6.)

(e) Subtract 1111_2 from $11\,100_2$. (Give answer in base 2.)

(f) Calculate $264_8 \times 24_8$. (Give answer in base 8.)

(South East Regional Examinations Board)

Unit 6

4 (i) State the number of significant figures in each of the following:

    (a) 40.02   (b) 0.00462.

 (ii) Evaluate (without using tables, or slide rule) 29.2×3.52, giving your answer

    (a) exactly

    (b) correct to four significant figures

    (c) correct to two decimal places.

(iii) (a) Write each of the following numbers in Standard Form:

      (i) 6480   (ii) 0.324.

    (b) Hence, or otherwise, evaluate $6480 \div 0.324$ giving your answer in Standard Form.

(iv) Express $\dfrac{9}{16}$ as an exact decimal.

(West Yorkshire and Lindsey Regional Examining Board)

Units 6, 12

5 The manufacturers of Glosso paint claim that 1 litre of paint will cover an area of 11 m².

   (a) Calculate, to two significant figures, the average thickness in metres of the paint. Give your answer in the standard index form $A \times 10^n$ where $1 \leqslant A < 10$ and n is an integer.

   (b) The paint is to be used to paint all of the outside of 35 closed boxes each measuring 1.87 m by 2.90 m by 0.53 m. Calculate the number of litres of paint required.

                                         (*East Anglian Examinations Board*)

Unit 9

6 (a) German butter was sold in Nottingham at $12\frac{1}{2}$ pence per half-pound packet. What would be an equivalent price in marks per kilogram in Germany if 1 kg = 2.2 lbs and the exchange rate is £1 = 5.72 marks.

   (b) Wine is imported from France at 4.60 francs per litre. What is the corresponding price per gallon in English money? (1 litre = 1.76 pints, £1 = 11.80 francs.)

   (c) The number of Danish Kroner that could be bought for £1 fell from 8.44 to 8.15. How much extra English money had to be paid for a Danish cheese that was priced at 211 Kroner?

                          (*East Midland Regional Examinations Board*)

Unit 10

7 Use tables to calculate:

   (a) 7.21×4.16, giving your answer to three significant figures

   (b) $\sqrt{42.8}$

   (c) $\sqrt{0.000826}$

   (d) $\sqrt{2.49^2 + 6.24^2}$

   (e) $0.178 \div \sin 26° 48'$.

              (*South East Regional Examinations Board*)

Unit 11

8

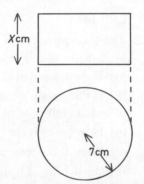

The diagram shows a circle of radius 7 cm, and a rectangle of width X cm, between the same parallels.

   (a) Write down the length of the rectangle.

   (b) Write down the area of the rectangle in terms of X.

   (c) Taking $\pi = \dfrac{22}{7}$, find the area of the circle.

   (d) If the areas of the circle and rectangle are equal, write down an equation, and hence find the value of x.

   (e) If the perimeters of the circle and rectangle are equal, write down another equation, and hence find the value of X in this case.

             (*East Midland Regional Examinations Board*)

Unit 12

9 The diagram (not drawn to scale) represents a solid triangular prism. The dimensions are given in centimetres.

   (a) Find the area of cross-section of the prism.

   (b) If the volume of the prism is 1848 cm³ find the length l.

   (c) If the material from which the prism is made weighs 17.5 g per cm³ and costs £2.10 per kilogram, find:

      (i) the weight of the prism,

      (ii) the cost of the prism, correct to the nearest penny.

   (d) If the prism is recast into a cylindrical bar of length 12 cm, calculate the radius of the bar.

$$\left(\text{Take } \pi \text{ to be } \frac{22}{7}\right).$$

                                       (*Welsh Joint Education Committee*)

Unit 13

10 A scale model of a car is one-hundredth (*i.e.* $\frac{1}{100}$th) as long as the car itself.

(*a*) If the length of the car is 3.5 m, what is the length of the model car?

(*b*) If the area of the glass in the back window of the model car is 50 mm², what is the corresponding area in the car? Give your answer in square metres (m²).

(*c*) If the amount of space within the car is 9 cubic metres (m³), what is the corresponding volume in the model car? Give your answer in mm³.

(*d*) If there are four seats in the model car, how many seats will there be in the car itself?

(*Yorkshire Regional Examinations Board*)

Units 13, 14

11 Three men decide to share the profits of their business in the ratio of their ages. At the end of the first year, Mr A's age was 20, Mr B's age was 35, and Mr C's age was 45.

(*a*) At the end of the first year the profits were £10 000. How much did each receive?

(*b*) What percentage of the total did each man receive?

(*c*) At the end of the eleventh year the profits are £26 000. Now that each man is ten years older, how much does each man receive?

(*d*) What percentage of the total does each man now receive? (Give your answers to one decimal place.)

(*e*) From your answers to (*b*) and (*d*) describe what will happen to each man's percentage of the profits as he gets older. As time goes on what will be the overall effect on their relative percentages?

(*Southern Regional Examinations Board*)

Unit 14

12 The shop price of a refrigerator is £67.20. At a discount warehouse it can be bought for cash at 15 % below the shop price.

(*a*) How much would it cost at the discount warehouse?

If it is bought on a hire-purchase agreement from a shop a deposit of 25 % of the shop price has to be paid followed by 104 weekly payments of 63p.

(*b*) How much is the deposit?

(*c*) What is the total cost of buying the refrigerator on hire purchase?

If after making 52 payments the buyer decides to close the account by paying the remaining payments altogether,

(*d*) How much would this amount to?

For closing the account early a rebate of 25 % of the total hire purchase interest would be given.

(*e*) How much interest would be returned as rebate?

(*South East Regional Examinations Board*)

Unit 15

13 (*a*) The following shows telephone charges for 3 months:

Rental   £9.50
Cost of metered units   £29.40
Cost of calls via the operator   £3.10

(*i*) Calculate the total cost of rental, metered units and calls via the operator.
(*ii*) If V.A.T. is charged at 15 % of the total cost, calculate the total amount of the bill.
(*iii*) If metered units cost 4p each, calculate the number of metered units used.

(*b*) Mr Brown has a gross monthly salary of £360. He can claim £1250 allowances against his tax each year, the remainder is taxed at the rate of 34p in the £. Calculate:

(*i*) his gross annual salary;
(*ii*) his taxable annual salary;
(*iii*) the amount of tax he pays each year; and
(*iv*) the amount of superannuation he pays each *month* if superannuation contributions amount to $6\frac{1}{2}$ % of his gross monthly salary.

(*West Yorkshire and Lindsey Regional Examining Board*)

Units 16, 50

14 The table shows the weekly rate of pay for 5 grades of workers in a small factory:

Grade	Weekly wage	Number of workers
I	£30	12
II	£35	8
III	£40	5
IV	£45	2
V	£50	3

(*a*) (*i*) Write down the modal wage.

(*ii*) Calculate the mean wage.

(*iii*) Find the median wage.

(*b*) Draw an accurate pie-chart to show the number of workers in each grade. Label each sector clearly.

(*c*) One of the employees made the statement, 'Most workers in this factory earn only £30 per week.' Discuss whether this statement is justified.

(Southern Regional Examinations Board)

Unit 18

15 Operations $\oplus$ and $*$ are defined on the set $\{1, 3, 5, 7\}$ as follows:

$a \oplus b$ = the remainder when the sum of a and b is divided by 8. For example $3 \oplus 7 = 2$, since $3 + 7 = 10$ and when 10 is divided by 8 the remainder is 2.

$a * b$ = the remainder when the product of a and b is divided by 8. For example $3 * 7 = 5$, since $3 \times 7 = 21$ and when 21 is divided by 8 the remainder is 5.

(*a*) Copy and complete the following tables for operations on the given set:

$\oplus$	1	3	5	7
1				
3		2		
5				
7				

$*$	1	3	5	7
1				
3		5		
5				
7				

(*b*) Explain why the set is closed under the operation $*$, but not under the operation $\oplus$.

(*c*) What is the identity element for the operation $*$?

(*d*) Show, by means of a clearly worked example, that the operation $*$ is associative.

(*e*) Use your tables to find solution sets for each of the following equations:

(*i*) $c * 5 = 3$,   (*ii*) $7 \oplus d = 2$,   (*iii*) $e \oplus e = 2$,   (*iv*) $(7 * f) \oplus 3 = 6$.

(East Midland Regional Examinations Board)

Unit 18

16 The operation $\oplus$ is defined by $a \oplus b = 2a - b$.

(*a*) Find the value of

(*i*) $3 \oplus 7$,   (*ii*) $4 \oplus -4$.

(*b*) Is the operation $\oplus$ commutative? Give an example to illustrate your answer.

(*c*) Find the value of $(5 \oplus 3) \oplus 2$ and of $5 \oplus (3 \oplus 2)$ and hence say whether or not the operation $\oplus$ is associative.

(*d*) If $2 \oplus x = 9$, what is the value of x?

(East Anglian Examinations Board)

Unit 19

17 In a works canteen tea costs 4p a cup and coffee 5p a cup. During one break-time the number of cups of tea sold was 30 more than the number of cups of coffee. Taking x as the number of cups of coffee sold, write down:

(*i*) the number of cups of tea sold;

(*ii*) the takings in pence for coffee sold;

(*iii*) the takings in pence for tea sold.

If the total takings were £15.60 write down an equation for x, and by solving it find the number of cups of coffee and of tea sold this break-time.

(Associated Lancashire Schools Examining Board)

Units 20, 24, 25

18 (*a*) Find the value of x for which:
$$(x+10) = 5(x-4)+2.$$

(*b*) Use any appropriate method to solve the following for x and y:
$$2x+3y = 4$$
$$3x+5y = 2.$$

(*c*) If x is an integer, solve the following inequality:
$$14 \leqslant (2x+5) \leqslant 23.$$

Unit 23 (*Yorkshire Regional Examinations Board*)

19 The sketch, which is not accurately drawn, shows a straight line through P and Q representing the equation $5x+2y = 8$. Calculate:

(*i*) the gradient of PQ,

(*ii*) the equation of the line through the origin parallel to PQ,

(*iii*) the area of triangle OPQ,

(*iv*) the co-ordinates of the mid-point of PQ.

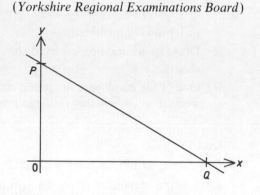

Unit 25

20 On a coach outing there are p children and q adults.

(*i*) The coach can seat 50 passengers. Write down the relation between p and q which satisfies this condition. Remember that the coach need not be full.

(*ii*) The number of children must be greater than or equal to twice the number of adults. Write down the relation between p and q which satisfies this condition.

(*iii*) (*a*) A charge of £2 is made for each child and £4 for each adult. Write down the total charge for p children and q adults.

(*b*) The total charge must be greater than or equal to £60. Write down the relation between p and q which satisfies this condition.

(*iv*) Using a scale of 2 cm to 10 units on each axis, draw a diagram to show the region which is satisfied by all these conditions together with the conditions $p > 0$ and $q > 0$. Shade out the unwanted regions and label all the lines.

(*v*) What is the smallest number of children on the outing if all the conditions are satisfied?

Unit 26

21 Matrices A and B are defined by:
$$A = \begin{pmatrix} 4 & 1 \\ -5 & -1 \end{pmatrix} \qquad B = \begin{pmatrix} 8 & 5 \\ 3 & 2 \end{pmatrix}.$$

(*i*) Calculate the product BA.

(*ii*) Calculate A^{-1}.

(*iii*) Calculate B^{-1}.

(*iv*) Calculate $(BA)^{-1}$.

(*v*) Find $A^{-1}B^{-1}$.

(*vi*) Use the inverse matrix method to solve the simultaneous equations:
$$8x+11y = 1$$
$$-11x-15y = 1.$$

Unit 29

22 (*a*) Solve each of the following equations:

(*i*) $x^2-9 = 0$.

(*ii*) $x^2-9x = 0$.

(*iii*) $x^2-6x+9 = 0$.

(*iv*) $x^2-x-6 = 0$.

(*b*) Solve $x^2-5x-3 = 0$, giving your answers correct to two decimal places.

Units 19, 29

23 (*a*) Multiply $(2x-3)$ by $(5x-4)$.

(*b*) Solve $3x^2-2x-8 = 0$. (*Yorkshire Regional Examinations Board*)

Units 19, 29

24 (*a*) Given that the solution of the equation $ax^2 + bx + c = 0$ is $x = \dfrac{-b \pm \sqrt{b^2 - 4ac}}{2a}$, solve the equation $2x^2 - 3x - 6 = 0$.

(*b*) A rectangle is 3 mm longer than it is wide. If it is x mm wide,

(*i*) write an expression for its length.

(*ii*) Write an expression for its perimeter.

(*iii*) Write an expression for its area.

(*iv*) If the area and the perimeter have the same numerical value, form an equation and solve it to find the width of the rectangle.

(East Anglian Examinations Board)

Unit 30

25 (*a*) Given that $y = \frac{1}{2}x^2 - 4$, copy and complete the following table:

x	-4	-3	-2	-1	0	1	2	3	4
y	4		-3.5	-4			-2	0.5	

(*b*) Taking 2 cm to represent one unit on each axis, draw the graph of $y = \frac{1}{2}x^2 - 4$ from -4 to 4.

(*c*) Use your graph to solve the equation $\frac{1}{2}x^2 - 4 = 2$.

(*d*) Mark on your graph, with the letters P and Q, the points from which the square roots of 6 can be determined and state these values correct to one decimal place.

(*e*) Mark on your graph, with the letter M, the point at which y is least and state the value of y.

(*f*) Draw the tangent to the curve at $x = 1$ and hence estimate the gradient of the curve at $x = 1$.

(East Anglian Examinations Board)

Unit 30

26 (*a*) On squared paper, and using scales of 2 cm to 1 unit on the x-axis and 1 cm to 1 unit on the y-axis, draw the graph of $y = x^2$ for whole number x values from -4 to $+4$.

(*b*) Using the same axes, draw the graph of $y = 2x + 3$.

(*c*) Write down the co-ordinates of the intersections of the two graphs.

(*d*) These intersections provide the solutions of the equation $x^2 = 2x + 3$. This equation can be written in the form $x^2 + bx + c = 0$. Write down the values of

(*i*) b,   (*ii*) c.

(East Anglian Examinations Board)

Unit 31

27 (*a*) Write down the values of

(*i*) 3^3,   (*ii*) 2^{-2}.

(*b*) Calculate the value of $(3 \times 10^3) - (4 \times 10^2)$. Give your answer in standard form.

(*c*) *Using logarithms*, calculate the value (to three significant figures) of $\dfrac{p - q}{p + q}$ when $p = 3.643$ and $q = 0.858$.

(East Anglian Examinations Board)

Unit 31

28 (*a*) Simplify:

(*i*) $x^2 \times x^5$,   (*ii*) $\dfrac{y^8}{y^2}$,   (*iii*) $(z^2)^5$.

(*b*) Use tables or slide rule to calculate answers to the following:

(*i*) $\dfrac{7.3 \times 0.153}{11}$ (to three significant figures).

(*ii*) A motorist travelled 15 300 kilometres in a year and spent £230 on petrol, oil and maintenance. Find the cost per kilometre, to the nearest $\frac{1}{10}$p.

(East Anglian Examinations Board)

Units 31, 54

29 (a) Use your tables to find:

(i) log 42.56,

(ii) the number of which the log is $\bar{1}.6132$,

(iii) tan 52° 30′.

(b) Use tables, or any other suitable method, to find the value of the following correct to three significant figures:

(i) $\dfrac{V}{I}$ where $V = 220$ and $I = 4.8$.

(ii) mc^2 where $m = 0.043$ and $c = 257.6$.

(Yorkshire Regional Examinations Board)

Unit 32

30 (a) (i) Make r the subject of the formula $A = s(r+8)$.

(ii) If $A = 253$ and $s = 22$, find the value of r.

(b) A gardener bought x trees at a total cost of £325. Four of the trees withered and died. He sold all the rest at £3 each. Express **in terms of** x:

(i) the number of trees sold,

(ii) the amount received from selling the trees,

(iii) the profit made.

If he made a profit of £32, form an equation and solve it to find the value of x.

(Welsh Joint Education Committee)

Unit 33

31 (a) When making a journey at a constant speed, the distance travelled, d km, is directly proportional to the time taken, t hours. If a distance of 252 km takes six hours to travel,

(i) write down a formula connecting d and t,

(ii) find the time taken to travel 336 km.

(b) The pressure, P, of a given mass of gas at a constant temperature is inversely proportional to its volume, V.

(i) Copy and complete the following table which is for values of P and V.

P	240	160	120		80	60	48		32	30
V	2		4	5	6		10	12	15	16

(ii) Draw a graph of P against V for the values given in your completed table, using the following scales:

Horizontal scale (V), 2 cm to 2 units.
Vertical scale (P), 2 cm to 20 units.

(iii) Write down a formula connecting P and V.

(East Midland Regional Examinations Board)

Units 34, 35, 17

32

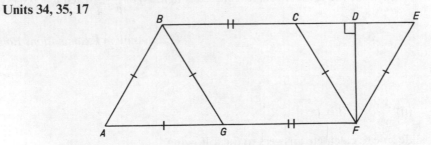

AB is parallel to FE. BE and AF are parallel straight lines:
FD is perpendicular to CE.

(a) Name the shapes (i) ABG, (ii) BGFC, (iii) ABCF.

(b) How many axes of symmetry have the following shapes?

(i) ABG,   (ii) BGFC,   (iii) ABCF,   (iv) CDF,   (v) ABEF.

(c) The shape *ABG* is reflected in the line *AG*. What is the name of the shape formed by *ABG* together with its reflection?

(d) Give the size of the angles: (i) *ABG*, (ii) *BGF*, (iii) *GBC*, (iv) *CFD*, (v) *CDF*.

(e) Given that *AB* is *x* units in length:

   (i) give length *CD* in terms of *x*,

   (ii) give length *DF* in terms of *x*,

   (iii) give area of *CFE* in terms of *x*.

(South East Regional Examinations Board)

Unit 36

33 The figure shows trapezium *ABCD* with *AB* parallel to *DC*. *AB* = 32 cm, *AE* = 12 cm and *EC* = 9 cm.

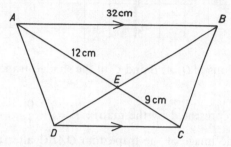

(a) (i) Name a pair of similar triangles in the figure.

   (ii) Calculate the length, in centimetres, of *DC*.

(b) (i) What fraction of the area of triangle *ADC* is the area of triangle *EDC*?

   (ii) If the area of triangle *EDC* is *x* square centimetres, what is the area of triangle *ABE*?

(East Anglian Examinations Board)

Unit 37

34 EITHER

A A ship leaves a port *P* and steams on a course 045° for one hour at 18 kilometres per hour to reach a point *A*. At *A* the ship changes course to 130° and steams for a further 1½ hours at the same speed to reach a point *B*.

 (i) Calculate how far the ship has travelled in going from *P* to *B* via *A*.

 (ii) Using a scale of 1 cm to represent 3 km draw a diagram of the course of the ship.

 (iii) Use your diagram to determine the bearing of *B* from *P*.

On reaching *B* the ship changes course and speed and steams for a further hour to a point *C* which is 21 km from *P* and on a bearing 120° from *P*. Determine:

 (iv) The speed and course set by the ship in going from *B* to *C*.

Unit 47

OR

B (i) Which of the following are represented by a great circle?

   (a) The equator.

   (b) The meridian of longitude 50°W.

   (c) The parallel of latitude 40°N.

   (d) The parallel of latitude 90°N.

 (ii) Calculate the radius of the parallel of latitude 60°S.

 (iii) *L* and *M* are two positions on the same parallel of latitude 53°N. *L* is also on the line of longitude 4°W whilst *M* is on the line of longitude 176°E. Calculate the distance between *L* and *M*:

   (a) Along the parallel of latitude 53°N.

   (b) Using the polar route.

   (You may use the fact that the radius of the earth is 6360 kilometres or 3960 statute miles, or the fact that 1 nautical mile is the distance between two positions on a great circle subtending an angle of 1′ at the centre of the earth.)

Unit 38

35

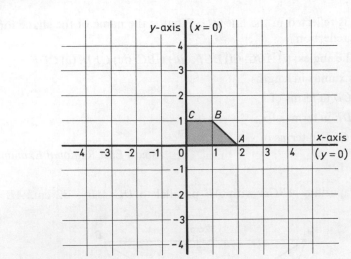

(a) Write down the positions of O, A, B and C in the shaded trapezium as a 2 by 4 matrix. Call the matrix R.

(b) A transformation is represented by the matrix $T = \begin{pmatrix} 0 & -1 \\ -1 & 0 \end{pmatrix}$. Calculate TR and, using your answer, draw the image of the trapezium $OABC$ after the transformation T. Call it $O'A'B'C'$.

(c) Translate $O'A'B'C'$ by the vector $\begin{pmatrix} 4 \\ 4 \end{pmatrix}$. Draw the image and call it $O''A''B''C''$.

(d) What single transformation would map $OABC$ onto $O''A''B''C''$? Describe it precisely.

(Yorkshire Regional Examinations Board)

Unit 38

36 (a) On one of your sheets of graph paper plot values of x and y from -8 to $+8$. (Let 1 cm represent 1 unit on each axis.) Plot the points $P(-2, 6)$, $Q(2, 3)$ and $R(-2, 3)$. Join these points to form a triangle.

(b) Reflect PQR in the line $x = -3$. Label the image $P'Q'R'$.

(c) Translate $P'Q'R' \begin{pmatrix} 10 \\ 2 \end{pmatrix}$. Label the image $P''Q''R''$ and write down the co-ordinates of the points.

(d) $P'''(6, -6)$, $Q'''(2, -3)$ and $R'''(6, -3)$ is the image of $P''Q''R''$ after a transformation. What was the transformation?

(e) Which single transformation would have mapped PQR onto $P'''Q'''R'''$?

(South East Regional Examinations Board)

Unit 39

37 (a) What properties remain the same under a shear transformation?

(b) (i) Apply the shear matrix $\begin{pmatrix} 1 & 2 \\ 0 & 1 \end{pmatrix}$ to the rectangle $ABCD$ and label it $PQRS$.

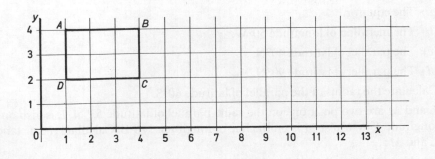

(ii) What is the area of the rectangle $ABCD$?

(iii) What is the area of the quadrilateral $PQRS$?

(iv) What is the special name given to the quadrilateral $PQRS$?

(Welsh Joint Education Committee)

Units 40, 11, 42

38 *ABCD* is a quadrilateral in which *DC* and *CB* are perpendicular. *AD* = 20 cm, *DC* = 24 cm, *BC* = 7 cm and angle *ADB* = 60°. Calculate:

   (*i*) the length of *DB*,

   (*ii*) the area of triangle *ADB*,

   (*iii*) the length of *AB*.

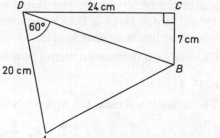

(*Associated Lancs. Schools Examining Board*)

Unit 41

39 The plan of a plot of ground *ABCD* is shown in the figure. Calculate to two significant figures

   (*a*) the length of *AE*,

   (*b*) the length of *AC*,

   (*c*) the length of *AB*,

   (*d*) the area of the plot of ground,

   (*e*) angle *ADC*.

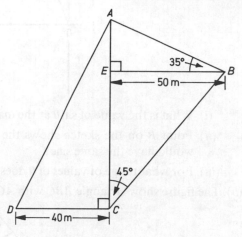

(*North West Regional Examinations Board*)

Units 41, 40

40 NOTE: YOU MAY NOT USE SCALE DRAWING IN THIS QUESTION. ALL ANGLES AND LENGTHS ARE TO BE FOUND AS ACCURATELY AS TABLES OR SLIDE RULE WILL ALLOW.

The diagram shows the rafters supporting a roof *CB*. The length of *CD* is 10 metres, the length of *DE* is 4 metres and angle *CBA* = 40°.

   (*a*) By using triangle *ABC*, find angle *ACB*.

   (*b*) By using triangle *DEB*, find

      (*i*) angle *EDB*,

      (*ii*) the length of *EB*.

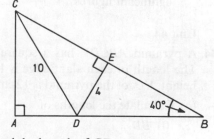

   (*c*) (*i*) By using Pythagoras' Theorem on triangle *CED*, find the length of *CE*.

      (*ii*) By using triangle *CED*, find the angle *DCE*.

   (*d*) (*i*) Find angle *ACD*.

      (*ii*) By using triangle *CAD*, find the length of *AD*.

(*Met. Regional Examinations Board*)

Unit 42

41 (*a*) *A* is a point on a straight coast due North of a second point *B*. The ship *S* is 4 km from *A* on a bearing of 137°, and is on a bearing of 068° from *B*.
Calculate the distance of *S* from *B*.

   (*b*) The diagram represents a crane carrying a load. If *PQ* = 6 m, *QR* = 8 m and *PR* = 12 m, **calculate** the size of angle *QPR*.

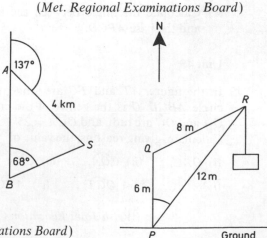

(*East Midland Regional Examinations Board*)

Unit 42

42 (*a*) A deep fielder in the school rounders team attempted to throw the ball directly to the bowler, a distance of 50 metres. Her throw was only 45 metres and instead of being straight was 15° off target. Draw a sketch to illustrate this information showing the two possible places where the ball may have landed.

(*b*) Calculate (to the nearest metre) how far the ball landed from the bowler.

(South East Regional Examinations Board)

Units 43, 11

43 (*a*) The figure is a sketch, not accurately drawn, of the sine curve for values of θ from 0° to 360°.

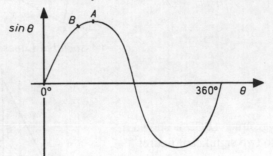

(*i*) What is the value of sin θ at the maximum point marked *A*?

(*ii*) Point *B* on the sketch shows the value of sin θ when θ is 50°. What other value of θ would have the same sine?

(*iii*) For what range of values of θ does the curve have a negative gradient?

(*b*) The figure shows triangle *ABC* with *AC* = 5 cm, *BC* = 7 cm and angle *C* = 70°.

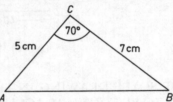

Calculate the area of the triangle, giving your answer in square centimetres, correct to three significant figures.

(East Anglian Examinations Board)

Unit 44

44 A pyramid *ABCDV* has a square base, *ABCD*. The length of each slant edge is 13 cm and the height, *VO*, of the pyramid is 12 cm.

(*a*) Calculate the lengths of

  (*i*) *BD*,

  (*ii*) *AB*.

(*b*) Calculate the angles

  (*i*) *VAB*,

  (*ii*) *VAC*.

(*c*) Calculate the angle between the face *VBC* and the base *ABCD*.

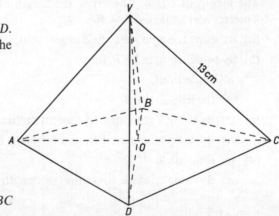

(East Midland Regional Examinations Board)

Unit 45

45 In the figure, *AT* and *TC* are tangents to the circle *ABCD*. *O* is the centre of the circle, *OA* and *OC* are radii and $O\widehat{C}A$ = 25°. Calculate, giving reasons, the value of

(*i*) $O\widehat{A}C$,   (*ii*) $C\widehat{O}A$,   (*iii*) $C\widehat{D}A$,

(*iv*) $A\widehat{B}C$,   (*v*) $O\widehat{C}T$,   (*vi*) $A\widehat{T}C$.

(Welsh Joint Education Committee)

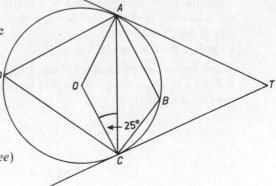

Units 46, 12

46 (*a*) The sketch represents a sector of a circle, centre *O* and radius 9 cm; the angle of the sector is 240°. Calculate

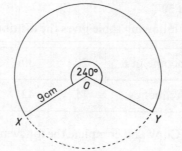

    (*i*) the length of the major arc *XY*,

    (*ii*) the radius of the base of the cone, with vertex *O*, which could be made from this sector by bringing together *OX* and *OY*.

(*b*) Another cone of perpendicular height 9 cm has a volume of 120 cm³. What is the radius of its base? (Take π to be 3.14.)

Unit 48

47 In a triangle *ABC*, *AB* = 9 cm, *BC* = 12 cm and angle *ABC* = 60°.

(*a*) Make a clearly labelled *sketch* of the triangle with side *BC* as the base. Add to your sketch

    (*i*) the point *X*, where the perpendicular bisector of *BC* cuts the side *AC*,

    (*ii*) the point *Y*, where the bisector of angle *ACB* cuts the side *AB*.

(*b*) Using *ruler and compasses only* construct triangle *ABC* full size. On your diagram show clearly the constructions which are necessary to fix the positions of *X* and *Y* given in part (*a*). Join the points *X* and *Y*.

(*c*) Measure the length of *XY* on your full size diagram giving your answer to the nearest millimetre.

(*d*) What further line would you need to construct to fix a point which is equidistant from the points *A*, *B* and *C*?

(South East Regional Examinations Board)

Unit 48

48 Use ruler and compasses only for this question.

Leave your construction marks clearly visible.

(*a*) Construct a parallelogram *ABCD* with sides *AB* = 10 cm, *AD* = 8 cm and angle *BAD* = 120°.

(*b*) Construct the bisector of angle *ADC*.

(*c*) Construct a circle to touch the sides *AB*, *AD* and *DC*.

(*d*) Shade the region which lies within the circle and less than 8 cm from *B*.

(Southern Regional Examinations Board)

Unit 49

49 (*a*) The figure shows triangle *PQR*, *X* and *Y* are the mid-points of *PQ* and *PR* respectively.

$$\overrightarrow{PQ} = \mathbf{a} \qquad \overrightarrow{QR} = \mathbf{b}.$$

Write down in terms of **a** and **b** the vectors representing the line segments

    (*i*) $\overrightarrow{PX}$,

    (*ii*) $\overrightarrow{PR}$.

    (*iii*) Show that $\overrightarrow{XY} = \tfrac{1}{2}\mathbf{b}$.

(*b*) $\mathbf{r} = \begin{pmatrix} 2 \\ 6 \end{pmatrix} \qquad \mathbf{s} = \begin{pmatrix} 8 \\ 10 \end{pmatrix} \qquad \overrightarrow{OR} = \mathbf{r} \qquad \overrightarrow{OS} = \mathbf{s}.$

    (*i*) Using a scale of 1 cm to 1 unit on each axis, draw a diagram on graph paper to show the points *O*, *R*, *S*, where *O* is the origin of co-ordinates.

    (*ii*) If $\overrightarrow{RS} = \mathbf{d}$ express **d** in vector form.

    (*iii*) If *M* is the mid-point of *RS* and $\overrightarrow{OM} = \mathbf{m}$, express **m** in vector form.

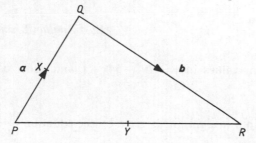

(East Anglian Examinations Board)

Unit 50

50 The following table gives the distribution of weekly incomes of a group of men:

Income in £	20–	30–	40–	50–	60–	70–	80–	90–100
Frequency	15	42	65	92	75	67	37	7

(a) Copy and complete the following cumulative frequency table:

Less than	20	30	40	50	60	70	80	90	100
Cumulative frequency	0		57			289		393	

(b) Draw a cumulative frequency curve.

(c) Use your curve to estimate

    (i) the number of men who earn between £45 and £75 a week,

    (ii) the 80th percentile of the distribution,

    (iii) the inter-quartile range of the distribution.

(West Midlands Examinations Board)

Unit 51

51 (i) A box contains five red balls, three white balls and two green balls. A ball is taken out at random. Determine the probability that it is

    (a) red,

    (b) white,

    (c) NOT green.

(ii) If the three balls are taken out in succession, determine the probability that they are drawn out in the order, GREEN, RED, WHITE, if each ball is

    (a) replaced,

    (b) not replaced.

(You may use a tree diagram if you wish.)

(iii) A bag contains white balls and black balls. The probability of picking out a white ball is $\frac{3}{5}$. What is

    (a) the probability of picking out a black ball,

    (b) the number of black balls in the bag, if it contains 15 white balls?

(West Yorkshire and Lindsey Regional Examining Board)

Unit 51

52 On my car there is, in any one year, a probability of $\frac{1}{2}$ that the brakes will need repair. The corresponding figures for the clutch and starter are $\frac{1}{3}$ and $\frac{1}{4}$ respectively.

(a) In any one year, what is the probability that repairs will not be needed by

    (i) my clutch,

    (ii) my starter,

    (iii) my clutch nor my starter?

(b) What is the probability that, in any one year,

    (i) none of the three items will need repair,

    (ii) at least one will need repair,

    (iii) just one item will need repair?

(East Anglian Examinations Board)

Unit 52

53 Find the maximum and minimum values of $y = 2x^3 - 54x + 1$ and show carefully how to distinguish between these values.

Unit 52

54 The velocity of a particle moving in a straight line is given by the equation $\dfrac{ds}{dt} = 5t - 2$ where s

metres is the distance from the origin, O, after t seconds of the motion.

  (*i*) For what value of t is the particle instantaneously at rest?

  (*ii*) Given that $s = 1$ when $t = 0$, obtain a formula for s in terms of t, and find the value of s when $t = 2$.

  (*iii*) Show that the acceleration is constant and find its value.

Unit 52

55

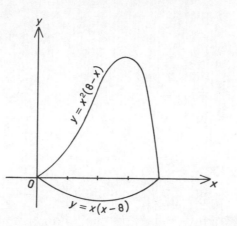

The sketch represents part of the curves $y = x^2(8-x)$ and $y = x(x-8)$.

  (*i*) Find $\displaystyle\int_0^8 x^2(8-x)\,dx$.

  (*ii*) Find $\displaystyle\int_0^8 x(x-8)\,dx$.

  (*iii*) Use your answers to (*i*) and (*ii*) to obtain the total area enclosed between the two curves in the above sketch.

Unit 53

56 A hiker and a motor cyclist both travelled from Rochester to Stapleford, a distance of 15 km. The hiker set out at 10.00 h and walked at a steady pace of 5 km/h for 1 hour. He then rested for $\frac{3}{4}$ hour. He continued at a steady speed until he reached Stapleford at 13.30 h. The motor cyclist left Rochester at 12.30 h and rode at a steady speed of 30 km/h until he reached Stapleford.

  (*a*) Set up distance-time axes using scales of 1 cm to represent $\frac{1}{4}$ hour and 1 cm to represent 1 km.

  (*b*) Using your axes draw a distance-time graph for the motor cyclist. At what time did he reach Stapleford?

  (*c*) Using your axes, draw a distance-time graph for the hiker. What was his speed on the last stage of his journey?

  (*d*) Find when and where the motor cyclist passed the hiker.

Unit 53

57 The following table gives the speed V (in kilometres per hour) of a train during the first 90 seconds of its journey.

Time t	0	10	20	30	40	50	60	70	80	90
Speed V	0	13.1	29.6	42.9	51.2	53.5	50.2	39.1	34.2	29.5

  (*a*) Using a horizontal scale of 2 cm to represent 10 seconds and a vertical scale of 2 cm to represent 10 kilometres per hour, plot these values of V and t.
Draw a smooth curve to show how V varies with t.
Use your graph to answer the following:

  (*b*) Find the acceleration of the train when $t = 40$.

  (*c*) For how long is the train travelling faster than 40 kilometres per hour?

  (*d*) Calculate the distance travelled in the first 60 seconds of its journey.

(*West Midlands Examinations Board*)

Answers to CSE questions

Part I

1 (*a*) 6; (*b*) 3.

2 $3^2 \times 5 \times 7^2$.

3 (*a*) 11 000; (*b*) 14.

4 (*b*) $\dfrac{3}{5}, \dfrac{3}{4}, \dfrac{7}{9}$.

5 1.5.

6 (*i*) 14; (*ii*) 14.5.

7 1017.

8 09 05.

9 5 hours 53 minutes.

10 £250.

11 (*a*) 1310.44; (*b*) 6.465.

12 21.5 cm².

13 (*i*) 1100 cm³; (*ii*) 2.2 g.

14 60 m.

15 £85.

16 (*a*) £3.84; (*b*) £1.16.

17 (*a*) £17.90; (*b*) £2.10.

18 80.

19 8.

20 7.7.

21 (*a*) 5; (*b*) 2.

22 (*i*) r; (*ii*) $q^{-1} = q, s^{-1} = p$.

23 (*a*) (*i*) $g + 7h$; (*ii*) $20gh$; (*iii*) $12g^2$; (*iv*) $\dfrac{g}{4h^2}$.
(*b*) (*i*) 1; (*ii*) -12.

24 (*i*) $x + 5y$; (*ii*) $x^2 + 4xy + 4y^2$; (*iii*) $x^2 - 4y^2$.

25 (*i*) 6; (*ii*) 5.

26 (*i*) $-2, 0, 2$; (*ii*) (*a*) $(-2, 8), (0, 0), (2, -8)$, (*b*) $(-2, -8), (0, 0), (2, 8)$; (*iii*) $x \to 4x$.

27 $x + 3y = 3$.

28 $x = 5, y = 1$.

29 $x = 8$.

30 $x > 0, y < 2, y > x$.

31 (*a*) $\begin{pmatrix} 5 & 1 \\ 2 & 3 \end{pmatrix}$; (*b*) $\begin{pmatrix} 4 & 2 \\ 4 & 0 \end{pmatrix}$; (*c*) $\begin{pmatrix} 4 \\ 2 \end{pmatrix}$.

32 (*a*) $5(a + 2)$; (*b*) $(3x + 4)(2x - 1)$.

33 $2x(3x + 1)$.

34 $2a - 5(a + 3b)$.

35 (*i*) $(x + 4)(x - 2)$; (*ii*) $(x - y)(x + y)$; 8600.

36 $\dfrac{x + 6}{12}$.

37 $x = -2$ or 7.

38 3.377.

39 118.

40 $t = \dfrac{v - u}{f}$.

41 (*i*) $a = 68°, b = 112°, c = 112°$, (*ii*) $x = 90°, y = 45°$.

42 150°.

43 (i) $\frac{2}{5}$; (ii) $\frac{4}{25}$.

44 (a) (i) 045°, (ii) 345°; (b) (i) 1 cm to 5 km, (ii) 15 km.

45 (a) $(-1, 8)$; (b) $(3, -2)$; (c) $(-3, -2)$.

46 Scale factor 3, $r = 3$, $y = 13.5$.

47 $\begin{pmatrix} 3 & 0 \\ 0 & 1 \end{pmatrix}$.

48 (a) 20 cm; (b) 36° 52′.

49 $AC = 16.08$ m, $BC = 36.64$ m.

50 (a) 45°; (b) equilateral; (c) 60°.

51 $x = 40$.

52 (a) $\frac{1}{6}$; (b) $7\frac{1}{3}$ cm.

53 (b) $BC = 3.2$ cm.

54 (a) $\begin{pmatrix} -5 \\ 1 \end{pmatrix}$; (b) $\begin{pmatrix} 5 \\ -1 \end{pmatrix}$.

55 (a) 105°; (b) $\frac{1}{8}$.

56 (i) $\frac{1}{5}$; (ii) $\frac{1}{45}$.

57 (a) DE; (b) BC.

58 (i) 0.3437; (ii) 0.7133; (iii) -0.9397.

Part II

1 (a) (i) 1, (ii) -8, (iii) 5; (b) (i) $-1, 0, 1$, (ii) $-10, -9, 9, 10$, (iii) 2, 3, (iv) $-8, -7, -6, 4, 5, 6, 7, 8$.

2 (a) (i) 16, (ii) 25; (b) 7; (c) 5; (d) 32 %.

3 (a) (i) 400_6, (ii) 100_{12}; (b) 49; (c) 441_5; (d) 4_6; (e) 1101_2; (f) 7020_8.

4 (i) (a) 4, (b) 3; (ii) (a) 102.784, (b) 102.8, (c) 102.78; (iii) (a) (i) 6.48×10^3, (ii) 3.24×10^{-1}, (b) 2×10^4; (iv) 0.5625.

5 (a) 9.1×10^{-5} m; (b) 50.6 l.

6 (a) 3.15 marks; (b) £1.77; (c) 71p.

7 (a) 30.0; (b) 6.542; (c) 0.02874; (d) 6.719; (e) 0.3948.

8 (a) 14 cm; (b) $14X$ cm²; (c) 154 cm²; (d) $X = 11$; (e) $X = 8$.

9 (a) 176 cm²; (b) $l = 10.5$; (c) (i) 32 340 g, (ii) £67.91; (d) 7 cm.

10 (a) 3.5 cm; (b) 0.5 m²; (c) 9000 mm³; (d) 4.

11 (a) A £2000, B £3500, C £4500; (b) A 20 %, B 35 %, C 45 %; (c) A £6000, B £9000, C £11 000; (d) A 23.1 %, B 34.6 %, C 42.3 %; (e) A's increases, B's and C's decrease. They will tend to get closer.

12 (a) £57.12; (b) £16.80; (c) £82.32; (d) £32.76; (e) £3.78.

13 (a) (i) £42; (ii) £48.30; (iii) 735.
(b) (i) £4320; (ii) £3070; (iii) £1043.80; (iv) £23.40.

14 (a) (i) £30, (ii) £36, (iii) £35.

15 (a)

$\oplus$	1	3	5	7
1	2	4	6	0
3	4	6	0	2
5	6	0	2	4
7	0	2	4	6

$*$	1	3	5	7
1	1	3	5	7
3	3	1	7	5
5	5	7	1	3
7	7	5	3	1

(c) 1; (e) (i) $c = 7$, (ii) $d = 3$, (iii) $e = 5$, (iv) $f = 5$.

16 (a) (i) -1, (ii) 12; (b) no; (c) $(5 \oplus 3) \oplus 2 = 12$, $5 \oplus (3 \oplus 2) = 6$, $\oplus$ is non-associative; (d) -5.

17 (i) $x + 30$; (ii) $5x$; (iii) $4(x + 30) = 4x + 120$. $5x + 4x + 120 = 1560 \Rightarrow 9x = 1440$. 160, 190.

18 (a) 7; (b) $x = 14, y = -8$; (c) $x = 5, 6, 7, 8, 9$.

19 (i) $-\dfrac{5}{2}$; (ii) $5x + 2y = 0$; (iii) $3\dfrac{1}{5}$ sq. units; (iv) $\left(\dfrac{4}{5}, 2\right)$.

20 (i) $p + q \leqslant 50$; (ii) $p \geqslant 2q$; (iii) (a) £$(2p + 4q)$, (b) $2p + 4q \geqslant 60$; (v) 15.

21 (i) $\begin{pmatrix} 7 & 3 \\ 2 & 1 \end{pmatrix}$; (ii) $\begin{pmatrix} -1 & -1 \\ 5 & 4 \end{pmatrix}$; (iii) $\begin{pmatrix} 2 & -5 \\ -3 & 8 \end{pmatrix}$; (iv) $\begin{pmatrix} 1 & -3 \\ -2 & 7 \end{pmatrix}$; (v) $\begin{pmatrix} 1 & -3 \\ -2 & 15 \end{pmatrix}$;
(vi) $x = -26, y = 19$.

22 (a) (i) $3, -3$, (ii) $0, 9$, (iii) 3 (twice), (iv) $3, -2$; (b) $5.54, -0.54$.

23 (a) $10x^2 - 23x + 12$; (b) $-\dfrac{4}{3}, 2$.

24 (a) $-1.137, 2.6375$; (b) (i) $(x + 3)$ mm, (ii) $2(2x + 3)$ mm, (iii) $x(x + 3)$ mm^2, (iv) 3 mm.

25 (c) $-3.5, 3.5$; (d) $-2.4, 2.4$; (e) -4; (f) 1.

26 (c) $(-1, 1), (3, 9)$; (d) (i) -2, (ii) -3.

27 (a) (i) 27, (ii) $\dfrac{1}{4}$; (b) 2.6×10^3; (c) 0.619.

28 (a) (i) x^7, (ii) y^6, (iii) z^{10}; (b) (i) 0.102, (ii) 1.5 p.

29 (a) (i) 1.6290, (ii) 0.4104, (iii) 1.3032; (b) (i) 45.8, (ii) 2850.

30 (a) (i) $r = \dfrac{A}{S} - 8$, (ii) 3.5; (b) (i) $x - 4$, (ii) £$3(x - 4)$, (iii) £$(3x - 337)$, (iv) $x = 123$.

31 (a) (i) $d = 42t$, (ii) 8 h; (b) (iii) $PV = 480$.

32 (a) (i) equilateral triangle, (ii) parallelogram, (iii) trapezium; (b) (i) 3, (ii) 0, (iii) 0, (iv) 0, (v) 0;
(c) rhombus; (d) (i) $60°$, (ii) $120°$, (iii) $60°$, (iv) $30°$, (v) $90°$; (e) (i) $\frac{1}{2}x$, (ii) $\dfrac{x \times \sqrt{3}}{2}$, (iii) $\dfrac{x^2 \times \sqrt{3}}{4}$.

33 (a) (i) $\triangle$'s ABE, CDE, (ii) 24 cm; (b) (i) $\dfrac{3}{7}$, (ii) $\dfrac{16}{9}x$ cm^2.

34 A (i) 45 km, (iii) $98°$ (approx.), (iv) 16 km h^{-1} on a course $251°$; B (i) (a) and (b); (ii) 3180 km or 1980 statute miles, (iii) (a) 12 026 km or 7488 statute miles or 6499 nautical miles; (b) 8215 km or 5115 statute miles or 4440 nautical miles.

35 (a) $R = \begin{pmatrix} 0 & 2 & 1 & 0 \\ 0 & 0 & 1 & 1 \end{pmatrix}$; (d) reflection in $x + y = 4$.

36 (c) $P''(6, 8), Q'' = (2, 5), R''(6, 5)$; (d) reflection in $y = 1$; (e) rotation of $180°$ about $(2, 0)$.

37 (b) (ii) 6 square units, (iii) 6 square units, (iii) parallelogram.

38 (i) 25 cm; (ii) 216.5 cm^2; (iii) 22.91 cm.

39 (a) 35 m; (b) 85 m; (c) 61 m; (d) 3825 m^2; (e) $64° 48'$.

40 (a) $50°$; (b) (i) $50°$, (ii) 4.767 m; (c) (i) 9.165 m, (ii) $23° 35'$; (d) (i) $26° 25'$, (ii) 4.449 m.

41 (a) 2.942 km; (b) $36° 20'$.

42 (b) 13 m.

43 (a) (i) 1, (ii) $130°$, (iii) $90° < \theta < 270°$; (b) 16.4 cm^2.

44 (a) (i) 10 cm, (ii) 7.07 cm; (b) (i) $74° 15'$, (ii) $67° 23'$; (c) $73° 35'$.

45 (i) $25°$, (ii) $130°$; (iii) $65°$; (iv) $115°$; (v) $90°$; (vi) $50°$.

46 (a) (i) 25.12 cm, (ii) 4 cm; (b) 3.57 cm (2 d.p.).

47 (c) 4.2 cm; (d) perpendicular bisector of AB or AC.

48 See unit 44.

49 (a) (i) $\frac{1}{2}\mathbf{a}$, (ii) $\mathbf{a} + \mathbf{b}$; (b) (ii) $\begin{pmatrix} 6 \\ 4 \end{pmatrix}$, (iii) $\begin{pmatrix} 5 \\ 8 \end{pmatrix}$.

50 (a)

Less than	20	30	40	50	60	70	80	90	100
Cumulative frequency	0	15	57	122	214	289	356	393	400

(c) (i) 235, (ii) £83, (iii) £25.

51 (*i*) (*a*) $\frac{1}{2}$, (*b*) $\frac{3}{10}$, (*c*) $\frac{4}{5}$; (*ii*) (*a*) $\frac{3}{100}$, (*b*) $\frac{1}{24}$; (*iii*) (*a*) $\frac{2}{5}$, (*b*) 10.

52 (*a*) (*i*) $\frac{2}{3}$, (*ii*) $\frac{3}{4}$, (*iii*) $\frac{1}{2}$; (*b*) (*i*) $\frac{1}{4}$, (*ii*) $\frac{3}{4}$, (*iii*) $\frac{11}{24}$.

53 Maximum value, minimum value.

54 (*i*) $\frac{2}{5}s$; (*ii*) $s = \frac{5}{2}t^2 - 2t + 1$; when $t = 1$, $s = 7$ m; (*iii*) 5 ms^{-2}.

55 (*i*) $\frac{1024}{3}$; (*ii*) $\frac{-128}{3}$; (*iii*) 384 square units.

56 (*b*) 13.00 h; (*c*) $5\frac{5}{7}$ km h^{-1}; (*d*) 12.49 h, 3.5 km from Stapleford.

57 (*b*) 1620 km h^{-2}; (*c*) 41 s; (*d*) 598 m.

Section IV   Hints for candidates taking Mathematics examinations

Examination nerves are common and understandable but if you have prepared yourself for the examination by doing a sensible course of revision, then they should not be too serious. However, you may not do yourself justice if you have a poor examination technique. The following hints should help you to tackle your examination with greater confidence.

BEFORE THE DAY

Before the actual day of your examination make sure you know:

- the date, day, time and place of each paper of your examination,
- how to get to your examination centre if it is not well known to you,
- your candidate number,
- your examination centre number,
- the telephone number of your examination centre.

Prepare any equipment you will need for your examination:

- pens which are comfortable to use and ink,
- sharp pencils, a pencil sharpener and a rubber,
- drawing instruments such as a ruler, compasses, protractor, set squares,
- calculator, if allowed, and spare batteries (check you know how to replace them quickly),
- an accurate watch or small clock,

ON THE DAY

Before the examination

Check that you have all the equipment you will need before setting off for your examination centre with plenty of time to spare. If you are delayed, contact your examination centre (have the telephone number with you) to explain what has happened. Arrive at the examination room early, a late start cannot be a good start.

Just before the start   Listen carefully to the invigilator. There may be some changes or special instructions which you were not expecting or some errors in the paper. Fill in any details such as your candidate number and examination centre number when the invigilator tells you to do so.

Reading the instructions   Read the instructions on your examination paper very carefully. Make sure that it is the correct examination paper! Although you will have used past papers, the way they are presented can change without notice. So make sure that you note from the actual paper in front of you:

(*i*) how many questions to attempt,

(*ii*) from which sections of the paper you should choose the questions (if you are a CSE candidate your school will have entered you for certain options; check with your teacher and **answer questions from these options only**),

(*iii*) how to present your answers (on the question paper or in an answer booklet; in one booklet or each section separately; each answer on a new page or immediately following the previous one),

(*iv*) the total time for the paper (it may recommend the time you should allow for each section).

Choosing the questions

Read the *whole* paper carefully. Some Examination Boards allow extra time at the beginning of the examination for reading the paper. Check whether your Board allows you this time. If the paper gives you a choice of questions, tick those you are going to answer. Always do your 'best' questions first, but remember that questions at the beginning of the paper are often the easiest and are worth attempting. Try to answer full questions if you can, but do not spend too long doing so. You can sometimes pass an examination by answering a lot of part questions. Indeed, questions are often structured—the first part being easier to answer than later parts. Some Examination Boards list the marks to be awarded for each question or part question. This information will help you to decide which questions or part questions to do. The harder questions usually carry the most marks.

Preparing your answers
Before you attempt to answer a question, read it again carefully. Whilst you are reading, jot down points relating to the question. These may be formulae you will need (*e.g.* $A = \pi r^2$), words you should know (*e.g.* parallelogram) or skills you will use (*e.g.* factorisation). If a diagram would be helpful, draw a sketch and label it with the information given. Be careful you do not do things you are not asked for (*e.g.* do not prove a geometrical theorem unless you are asked to do so). Write your answers neatly and carefully. Marks will be given for legible working, not just 'right' answers.

More hints on answering questions are given on page 150.

Timing the questions
The total time for the examination will be given on the paper. Allow a sensible proportion of time for each section you are to answer. You should have practised doing this during your revision. Quite often the first section of a paper will contain easier questions than the later sections. You should normally allow less time for this part of the paper. Divide the time you have allowed for a section between the number of questions you have to answer. If you find you are spending too long on a question it is wise to leave it and move on to the next. Try to allow about ten minutes at the end for checking your paper.

Doing the correct number of questions
Make sure you answer the correct number of questions. If you answer less than the number required, you are limiting the number of marks available to you. Remember the first part of many questions are easier than the later parts. Different Examination Boards have different policies regarding candidates who have answered too many questions. This can vary from year to year so try to find out your Board's policy. If you answer too many questions and your Board:

(*i*) marks all your questions and ignores your worst marks
   —hand in all your answers,
(*ii*) ignores your last questions,
   —cross out the questions you feel you have done badly, leaving only the correct number to be marked.

At the end   Before handing in your examination paper check that:
   ● any 'front sheet' is completed according to the instructions,
   ● every loose page is clearly marked with your examination number, *etc.*,
   ● every answer is numbered correctly,
   ● pages are numbered clearly and in order.

Formula check list

Standard form (Unit 6)

A number in standard form $= A \times 10^{n}$

$1 \leqslant A < 10$ ⎦ ⎣positive or negative integer

Perimeters of plane shapes (Unit 11)

Name	*Sketch*	*Perimeter*
square		$4 \times$ (length of a side) $= 4a$
rectangle		$2 \times$ (length + breadth) $= 2(l + b)$
triangle		sum of lengths of sides $= a + b + c$
parallelogram		$2 \times$ (sum of lengths of two adjacent sides) $= 2(l + m)$
trapezium		sum of lengths of sides $= a + b + c + d$
circle		$2 \times \pi \times$ radius $= 2\pi r$

Areas of plane shapes (Unit 11)

Name	Sketch	Area
square		$(\text{length})^2$ $= a^2$
rectangle		$\text{length} \times \text{breadth}$ $= lb$
triangle		$\frac{1}{2} \times \text{base} \times \text{height}$ $= \frac{1}{2}bh$
		$\frac{1}{2} \times (\text{product of two sides}) \times (\text{sine of included angle})$ $= \frac{1}{2}ab \sin C$ (or $\frac{1}{2}bc \sin A$ or $\frac{1}{2}ca \sin B$)
		$\sqrt{S(S-a)(S-b)(S-c)}$ where $S = \frac{1}{2}(a+b+c)$
parallelogram		$\text{base} \times (\text{perpendicular height})$ $= bh$
trapezium		$\frac{1}{2} \times (\text{sum of parallel sides}) \times (\text{perpendicular height})$ $= \frac{1}{2} \times (a+b) \times h$
circle		$\pi \times (\text{radius})^2$ $= \pi r^2$

Volumes of solid shapes (Unit 12)

Name	Sketch	Volume
cube		$(\text{length})^3$ $= a^3$
prism		$(\text{area of end section}) \times \text{length}$ $= Al$
cuboid*		$(\text{area of end section}) \times \text{length}$ $= abc$
right circular cylinder*		$(\text{area of base}) \times \text{height}$ $= \pi r^2 h$
sphere		$\frac{4}{3} \times \pi \times (\text{radius})^3$ $= \frac{4}{3}\pi r^3$
pyramid		$\frac{1}{3} \times (\text{base area}) \times \text{height}$ $= \frac{1}{3}Ah$
square based pyramid†		$\frac{1}{3} \times (\text{base area}) \times \text{height}$ $= \frac{1}{3}a^2 h$
tetrahedron†		$\frac{1}{3} \times (\text{base area}) \times \text{height}$ $= \frac{1}{3}Ah$
right circular cone†		$\frac{1}{3} \times (\text{base area}) \times \text{height}$ $= \frac{1}{3}\pi r^2 h$

* – Special prisms
† – Special pyramids

Surface areas of solid shapes (Unit 12)

Name	Sketch	Net	Surface area
cube			$6 \times$ (area of one face) $= 6a^2$
prism			$(2 \times$ area of end face$) +$ (perimeter of end face $\times$ length) $= 2A + Pl$
cuboid*			$(2 \times$ area of end face$) +$ perimeter of end face $\times$ length) $= 2ab + (2a + 2b)c =$ $2(ab + ac + bc)$
right circular cylinder*			$(2 \times$ area of end face$) +$ (perimeter of end face $\times$ length) $= 2\pi r^2 + 2\pi rh$
sphere		not possible	$4 \times \pi \times$ (radius)^2 $= 4\pi r^2$
pyramid			(area of base) $+$ (areas of triangular faces)
right circular cone†			(area of base) $+$ (area of curved surface) $= \pi r^2 + \pi rl$

* – Special prisms
† – Special pyramid

Percentages (Unit 14)

x as a percentage of y is $\dfrac{x}{y} \times 100\%$

Profit and loss (Unit 14.2)

$$\text{Percentage profit (or loss)} = \frac{\text{selling price} - \text{cost price}}{\text{cost price}} \times 100\%$$

Simple interest (Unit 14.3)

Simple interest (SI) $= \dfrac{P \times T \times R}{100}$ where: P—principal, T—time, $\dfrac{R}{100}$—rate as a percentage

Amount $(A) = $ Principal $(P) + $ Interest (I)

Averages (Unit 16)

Arithmetic mean $= \dfrac{\text{Total}}{\text{Number of quantities}}$

Average speed $= \dfrac{\text{Total distance travelled}}{\text{Total time taken}}$

Straight line gradient (Unit 23.2)

Gradient of a straight line $= \dfrac{\text{vertical displacement}}{\text{horizontal displacement}}$

Displacements:

An 'upwards' sloping line has positive gradient

A 'downwards' sloping line has negative gradient.

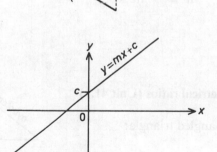

Equation of a straight line (Unit 23.3)

The equation of a straight line is
$$y = mx + c$$
Where: m is the gradient,
$\quad\quad\quad c$ is the intercept on the y-axis

Quadratic expansions (Unit 29.1)

$(a+b)^2 = (a+b)(a+b) = a^2 + 2ab + b^2$

$(a-b)^2 = (a-b)(a-b) = a^2 - 2ab + b^2$

$\quad\quad (a+b)(a-b) = a^2 - b^2$, the difference between two squares

Solution of a quadratic equation (Unit 29.5)

If $ax^2 + bx + c = 0$ is any quadratic equation, then, $x = -\dfrac{b \pm \sqrt{(b^2 - 4ac)}}{2a}$ is the formula which will give the two solutions.

Rules of indices (Unit 31.1)

$$x^m \times x^n = x^{m+n}$$
$$x^m - x^n = x^{m-n}$$
$$x^0 = 1$$
$$p^{-n} = \frac{1}{p^n}$$
$$(x^m)^n = x^{m \times n}$$
$$\sqrt[n]{x^m} = x^{\frac{m}{n}}$$
$$p^{\frac{1}{n}} = \sqrt[n]{p}$$

Variation (Unit 33)

Direct	*Inverse*
If *a* is proportional to *b*,	If *c* is inversely proportional to *d*,
or, *a* varies directly as *b*,	or *c* varies inversely as *d*,
i.e. $a \propto b$	i.e. $c \propto \dfrac{1}{d}$
then $\dfrac{a}{b} = K$	then $c = \dfrac{k}{d}$

K and *k* are constants of proportionality

Angles of a polygon (Unit 34.4)

For a polygon with *n* sides,
the sum of the interior angles is $(2n-4) \times 90°$,
the sum of the exterior angles is $360°$
If the polygon is regular (equal sides and angles),

each exterior angle is $\dfrac{360°}{n}$

Similar shapes (Unit 36)

Area factor $= (\text{scale factor})^2$

Volume factor $= (\text{scale factor})^3$

Enlargement (Unit 38.4)

Scale factor $= \dfrac{\text{image length}}{\text{object length}}$

Pythagoras' theorem (Unit 40)

In a right-angled triangle,
'the square on the hypotenuse
is equal to the sum of the
squares on the other two sides'.

$$a^2 = b^2 + c^2$$

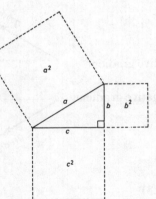

Trigonometrical ratios (Unit 41.1)

In a right-angled triangle:

$$\sin \angle = \frac{\text{opposite}}{\text{hypotenuse}} \qquad \cos \angle = \frac{\text{adjacent}}{\text{hypotenuse}} \qquad \tan \angle = \frac{\text{opposite}}{\text{adjacent}}$$

Rearranging gives:

opposite $=$ hypotenuse $\times \sin \angle$

adjacent $=$ hypotenuse $\times \cos \angle$

opposite $=$ adjacent $\times \tan \angle$

Ratios of standard angles (Unit 41.2)

	0°	30°	45°	60°	90°
sine	0	$\dfrac{1}{2}$	$\dfrac{1}{\sqrt{2}}$	$\dfrac{\sqrt{3}}{2}$	1
cosine	1	$\dfrac{\sqrt{3}}{2}$	$\dfrac{1}{\sqrt{2}}$	$\dfrac{1}{2}$	0
tangent	0	$\dfrac{1}{\sqrt{3}}$	1	$\sqrt{3}$	*

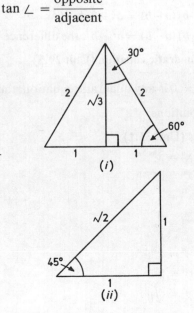

∗ means the ratio is undefined

Sine rule (Unit 42.1)

In any triangle ABC, the sine rule can be written as:

$$\frac{a}{\sin A} = \frac{b}{\sin B} = \frac{c}{\sin C}$$

or

$$\frac{\sin A}{a} = \frac{\sin B}{b} = \frac{\sin C}{c}$$

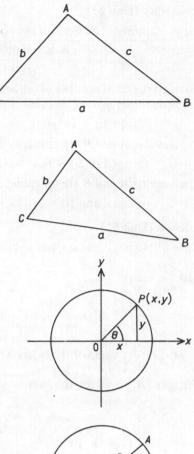

Cosine rule (Unit 42.2)

In any triangle ABC, the cosine rule can be written as:

$$a^2 = b^2 + c^2 - (2bc \cos A)$$

Rearranging gives:

$$\cos A = \frac{b^2 + c^2 - a^2}{2bc}$$

Trigonometrical ratios for any angle (Unit 43.1)

For any angle θ:

$\sin \theta =$ the y co-ordinate of P

$\cos \theta =$ the x co-ordinate of P

$\tan \theta = \dfrac{\text{the } y \text{ co-ordinate of } P}{\text{the } x \text{ co-ordinate of } P}$

Arc length and sector area (Unit 46.2)

If θ is measured in degrees:

$$\text{Arc length } AB = \frac{\theta^\circ}{360^\circ} \times 2\pi r$$

$$\text{sector area } AOB = \frac{\theta^\circ}{360^\circ} \times \pi r^2$$

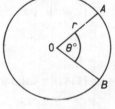

Radian measure (Unit 46.4)

$$\pi \text{ radians} = 180^\circ$$

If θ is measured in radians:

$$\text{arc length } AB = r\theta$$

$$\text{sector area } AOB = \tfrac{1}{2}r^2\theta$$

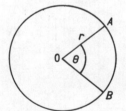

Latitude and longitude (Unit 47)

If the difference in latitude between two places on the same circle of longitude is θ°, then the distance between them is:

(a) $\dfrac{\theta}{360} \times 2\pi R$ km, if R is the radius of the earth in km,

(b) $60 \times \theta$ nautical miles

If the difference in longitude between two places on the same circle of latitude α°N is θ°, then the distance between them is:

(a) $\dfrac{\theta}{360} \times 2\pi(R \cos \alpha^\circ)$ km, if R is the radius of the earth in km,

(b) $60 \times \theta \cos \alpha^\circ$ nautical miles

Vectors (Unit 49)

Addition of vectors:

$$a + b = c$$

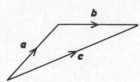

Subtraction of vectors:

$$a - b = a + -b$$

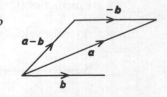

Probability (Unit 51)

The probability of an event A occuring is:

$$p(A) = \frac{\text{number of different outcomes in which } A \text{ occurs}}{\text{total number of outcomes}}$$

provided the total number of outcomes is finite and all the outcomes are equally likely.
The probability $q(A)$ of an event A *not* occurring is:

$$p(A') = 1 - p(A).$$

If two events A and B are mutually exclusive,

$$p(A \text{ or } B) = p(A) + p(B)$$

If two events A and B are independent,

$$p(A \text{ and } B) = p(A) \times p(B)$$

Calculus (Unit 52)

If $y = ax^n$ (a is a constant, n is any real number)

then $\dfrac{dy}{dx} = anx^{n-1}$

$$\int x^m \, dx = \frac{x^{m+1}}{m+1} + C \; (m \neq -1 \text{ and } C \text{ a constant})$$

$$\int_a^b f(x) \, dx = \left[\text{value of } \int f(x) \, dx \text{ when } x = b \right] - \left[\text{value of } \int f(x) \, dx \text{ when } x = a \right].$$

The area (A_1) between the curve $y = f(x)$, the x-axis and the lines $x = a$ and $x = b$ is:

$$A_1 = \int_a^b y \, dx$$

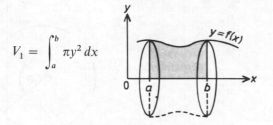

The volume (V_1) of a solid formed by rotating the area A_1 once round the x-axis is:

$$V_1 = \int_a^b \pi y^2 \, dx$$

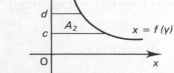

The area (A_2) between the curve $x = f(y)$, the y-axis and the lines $y = c$ and $y = d$ is:

$$A_2 = \int_c^d x \, dy.$$

The volume (V_2) of a solid formed by rotating the area A_2 once round the y-axis is:

$$V_2 = \int_c^d \pi x^2 \, dy.$$

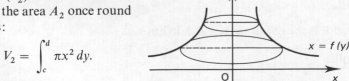

Kinematics (Unit 53)

$$\text{Average velocity} = \frac{\text{total displacement}}{\text{total time}}$$

$$\text{Average acceleration} = \frac{\text{change in velocity}}{\text{time taken for change}}$$

Displacement of a moving object
= area under its velocity-time graph

Velocity of a moving object
= area under its acceleration-time graph

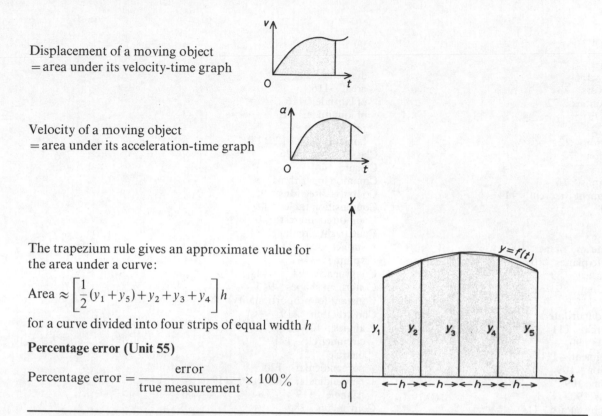

The trapezium rule gives an approximate value for the area under a curve:

$$\text{Area} \approx \left[\frac{1}{2}(y_1 + y_5) + y_2 + y_3 + y_4 \right] h$$

for a curve divided into four strips of equal width h

Percentage error (Unit 55)

$$\text{Percentage error} = \frac{\text{error}}{\text{true measurement}} \times 100\%$$

Index